Carnegie Commission on Higher Education
Publications in Print

FINANCING MEDICAL EDUCATION:
AN ANALYSIS OF ALTERNATIVE POLICIES
AND MECHANISMS
Rashi Fein and Gerald I. Weber

HIGHER EDUCATION IN NINE COUNTRIES:
A COMPARATIVE STUDY OF COLLEGES AND
UNIVERSITIES ABROAD
*Barbara B. Burn, Philip G. Altbach, Clark Kerr,
and James A. Perkins*

BRIDGES TO UNDERSTANDING:
INTERNATIONAL PROGRAMS OF AMERICAN
COLLEGES AND UNIVERSITIES
Irwin T. Sanders and Jennifer C. Ward

HIGHER EDUCATION AND THE NATION'S
HEALTH: POLICIES FOR MEDICAL AND
DENTAL EDUCATION
*a special report and recommendations by the
Commission*

GRADUATE AND PROFESSIONAL EDUCATION,
1980:
A SURVEY OF INSTITUTIONAL PLANS
Lewis B. Mayhew

THE AMERICAN COLLEGE AND AMERICAN
CULTURE:
SOCIALIZATION AS A FUNCTION OF HIGHER
EDUCATION
Oscar Handlin and Mary F. Handlin

RECENT ALUMNI AND HIGHER EDUCATION:
A SURVEY OF COLLEGE GRADUATES
Joe L. Spaeth and Andrew M. Greeley

CHANGE IN EDUCATIONAL POLICY:
SELF-STUDIES IN SELECTED COLLEGES AND
UNIVERSITIES
Dwight R. Ladd

THE OPEN-DOOR COLLEGES:
POLICIES FOR COMMUNITY COLLEGES
*a special report and recommendations by the
Commission*

QUALITY AND EQUALITY: REVISED
RECOMMENDATIONS
NEW LEVELS OF FEDERAL RESPONSIBILITY
FOR HIGHER EDUCATION
*a supplement to the 1968 special report by
the Commission*

STATE OFFICIALS AND HIGHER EDUCATION:
A SURVEY OF THE OPINIONS AND
EXPECTATIONS OF POLICY MAKERS IN NINE
STATES
Heinz Eulau and Harold Quinley

A CHANCE TO LEARN:
AN ACTION AGENDA FOR EQUAL
OPPORTUNITY IN HIGHER EDUCATION
*a special report and recommendations by the
Commission*

ACADEMIC DEGREE STRUCTURES:
INNOVATIVE APPROACHES
PRINCIPLES OF REFORM IN DEGREE
STRUCTURES IN THE UNITED STATES
Stephen H. Spurr

COLLEGES OF THE FORGOTTEN AMERICANS:
A PROFILE OF STATE COLLEGES AND
REGIONAL UNIVERSITIES
E. Alden Dunham

FROM BACKWATER TO MAINSTREAM:
A PROFILE OF CATHOLIC HIGHER
EDUCATION
Andrew M. Greeley

ALTERNATIVE METHODS OF FEDERAL
FUNDING FOR HIGHER EDUCATION
Ron Wolk

INVENTORY OF CURRENT RESEARCH ON
HIGHER EDUCATION 1968
Dale M. Heckman and Warren Bryan Martin

QUALITY AND EQUALITY:
NEW LEVELS OF FEDERAL RESPONSIBILITY
FOR HIGHER EDUCATION
*a special report and recommendations by the
Commission, with 1970 revisions*

*The following reprints are available from the Carnegie Commission on
Higher Education, 1947 Center Street, Berkeley, California 94704*

RESOURCES FOR HIGHER EDUCATION:
AN ECONOMIST'S VIEW
Theodore W. Schultz

INDUSTRIAL RELATIONS AND UNIVERSITY
RELATIONS
Clark Kerr

STUDENT PROTEST—
AN INSTITUTIONAL AND NATIONAL PROFILE
Harold L. Hodgkinson

WHAT'S BUGGING THE STUDENTS?
Kenneth Keniston

Financing
Medical Education

Financing Medical Education

AN ANALYSIS OF ALTERNATIVE POLICIES AND MECHANISMS

by **Rashi Fein**

Professor of the Economics of Medicine,
Harvard Medical School

and **Gerald I. Weber**

Visiting Lecturer,
Graduate School of Public Affairs,
University of California, Berkeley

A General Report Prepared for
The Carnegie Commission on Higher Education
and *The Commonwealth Fund*

MCGRAW-HILL BOOK COMPANY

New York   St. Louis   San Francisco   Düsseldorf
London   Sydney   Toronto   Mexico   Panama

The Carnegie Commission on Higher Education
and the Commonwealth Fund have sponsored
the preparation of this report to present
significant information for public discussion.
The report was begun when the authors
were on the staff of The Brookings
Institution and received the Institution's
continued support until completion.
The views expressed are those of the authors.

FINANCING MEDICAL EDUCATION
An Analysis of Alternative Policies and Mechanisms

Library of Congress catalog card number 72-132353
123456789MAMM7987654321
07-10020-9

Foreword

Medical schools in the United States bear heavy burdens. They train the nation's practicing physicians; they engage in research in the health sciences; and, through their teaching hospitals, they render health services directly—often to people who cannot afford to get them anywhere else. Their performance influences health standards of the cities and states in which they are located and affects the size of everybody's doctor and hospital bills.

Medical schools perform their important responsibilities despite what appear to be organizational weaknesses. Many of their faculty members divide their time and loyalty among the school, private practice, and research. They often derive much of their income from sources other than medical schools. The deans, to whom these schools look for leadership, are frequently only as powerful as the size of the budgets from which they allocate funds to divisions and departments. And at least a score of these schools have been in financial difficulty for many years.

As Rashi Fein and Gerald Weber point out, however, more money, as badly as it may be needed, is not, by itself, the answer. The economic relationships of the students, faculty, and administrators within the schools, and the relationships of the schools to their teaching hospitals, their communities, and the medical profession externally are remarkably sensitive. Financial inputs for any specific purpose, or provided through any one constituency, inevitably affect other goals and constituencies and, eventually, the cost of health care given to the public. It follows that relief of the medical schools' financial plight must be undertaken on the basis of a full understanding of such complicated factors as the number, ability, and socioeconomic status of students; the length of time it takes to become a practicing physician; the balance of service, education and research among the schools' objectives; the qualifications, commitments, and interests of faculty members; the distribution and financing of health delivery systems throughout the country; and the responsibilities of individual citizens, states, and the federal government in providing support for medical schools. By making this kind of analysis of financing medical schools, the authors have rendered a valuable service to all those who are responsible for planning medical education.

Clark Kerr

Chairman
The Carnegie Commission
on Higher Education

September, 1970

Preface

This monograph is, in part, an outgrowth of a Conference on the Financing of Medical Education held at The Brookings Institution in October, 1967. At that time both authors were members of the resident staff of The Brookings Institution. The conference discussion made clear that there was need for study of the sources and effects of financing medical education. Such a study, it was felt, would be helpful to those concerned with and interested in the economics of higher education and in the economics of medicine. This monograph represents the results of our research efforts on such matters.

It should be evident, however, that the monograph is not presented as *the* definitive study. Many important areas were left untouched or were inadequately analyzed, and considerable improvement in, and refinement of, basic financial data is required. Some brief comments on these matters are in order.

The discussion of medical education usually focuses on the medical school and the first four years of the physician's professional training. Yet, one of the first things that strikes the analyst is the importance of the teaching hospital in the education of the M.D. candidate, the intern, and the resident. Unfortunately, the only institutional data that are collected and available on a somewhat systematic basis deal with the medical school. This forced us to turn our efforts toward the medical school to a greater extent than we would have preferred (see Chapters 2 and 3). While the teaching hospital has been brought into the discussion where possible, we were unable to submit it to the detailed empirical analysis required. It should also be noted that our analysis was focused entirely on the M.D. and did not touch upon the training of osteopaths.

We also did not adequately study the behavioral processes within the medical school. While we did attempt to portray the institutional environment within which the medical schools perform, and while we tried to relate the outputs of the medical school to the system of financing, the intermediate process of decision making within the medical school is only briefly and incompletely touched upon. Until it is possible to make systematic predictions of the reactions of medical schools to changes in financing policy, there will remain a great deal of uncertainty with respect to the effects of such changes.

Finally, much of the data that we used had serious weaknesses, in terms of both precision and scope. These inadequacies affected the nature of our empirical analysis. For example, we found that there were inconsistencies (and errors in some years) in the financial data collected by the Association of American Medical Colleges–American Medical Association (AAMC–AMA). We therefore decided to forgo the systematic statistical analysis, sensitive to random error, of the six years (1959–1965) of data available to us and to limit our use of the information to descriptive analyses of the data for 1957 and 1965. We do have confidence that the averages presented in our analyses provide an acceptable portrayal of the existing situation. We used simple regression analysis in Chapter 5, where we felt that the need for such analysis was great and that given the available information, even beginning work would be beneficial. However, additional improved data on physician fees and income by state will be required before the evidence of the effect of the location of medical schools on the physician's place of practice can be conclusive.

The discussion of data does impel us to make one additional observation. We believe that it is imperative that medical educators and others with responsibilities in medical education recognize the shortcomings of existing data sources and implement better and more thorough data-generating systems. Those connected with the medical education sector can, and should, develop better and more comprehensive accounting systems. Schools should do so in concert with one another so that the data generated are comparable. Furthermore, it is necessary, and, we believe, will be increasingly necessary, that studies be conducted of individual (or of small groups of) schools. Such studies will provide additional information that will go well beyond the more aggregative findings that we were able to provide. Such studies will also be of value in helping develop the better data base we seek. We do not underestimate the difficulties involved in conducting such microexamination.

Nonetheless, this type of research, done in a number of institutions and using a common framework and classification system, is required if this field of inquiry is to be enriched in the years ahead. The need for such studies and for better data will become even greater if the federal government moves to support medical education in the more direct fashions that we urge in Chapter 7.

Even with the shortcomings that we refer to, the discussion and analyses we present will, we believe, clarify the economic questions related to the financing of medical education, provide the general institutional and historical framework necessary for the intelligent discussion of the issues, and provide a start in the systematic empirical analyses of behavioral patterns which will be useful in making policy decisions in the area.

We should like to express our deep appreciation for the cooperation and stimulus provided by numerous individuals and organizations. The Association of American Medical Colleges and the American Medical Association were most helpful in providing us with the data necessary for the preparation of the study. Dr. Robert C. Berson, Dr. Thomas Campbell, Dr. Davis G. Johnson, Dr. Dale E. Mattson, Dr. Lee Powers, Mr. Ray Rathburn, Dr. Walter Rice, and the late Augustus C. Carroll of the AAMC lent their personal advice and cooperation to our efforts as did Dr. C. H. William Ruhe of the AMA. Several divisions of the National Institutes of Health (NIH) also provided us with data and advice. Marion Altenderfer, Dr. Philip S. Chen, Anna R. Crocker, Louis C. R. Smith, Margaret D. West, and Dr. Marjorie P. Wilson, all of the NIH, cordially responded to our many requests and questions. Charles R. Dean of C. R. Dean Economics, Inc. prepared the analysis of the data which he had collected for his study of pediatric departments for our use in Chapter 2. We wish to thank the Association of Professors of Gynecology and Obstetrics and the Association of Medical School Pediatric Department Chairmen for permission to use the unpublished analyses of their departments.

Whatever errors remain in this manuscript, they are far fewer than would have been the case in the absence of the helpful and constructive recommendations made by the following individuals who read and commented on preliminary drafts, even though severe time constraints were placed upon them: Dr. Henry Aaron, Dr. Mark Blumberg, Dr. John A. D. Cooper, Dr. Robert Ebert, Dr. Joseph Froomkin, Dr. Eli Ginzberg, Dr. Margaret Gordon, Dr. David Kessner, Dr. Charles V. Kidd, Dr. Sidney Lee, Miss

Margaret Mahoney, Dr. Lucy Mallen, Mr. Henry Meadow, Dr. John S. Millis, Mr. Joseph Murtaugh, Mrs. Cecile Papirno, Dr. Joseph Pechman, Mrs. Dorothy Rice, Dr. Alice Rivlin, Dr. Jeffrey H. Weiss, Dr. Robert Weiss, and Dr. Marjorie P. Wilson.

The research assistance of Dulcy Brown, Virginia Dailey, Betsy Flint, and Leigh Hallingby was invaluable in the preparation of this study. Computer programming was provided by Pat Cantor and Sara Clark. Evelyn Fisher and Margaret Lyerly painstakingly checked our data, references, and computations. Betsy Flint, Camille Miller, and Marilyn Spellmeyer typed the several drafts of the study.

This monograph represents the collaborative effort between two authors. We both bear and accept responsibility for the manuscript. Since that is the case, it is unnecessary, and indeed impossible, to provide a detailed description of the individual contribution that each of us made to the final product. It is appropriate, however, to note that the regression analyses presented in Chapter 5 and in Appendix D were conceived and carried forward by Dr. Weber. This also holds true for the analysis of the rate of return to medical education presented in Appendix C.

Rashi Fein
Gerald Weber

September, 1970

Contents

1. *Introduction*

The task that we have set for ourselves is to examine the financing of medical education. We shall ask how medical education is being financed and what roles the students, the public, and others play in providing the required funds. Our study is focused on the education and training of the M.D. candidate, the intern, and the resident, and since most of these individuals receive their training under the auspices of medical schools, our examination will frequently require us to look at the overall support of those institutions. It will be necessary to discuss some of the characteristics and traditions of medical schools because these influence decisions and responses in the various institutions.

Aware that the future is, in part, a function of the past and the present, but also aware that it can be molded, we shall ask what the impact of alternative funding mechanisms might be both on the recipient and on the provider of funds. We are not searching for a single, most desirable financing mechanism. There are, after all, a number of medical schools. Their differences may be troublesome to the analyst, but we believe they are a source of strength to the nation. In considering financing mechanisms, we shall therefore seek arrangements that contribute to responsible diversity and flexibility.

The education of a physician — from his entrance into medical school until the completion of his residency — is a long, complicated, and costly process. During that time, society (and the student) forgoes the productive contribution that he might make if his efforts were not allocated to training. This forgone production represents the opportunity cost in medical education. Since a considerable part of medical education involves learning by doing, that is, by performing service, this cost is difficult to measure, particularly in the more advanced stages of the educational process. We shall find, however, that the opportunity cost, both to the student and to society, represents a major portion of the total cost of medical education. In addition, the medical student requires the scarce and valuable time of skilled physicians and scientists, complemented by costly capital equipment. These inputs are combined at the medical school and teaching hospital to produce different outputs: service to individual patients and to the community, research in various fields, and education of many kinds of students for different kinds of tasks. What are the priorities among the three outputs? How should resources be combined? How many resources are required to educate how many students? What proportion of the total student body should be prepared for the clinical practice of medicine? How do service, research, and education complement and how do they compete with one another?

Similar questions are asked by other parts of the higher education system, but they are particularly difficult to answer in medical education. This is the case, in part, because the medical school is more involved in the delivery of service, a process intimately bound up with the education of students, than other units of the university are. Another special difficulty is that both students and faculty are learning and teaching in hospitals and are away from the academic center during a large proportion of the educational experience. The medical school and teaching hospital (and the latter's role in medical education is crucial) are so unlike other units of the university that only confusion can result if the graduate school, the school of law, or other sectors of higher education are used as an analogy.

Multiple ways to produce and combine service, research, and education; multiple sources of funding; and multiple beneficiaries of the activities of the medical educational institution—all these compound the difficulty of analysis. Our task is also hard because of the multiplicity of legal arrangements that exist between hospitals and schools and the multiplicity of bookkeeping and accounting methods used. On occasion, because of these variables, the data will unfortunately be "softer" than one would like. The need for an organizational framework, for exploring and finding a way of thinking about the problem of financing, will in turn be that much greater.

THE PROVIDERS OF FUNDS Funds for the medical educational institution are provided chiefly by students, patients, and society. In return for the funds made available, the individuals and organizations place certain demands and restrictions upon the medical school and hospital.[1] The financing structure or system within which the medical school operates often reflects these demands. (For the sake of convenience we shall frequently refer to the medical school alone. Much of what we say, however, can be applied to the teaching hospital as well.) Decision makers in the medical school[2] are therefore faced with choices, some conflicting, some complementary. In deciding upon the allocation of resources within the school, the decision makers must take account of the level of demand for and the costs of producing each of the various outputs.

The choices confronting the decision makers, the demands placed upon them, and the costs of meeting these demands are seldom stated explicitly. Medical school deans do not, for example, have detailed information or exact quantitative data on relevant costs, long- and short-run constraints and options, and other important variables. To argue, however, that making rational decisions requires consideration of the relevant choices and assessment of the costs and benefits of each option is not to suggest that the thought process works only in the context of complete, hard, quantitative data. Though decision makers may not have as much information as they might desire, they do not operate without a framework of analysis or in total ignorance.

The demand for the outputs of the medical educational institutions can be placed into four categories:

1 The *private demand* for education comes from the potential medical and medical science students, interns, and residents. It is based upon the net monetary and nonmonetary benefits the potential students expect to derive from their medical education. In turn, it is a reflection of the anticipated private and public demands for their services.

2 *Governmental demands* are based on the assumed existence of benefits beyond those which accrue to the students themselves—public benefits from the training and education of the additional

---

[1] A small amount of funds from gifts, unrestricted endowments, and government come with no apparent requirements placed upon their use. Even these gifts, however, may be related to the quantity and quality of outputs over a period of time.

[2] Who the decision makers are in part is a function of the sources of funds and the uses to which they may be put. The issue of authority in a medical school will be discussed more fully later.

manpower, desired reduction of inequalities in the distribution of educational opportunities among different socioeconomic groups, and more equitable geographic distribution of health personnel. Additionally, government may feel that medical care would be improved by attracting into medicine persons with particular characteristics and might be willing to increase such persons' demand for the education by sharing in the costs.[3] Finally, government may recognize that the quality of medical care in a given area may be improved by the presence of a medical school. It may, under those conditions, exercise a demand for medical education, not because of the demand for education itself, but because of the demand for an associated output—the potential upgrading of the quality of health services.

3 The third demand is focused on the *research activities* of the faculty. Most of the funds that support and exercise demand for this activity have come from government (both federal and state) and foundations. A number of factors suggest why this is so. The success of any research project is difficult to predict; research activities are often carried on in a number of institutions jointly; and much of the research activity is basic, with benefits that are shared by all, regardless of the source of funding. Since research findings are available to everyone and know no geographic boundaries, there is likely to be underinvestment in research unless it is supported by national sources.

4 Finally, the fourth source of demand: the *demand for health services* that are produced by the faculty and (in varying amounts) by the students. This demand is presented by individual patients and by the larger community, though, of course, the payment for the services may be provided in whole or in part by the patient, by third parties (such as insurance carriers), or by local, state, or federal governments.

The response of the medical schools and teaching hospitals to these demands helps determine the types, qualities, and quantities of the various outputs produced. The demands thus interact with

---

[3] Which of these various reasons is of greatest importance at a particular moment may help shape the characteristics of the government assistance in the funding of medical education, for example, whether aid is given to certain students and not to others, to all students, or to the school itself. Different approaches are likely to have different impacts.

the desires of the faculty, students, and administration; with the possible relationships between the quantity of the inputs utilized and the quantity of the outputs produced; and with the fact that the outputs must be produced jointly. Teaching must be accompanied by some (but it is not clear how much) research and some delivery of service. There is evidence that the quality of service is positively correlated with the presence of research and teaching. Research may be improved if assisted in by students and, perhaps, if associated with the delivery of service. The medical school's products are therefore multiple and intertwined; it must produce all if it is to produce one.

Nonetheless, the relative proportions in which the different outputs can be (and are) produced is not fixed. These proportions will vary from school to school and over time. Different groups—students, faculty, administrators, government officials, the public—often have divergent views as to which of the various outputs should be emphasized. Choices will be made, in part, in an attempt to reconcile these views and the demands we have discussed. In part, they will be made in accordance with the principle that "he who pays the piper calls the tune." We shall find that medical schools now receive funds from multiple sources—that there are many payers; thus many tunes are being called for. The medical school must somehow play the various tunes and yet not become discordant. Furthermore, since it is an educational institution, it must attempt to educate those who provide funds to the importance of the missions it feels should have priority.

That the views on the relative importance of various outputs and on the possible missions of a medical school and teaching hospital can differ is not surprising. These differences arise, in part, out of differences in the perception of priorities. They also arise because the medical school is linked to—affects and is affected by—the health delivery system. Finally, they arise because there is disagreement concerning the optimum way to achieve the ultimate goal—better health (rather than simply more physicians). Views on these issues help determine the climate within which the medical center functions. They therefore warrant some consideration.

GOALS AND RESOURCES The ultimate goal we seek is health. Health is desired and desirable both as a consumption good—it contributes to an enjoyable life—and as an investment good—it makes possible productive economic activity. Health manpower, including physicians, is a means toward achieving health. Yet we know very little about what physicians in practice actually do and have relatively little information concerning the contribution that physicians' services make to health. Indeed, there is evidence that there are alternative ways to produce health even as there are alternative ways to produce the resources (personnel and facilities) that contribute to health.[4]

Relatively little analytical work has been undertaken to ascertain the ways in which health can be produced. We do not know the health implications of the fact that in 1961 the United States had 13 physicians, 91 hospital beds, and 42 nurses and midwives (1962 data) per 10,000 population, while Israel had 26 physicians, 74 hospital beds, and 24 nurses and midwives, and Sweden had 10 physicians, 159 hospital beds, and 108 nurses and midwives.[5] Furthermore, beginning efforts to investigate the incremental effects that various inputs have on health indices have yielded contrasting results: different findings concerning the relative contributions that per capita income, industrialization, urbanization, and the availability of physicians make to changes in mortality rates (Adelman, 1963, pp. 314–339; Larmore, 1967). In part this may be related to the fact that countries with different levels of living have different disease patterns. In many, the bulk of human disease must still be dealt with in mass terms: through sanitation, water, food, and immunization. In others, diseases must be dealt with by personal medical services. Since disease patterns differ, optimum health strategies also differ.

Alternative strategies would also be required because of differences in the availability and cost of various inputs, the organizational structure of medical care, and the delivery system itself. Changes in these variables would call for new strategies and for

[4] The measurement of the health level of an individual or of a community is a complex affair, both conceptually and statistically. For this reason, indicators which serve as proxies are often utilized: infant mortality, life expectancy, and morbidity days, for example. For a discussion of a health index, see Chiang, 1965.

In considering the number of physicians and other health workers to be trained and the total resources to be devoted directly to the health endeavor, attention must be paid to the fact that nonmedical goods and services also help raise health levels. Increased availability of food and housing, for example, can contribute to better health, as well as to satisfaction directly. Nonetheless, at the margin, the production of health services and the production of other goods and services must compete for resources.

[5] See Abel-Smith, 1967, for more complete data for a number of countries. These data are from p. 18.

changes in medical education. It is clear, for example, that substitution among health inputs is possible—and not only between manpower and facilities. Alternative kinds of manpower combinations can also be utilized. Nor are these combinations limited to the traditional types of health personnel. New types of personnel can be created to work with the physician and others.[6] Such personnel, for example, would be prepared to deliver a substantial amount of the medical care services that are now delivered by physicians.

We would anticipate that the medical care delivery system of the future would include more groupings of physicians enabling these physicians to work more effectively with new kinds of health professionals. Such groupings and the training of different kinds of personnel would, necessarily, have considerable implications for medical care and practice and, perforce, for medical education. Other changes would also affect the outputs of the medical center. Present dissatisfactions with the medical care delivery system will most probably lead to a greater emphasis on ambulatory health care and on community and social medicine. Organized units (medical schools, community hospitals, group practices, government itself) will assume increased responsibilities for delivering care outside the walls of the hospital. Agreement that the economic barrier to care should be reduced and that Americans have a right to obtain care will require the assumption of responsibility to see that care is available and accessible.

Since the education of the physician is designed, at least in part, to prepare him for the practice of medicine, and since the characteristics of future medical practice—the things that the physician will do and the settings in which he will do them— will alter, the education of the future physician will change. Yet, although there is a substantial agreement that tomorrow's medical care system will be different from today's and some agreement on the general nature of the differences, the specific changes and the speed with which they will be instituted remain at issue. The different perceptions of the future, combined with different views as to the nature of today's health "crisis," reflect themselves in different attitudes concerning the missions of the medical schools, the proportion of effort to be

[6] It is difficult to define the term *traditional personnel* since the educational and licensing requirements are not the critical parts of the definition. What is critical, rather, are the tasks assigned, the work done. These can and do change, even though certification requirements may remain the same (or change more slowly). In examining an occupational distribution, it is therefore necessary to adopt a task rather than a licensing orientation.

devoted to meeting the various demands placed upon them, and the role they should play in helping to foster change.

Moreover, even if there were agreement concerning the nature of medical practice in the future, the speed with which the delivery system would change, and the role that the medical school should play in speeding change, differences in the educational and other programs of the various medical schools would remain. This is the case because there are many ways to educate a physician. There is choice in the characteristics of the student—his age, abilities, interests, previous educational attainment, residence, family income, and so forth. The length of his training can be varied, as can the characteristics of the total curriculum and the contents of the individual courses. Choices in these matters not only are possible but are being made. The characteristics of student bodies in American medical schools do differ. There are also curricular differences between schools in the United States (and, perforce, between schools in different countries). Some of these differences reflect the different kinds of work that physicians might do in the various countries or locations. Some reflect different costs of the inputs required to educate a physician. Some, however, reflect differences in tradition and in educational concepts and philosophies. As is true of education in general, relatively little is known concerning whether different combinations of inputs in medical education alter the output, and in what ways and with what costs.

There is, for example, considerable variation in American medical schools in the number of hours that different subject matter is presented to the student, in the number of electives, and in the amount of time devoted to introduction to patient care (that is, in the various inputs that are used to produce medical education). Yet there have been few studies of the impact that such differences have on the capabilities of the practicing physician. Indeed, it is even difficult to explain the substantial variation in the performance of students from different schools on National Board examinations, taken after the second and fourth years of medical school and perhaps a substitute measure of physician quality.

Ignorance of the relationship between performance on the National Boards and performance as a physician reduces the value that can be ascribed to the information revealed by the relationship between performance on Boards and medical school inputs. Nonetheless, to the extent that Boards are an adequate measure of what was learned and to the extent that they are an adequate proxy for potential (if not actual) future performance, the relationships would be revealing.

Analyses do show that schools that have the most dollar resources relative to their overall student population have students that perform best on the National Boards. These, however, are the schools whose freshmen have the highest average scores on the science section of the Medical College Admission Test (MCAT). It is thus clear that no simple explanation of variation in performance on the National Board examinations can be offered. Are the variations in performance ascribable to the inputs of the schools or to the students themselves? The schools with the greatest expenditures do, after all, attract the more able students (or at least the students who performed better on certain types of tests). Starting with better students or with better-performing students, they subsequently graduate students who perform better on the National Board examinations. That the schools with the most to spend on students start with the students who, on the average, are most able (to learn or to do well on tests) is itself an interesting commentary on resource allocation—but one which can be made of most of higher education and, in spite of equalization policies, of most of elementary and high school education as well. That these doubly advantaged students then perform better on tests taken during and at the conclusion of the educational experience does not come as a surprise. What one would like to know, however, is how the result would be altered by changes in inputs, that is, the relationships at the margin.

The absence of such information, and of even more general information on the educational process, and the lack of agreement on how a physician is to be best educated and on what kind of a physician is to be produced helps explain why medical schools educate their students in different ways. The fact that education is combined with service and research also helps explain why it is so difficult to reach agreement on the degree of effort to be devoted to the production of each of the various intertwined outputs.

It is in this general milieu that the medical school functions. Unsure of the optimum combination of resources required to maximize favorable health impacts, of the future structure of the delivery system, of the kinds of physicians to be educated for tasks not fully known, and of the optimum way to organize its own resources for education, the medical school must, nonetheless, reconcile the demands placed upon it. In such a situation, the desires of those who provide the funds for the operation of the school—and the desires of faculty members who receive some of the funds—are likely to play a major part in determining the balance achieved between the various possible outputs: service, research, and education. The funding structure becomes a central concern.

Our examination will address itself to financing: to the funds received and the funding structure. We shall analyze the manner in which the medical school is financed, the sources from which funds are received, and the uses to which they are put. We shall ask how those sources have changed over the years and how these movements have been associated with changes in the medical school itself. We shall pay particular attention to the roles that students, state governments, and the federal government might play in financing medical education, and we shall discuss alternative funding patterns and their policy implications. In undertaking these tasks we shall attempt to provide an analytical framework and a set of principles that can be used to assess relevant new data as they become available. Such reassessments will be necessary since funding structures, the medical care delivery system, and medical education will change. Only a continuing analysis of new information in the light of general principles will permit us to determine the impacts of those changes.

2. The Medical School: Some General Characteristics

American medical schools have evolved within a structure of constraints introduced by university goals, geographic locations, local preferences and traditions, trustee decisions, state laws and regulations, federal legislation, financial limitations, and various other factors. These have helped to mold medical schools into institutions with widely varying characteristics and missions. There is no single pattern, no "master plan" for the whole country. Some schools emphasize research, and others education. Some offer only as much service as they feel is required to carry on their educational activity, and others do far more. Since the manner and cost of producing different possible outputs will vary, and since the cost of acquiring different inputs will also vary, the diversity in outputs and inputs leads to diversity in funding levels and sources and to different financial considerations and problems.

This diversity implies that a researcher cannot single out any one institution as representative and examine it in detail in order to learn about medical education in depth. He cannot ignore the range of differences, for probably there will be exceptions to almost every generalization that he might note. Yet, as we examine medical education, we shall be forced to generalize and summarize in order to avoid presenting more than can be grasped or understood. In doing so, we shall attempt to select what seems important, hoping that we do not exclude critical variables.

In the first part of this chapter we describe the characteristics of medical school outputs and inputs, focusing on some of the relationships between the more significant variables. Aware of the dangers, just noted, of citing averages, we shall provide data for eight groupings of medical schools: four for private and four for public institutions. The schools in each quartile (within the categories of public and private) will be determined by a ranking based on the

TABLE 1 Quartile averages for schools grouped by rank for four medical school characteristics, 1965–66

Type of school and quartile*	Total expenditures per school (millions)†	Total expenditures per full-time student‡	MCAT science score for entering M.D. candidates	Ratio of M.D. candidates to full-time students§
Public				
Highest	$16.0	$16,890	577	0.39
Second	9.6	12,723	547	0.53
Third	7.5	9,965	525	0.58
Lowest	4.2	7,901	495	0.67
Private				
Highest	20.3	21,079	618	0.34
Second	12.1	14,663	579	0.42
Third	6.8	9,767	559	0.54
Lowest	4.0	7,335	509	0.70

*Each group includes 10 schools except the "lowest public," which includes 11 schools, and the "lowest private," which includes 12 schools. The quartile in which a specific school appears may differ from column to column depending on the value for that school of the variable determining the ranking. See Table 6 for the simple and rank correlations of indices.

†In all computations, expenditures connected with Agency for International Development (AID) contracts and one-half the expenditures funded by federal teacher and training grants have been excluded. The latter were excluded because our information suggests that about one-half of those teacher and training grant funds were used to provide stipends to support graduate students.

‡Full-time students include M.D. candidates, graduate and postdoctoral students in the basic sciences, interns, residents, clinical fellows, and postdoctoral students in the clinical sciences.

§This column reads from lowest to highest since schools which rank high on the other three indices tend to have low ratios of M.D. candidates to full-time students.

SOURCES: Unpublished data from the AAMC and AMA annual questionnaires. Published data from *Journal of the American Medical Association,* 1966. The data are for the 83 four-year medical schools in active operation in the continental United States in 1965–66.

variable under examination: (1) dollar expenditures per student, (2) MCAT science achievement scores of entering students, or (3) the ratio of M.D. candidates to the total number of full-time students (including interns, residents, clinical fellows, and graduate and postgraduate students in the basic sciences) who are the responsibility of the medical school faculty. A summary of the values of the three ranking factors for the schools grouped by quartiles illustrates the diversity among medical schools (see Table 1).[1]

The expenditure-per-student figures presented in Table 1 and in succeeding tables do not represent the cost of educating an M.D. candidate. This cannot be stressed too strongly. The reasons for this

[1] Diversity is also shown by the data in column 1 of Table 1, which relate to total dollar expenditures. These data are not used to provide quartile groupings in the subsequent analysis. We speak of quartile groupings even though two of the groupings include more schools than are included in the other six groups.

are (1) the medical school produces multiple outputs, (2) some of the funds budgeted in one category (for example, sponsored research) may be used for teaching purposes, (3) the costs of educating different types of students (M.D. candidates, interns, residents, and graduate students in the basic sciences) differ, and (4) accounting for activities in the teaching hospital creates problems.[2]

Our analysis will show that schools exhibit considerable variation in size, wealth, the apparent quality of their students, the allocation of their efforts among the different outputs of the medical school, and the types of physicians they train. On the average, the characteristics of the schools will be interrelated. Those schools, for example, with the largest expenditures per full-time student tend to attract M.D. candidates who, on the average, have higher scores on the MCAT science test. They also tend to allocate relatively more effort to the training of interns, residents, and graduate students in the basic sciences.

The second part of this chapter will provide a broad description of the institutional setting of the medical school. We shall discuss the medical school–teaching hospital relationship, the arrangements for compensating the clinical faculty, and the structure of decision making.

EDUCATION OUTPUTS When examining the functions of medical schools and teaching hospitals, one speaks of teaching, research, and service. Often it is incorrectly assumed that the educational component is related exclusively (or in the largest measure) to educating and training the M.D. candidate—the undergraduate medical student. This conception, together with inadequate medical school budgeting and accounting procedures, has led to the development of badly mistaken views concerning the costs of medical education. In 1967 only 49 percent of the total number of students in American medical schools were undergraduate medical students. The others included interns, residents, and graduate and postgraduate students in the

---

[2] Some schools receive a substantial portion of their funds from teaching hospitals. These funds may include faculty salaries and rental value of classroom space, offices, and other space, plus plant maintenance and business services. A number of these are imputed values, however, and there is little reason to believe that the accounting, costing, and budgeting procedures are reliable enough to give confidence to the view that the figures used in such budgets are consistent.

TABLE 2 *Student composition, expenditures, and professional activity of graduates of United States medical schools; quartile averages for schools grouped in order of ratio of M.D. candidates to full-time students, 1965–66*

Quartile*	M.D. candidates per full-time students	Other clinical students per full-time students	Nonclinical students per full-time students	Number of M.D. candidates in first-year class
Public				
Highest	0.67	0.24	0.08	121
Second	0.58	0.31	0.11	100
Third	0.53	0.34	0.13	123
Lowest	0.39	0.44	0.18	98
Private				
Highest	0.70	0.22	0.08	102
Second	0.54	0.36	0.11	103
Third	0.42	0.43	0.15	88
Lowest	0.34	0.49	0.17	84

*Each group includes 10 schools except "highest public," which includes 11 schools, and "highest private," which includes 12 schools. The data are means for the quartiles.

†Expenditure data have been adjusted to omit contract funds provided by the AID and one-half of the federal teacher and training funds. The latter adjustment in the total expenditure figures (as received from the AAMC) was made because our information suggests that about one-half of these teacher and training grant funds were used to provide stipends to support graduate students.

clinical and basic sciences. In many schools, the candidates for the doctorate in medicine were only a minority of all students that are the responsibility of the faculty. Among individual schools, the proportion of M.D. candidates in the total full-time student body ranged from 88 percent at one extreme to 25 percent at the other.

More detailed information on characteristics related to the ratio of medical students to full-time students is presented in Table 2. A number of facts stand out:

1 On the whole, private schools have a smaller proportion of M.D. candidates to full-time students than the public institutions.

2 On the average, the private schools that place the greatest emphasis on non-M.D. candidates have relatively small, high-quality (to the extent that MCAT scores indicate quality) entering classes of medical students. As the emphasis on the M.D. candidate increases, the size of the entering class increases, and average MCAT scores

Number of full-time students	MCAT science score	Total expenditures† (in thousands)	Total expenditures per full-time student	Percent of physician graduates, 1950–1959, who were general practitioners in 1967	Percent of physician graduates, 1950–1959, on medical school faculties in 1967
658	505	$ 5,812	$ 8,833	33	4
643	542	7,402	11,505	23	7
865	542	10,243	11,844	25	5
952	565	13,629	14,317	22	7
559	538	4,659	8,335	26	4
736	562	9,098	12,355	16	6
808	576	11,731	14,518	13	9
997	599	17,486	17,544	10	14

SOURCES: Unpublished data from the AAMC and AMA annual questionnaires. Published data from *Journal of the American Medical Association,* 1966; and Theodore, Sutter, & Haug, 1968. The data are for the 83 four-year medical schools in active operation in the continental United States in 1965–66.

decline. Substantially the same pattern exists for the public schools (with the exception of the third-quartile schools).[3]

3 Though the schools with the lowest ratio of M.D. candidates to full-time students have small entering first-year classes, they have large numbers of full-time students. This is true for both private and public institutions. There is considerable variation in the size of the total student body among both public and private schools.

[3] The MCAT has four sections: verbal ability, quantitative ability, general information, and science. There is divided opinion among medical school faculties about the reliability of MCAT scores as a measure of capabilities and potential, that is, as a measure of the quality of students. Faculties therefore rely upon a number of other measures to evaluate applicants. Nonetheless, MCAT scores are considered, and the science section appears to be given particular weight by admissions committees. Less than 6 percent of applicants for the 1965–66 entering class scored above 649 on that examination, about 16 percent scored above 600, about 33 percent scored above 550, about 54 percent scored above 500, and about 74 percent scored above 450 (Sedlacek, 1967, p. 40).

4   Schools that emphasize undergraduate medical education have substantially smaller budgets than schools which emphasize other educational outputs.

5   The variation in expenditures is cut down considerably when we examine average expenditures per full-time student. Even so, there are considerable differences between the averages for the individual quartiles. Among private schools, for example, per-student expenditures range from an average of $17,500 for the group of schools with the lowest ratio of undergraduate medical students to $8,300 for the schools whose student body is composed predominantly of M.D. candidates.

6   Particularly among private schools, those which place the greatest emphasis on non-M.D. candidates have a much greater proportion of their graduates on medical school faculties and a much smaller proportion of their graduates in general practice. Substantially the same general trends are found among the public institutions.[4]

SERVICE AND RESEARCH OUTPUTS   Medical schools also differ greatly in their production of services and research. Unfortunately, however, there is little comparative information available on the amounts of services and research provided.[5] Some indication of the extent of the variations is given by data computed from a survey of departments of pediatrics in a number of medical schools. The faculty of these departments were asked to estimate the time spent on administrative work and various combinations of teaching, patient care, and research. The greatest total proportion of departmental time allocated to research was 58 percent; the lowest proportion was only 10 percent. The proportion of time allocated to service ranged from 79 to 34 percent. In Table 3 we present the results of this survey by quartile averages for

---

[4] As will be seen in Tables 4 and 5, the percentage of students who graduated during the period 1950–1959 and who are full-time members of medical school faculties is higher in private than in public institutions. In general, it is also higher in schools which spend more dollars in total, which spend more dollars per full-time student, and which have student bodies with high MCAT scores. The percentage of graduates who, by their own definition, are in general practice is inversely related to these same variables.

[5] It is sometimes suggested that the ratio of sponsored research funds received by a medical school to the level of its total expenditures might serve as an adequate proxy for the effort allocated to research. Such a ratio, however, is misleading because some of the sponsored research funds may be used for nonresearch purposes and also because additional research may be financed out of the school's general budget.

the schools grouped according to total expenditures per full-time student. Because this survey is related to a single *clinical* department, it is not representative of the mix of outputs for other clinical departments or for the entire school.

These conclusions are apparent from the results presented in Table 3:

1 The allocation of faculty time is a very complex matter, and there is considerable variation among the schools in the various groupings.

2 Relatively little time (in this clinical department) is allocated to teaching alone, research alone, or patient care alone. Most of each type of activity is done in conjunction with other activities. Thus most of the faculty time is allocated to the production of joint outputs.

3 In all cases, teaching is most often done in conjunction with patient care; research is more often done by itself, rather than in combination; and patient care is most often carried on in conjunction with teaching.

4 In all cases, more time is devoted to patient care (by itself and in combination with other activities) than to either of the other two activities—teaching (by itself and in combination with research, patient care, or both) or research (by itself or in combination). The service aspect of the medical school is clearly very different from that found in other units of the university.

Medical school faculties are far less compartmentalized in their activities than other parts of the higher education system are likely to be. Creating many outputs at the same time, they are surely aware of the many masters that they serve, of the varying demands placed upon them, and of the multiple sources of funding these diversities imply.

INPUT: DOLLAR RESOURCES There is a wide range in the total dollar resources utilized in the operation of medical schools. In 1966, total expenditures in the four-year schools ranged from almost $2 million to about $35 million. Reasons for such differences include the size and composition of the student body and the faculty, the amount and type of research undertaken, and the level of salaries and costs of other resources. The 10 private schools with the highest total expenditures ac-

| Time allocation | Percentage distribution of time | | | |
| | Public schools, by quartiles* | | | |
	Highest	Second	Third	Lowest
Teaching, alone	7.7	9.3	7.9	8.4
Teaching, with patient care	25.8	21.5	25.4	28.3
Teaching, with research and patient care	10.2	7.0	7.6	8.0
Teaching, with research	5.9	3.6	4.8	3.0
Research, alone	18.9	20.0	15.3	11.4
Research, with patient care	7.4	7.5	8.5	6.7
Patient care, alone	7.3	9.3	9.3	13.8
TOTAL (excluding administration and miscellaneous)	83.2	78.2	78.8	79.6
Administration‡	13.9	18.1	18.5	17.0
Teaching‡	50.7	42.6	46.6	48.8
Service‡	52.0	46.8	51.8	58.0
Research‡	43.7	39.5	37.4	30.3

*The quartile *groupings* are based upon the 83 schools that were presented in Table 1. The "highest" quartiles include the schools with highest expenditures per full-time student. Only 69 schools participated in the survey from which these data are taken and are represented as follows: Public—highest and second, 10 schools each; third, 8 schools; and lowest, 11 schools. Private—highest, 7 schools; second and third, 9 schools each; and lowest, 5 schools.

counted for almost 25 percent of the total expenditures of all 83 schools, and yet they were responsible for only 11.3 percent of the first-year medical students. Thus their high total expenditures were not entirely related to larger numbers of M.D. candidates,[6] but, in part, represent greater dollar expenditures per medical student and per full-time student as well as a different mix of the three outputs: education, research, and service. In Table 4 we present data on private and public medical schools grouped by rank of total expenditures per full-time student for the academic year 1965–66. From Table 4, these facts stand out:

1 Private schools spend more total dollars than public schools. The 42 private schools account for about 54 percent of total expenditures and about 47 percent of first-year students.

[6] They did have large student bodies since, of the various groups of schools analyzed, they had the highest ratio of non-M.D. students to M.D. candidates. Undergraduate medical students accounted for only 37 percent of the full-time student body.

Percentage distribution of time			
Private schools, by quartiles*			
Highest	*Second†*	*Third*	*Lowest*
8.1	7.9	11.1	12.0
22.9	17.0	29.9	25.0
12.0	9.7	6.6	5.4
5.6	3.8	4.7	4.6
20.1	20.2	12.4	9.2
5.7	9.1	6.2	5.2
8.7	12.9	9.4	12.6
83.1	80.6	80.3	74.0
13.1	15.6	16.1	23.4
49.9	39.6	53.4	47.8
50.3	50.0	53.6	49.2
44.4	43.8	31.1	25.0

†Eleven cases (two schools reported for two separate units each).

‡Totals of administration, teaching, service, and research exceed 100 percent because time is spent in combinations of the latter three activities.

SOURCE: Unpublished data from C. R. Dean Economics, Inc., New York, printed with permission of the Association of Medical School Pediatric Department Chairmen.

2   The range in quartile average expenditures per student is greater among the private schools than among the public institutions. The two highest-expenditure quartiles of the private schools spend more dollars than the two high quartiles of the public medical schools, but this is reversed for the lower-expenditure institutions (where the private institutions spend less than the public). Put simply, the "rich" private schools are richer than the "rich" public schools, but the "poor" private schools are poorer than the "poor" public schools. Public institutions have a lower ceiling but also a higher floor.[7]

3   Private schools with large total expenditures per student have a student body with high averages MCAT science scores (the range is from 609 down to 540). The same pattern holds for public schools examined separately (from 550 to 516). The relationship

[7] "Rich" and "poor" are shorthand expressions. The statement is correct only to the extent that richness and poverty are adequately measured by the level of expenditures per full-time student.

TABLE 4
*Expenditures,
student
composition,
and professional
activity of
graduates of
United States
medical schools;
quartile
averages for
schools grouped
in order of
total
expenditures
per full-time
student,
1965–66*

Type of school and quartile*	Total expenditures per full-time student	Expenditures as percent of total expenditures of all schools	MCAT science scores	M.D. candidates per full-time student
Public				
Highest	$16,890	16.4	550	0.44
Second	12,723	11.8	550	0.53
Third	9,965	10.2	536	0.56
Lowest	7,901	7.7	516	0.60
Private				
Highest	21,079	22.8	609	0.40
Second	14,663	16.2	581	0.40
Third	9,767	7.8	544	0.56
Lowest	7,335	6.9	540	0.61

*Each group includes 10 schools except "lowest public," which includes 11 schools, and "lowest private," which includes 12 schools. The data are means for the quartiles.

does not hold, however, when private and public institutions are examined together. Private schools in the lowest-expenditure quartile, with average total expenditures of $7,335 per student, have a student body whose MCAT scores, on the average, are higher than those of students in the second-lowest-expenditure public institutions (with average total expenditures of $9,965 per student). Apparently, even the private schools with fewer resources are able to adopt more selective admissions policies (in terms of MCAT scores).

4 Full-time students are almost equally divided between private and public institutions. Among private schools, particularly, there are significant variations among the quartile groups in the size of the student bodies, with the total size of the student body positively related to total expenditures. In contrast, the schools with higher expenditures per student have smaller first-year medical student classes.

It is clear that there are important differences between private and public schools and that there are significant differences between schools in each category. At times it appears that the critical association is with the control of the institution (often a matter of

Number of M.D. candidates in first-year class	Percent of all first-year students	Number of full-time students	Percent of all full-time students	Percent of physician graduates, 1950–1959, who were general practitioners in 1967	Percent of physician graduates, 1950–1959, on medical school faculties in 1967
90	10.6	794	12.4	24	8
106	12.4	756	11.8	26	6
127	14.9	836	13.1	24	5
119	15.4	725	12.5	30	4
88	10.4	884	13.8	10	13
90	10.6	902	14.1	13	10
96	11.2	655	10.2	19	5
102	14.4	643	12.1	23	4

SOURCES: Unpublished data from the AAMC and AMA annual questionnaires. Published data from *Journal of the American Medical Association,* 1966; and Theodore et al., 1968. The data are for the 83 four-year medical schools in active operation in the continental United States in 1965–66.

tradition rather than source of funds, since in all schools public moneys play a key role); at other times the association seems to be with the level of expenditures or with the resources available to the institution.

INPUT: STUDENT ABILITY AND POTENTIAL
Another important input involves the basic capabilities and potentials of the students themselves. Though these are difficult to assess, the scores on the science section of the MCAT have generally been given significant weight by medical school faculties, and there is evidence that they do serve as a measure of the applicant's preparation for medical school (at least as medical education is oriented at the present time (Funkenstein, 1966; Sedlacek & Hutchins, 1966). It is therefore useful to look at the schools under examination as ranked by student performance on the science section of the MCAT (Table 5). The average score on the science examination for the freshman classes entering medical school in 1965 ranged from a high average of 656 in one school to a low of 446. In general, we find that students in schools whose student bodies have higher average MCAT scores are in schools in which more resources—as measured by average expenditures per full-time student—are (or can be) devoted to their education. The highest quartile of private

TABLE 5 *Expenditures, student composition, and professional activity of graduates of United States medical schools; quartile averages for schools grouped in order of MCAT science performance, 1965–66*

Type of school and quartile*	MCAT science score	Total expenditures per full-time student	M.D. candidates per full-time student	Number of M.D. candidates in first-year class	Percent of all first-year students
Public					
Highest	577	$13,942	0.46	120	14.1
Second	547	10,934	0.49	117	13.7
Third	525	11,568	0.60	92	10.8
Lowest	495	10,266	0.63	114	14.8
Private					
Highest	618	16,971	0.41	102	12.0
Second	579	16,798	0.43	93	10.9
Third	559	8,647	0.51	97	11.4
Lowest	509	10,159	0.62	88	12.4

*Each group includes 10 schools except "lowest public," which includes 11 schools, and "lowest private," which includes 12 schools. The data are means for the quartiles.

schools have a student body with average MCAT scores of 618 and average expenditures of $17,000 per full-time student. They account for 21 percent of total expenditures (though for only 12 percent of first-year students and 16 percent of total full-time students). At the other extreme is the lowest quartile of public institutions, whose student bodies have average MCAT scores of 495 and who have average expenditures per full-time student of $10,300. They account for only 9 percent of total expenditures but for 15 percent of first-year students and 11 percent of total full-time students.

From the data presented thus far, it is evident that America's medical educational institutions have differing output mixes and graduate students who go on to differing tasks. They bring together different combinations of inputs and admit students with different preparation and abilities.

Table 1 illustrated the wide range of differences that exist in American medical schools (even when the range is reduced by grouping schools in quartiles and presenting averages for quartiles). Successive tables examined some of these differences in greater detail. These cross-tabulations indicated that the various indices for medical schools are related on the average. Table 6 presents

Number of full-time students	Percent of all full-time students	Total expenditures per school (in thousands)	Expenditures as percent of total expenditures of all schools	Percent of physician graduates, 1950–1959, who were general practitioners in 1967	Percent of physician graduates, 1950–1959, on medical school faculties in 1967
993	15.5	$13,838	17.0	18	7
897	14.0	9,802	12.0	26	5
563	8.8	6,511	8.0	31	6
666	11.4	6,833	9.2	32	4
1,012	15.8	17,173	21.1	10	12
829	13.0	13,924	17.1	17	9
740	11.6	6,399	7.8	19	6
526	9.9	5,342	7.9	23	4

SOURCES: Unpublished data from the AAMC and AMA annual questionnaires. Published data from *Journal of the American Medical Association*, 1966; and Theodore et al., 1968. The data are for the 83 four-year medical schools in active operation in the continental United States in 1965–66.

simple and rank correlation matrices for the various indices. A number of the correlations are quite high. Furthermore, the correlations are considerably higher for the private schools than for the public institutions: the various characteristics (and their relationships) exhibit much more variation for the public schools within each grouping than they do for the private schools. In general, however, the data portray groups of schools sharply differentiated in the amount of resources available to them, as well as in the proportion of their educational effort allocated among M.D. candidates and graduate students (including interns and residents) in the basic and clinical sciences and in the apparent abilities of the M.D. candidates as demonstrated on the science section of the MCAT.

These differences affect and are affected by financial considerations and by the various sources and mechanisms of funding. They also affect and are affected by institutional arrangements and the decision-making process within the institution.

INSTI-TUTIONAL ARRANGE-MENTS   Medical schools, unlike other parts of universities, are heavily engaged in service. Some members of their faculties spend a high proportion of their time in patient care. Much of this time is spent

TABLE 6
Simple and rank correlations for expenditures and student composition, United States medical schools, 1965–66

Type of school and correlation	Total expenditures	Expenditures per full-time student	MCAT science score
Public			
Simple correlations			
Expenditures per full-time student	0.612		
Average MCAT science score	0.578	0.317	
M.D. candidates per full-time student	−0.631	−0.529	−0.661
Rank (Spearman) correlations			
Expenditures per full-time student	0.544		
Average MCAT science score	0.566	0.370	
M.D. candidates per full-time student	−0.621	−0.558	−0.634
Private			
Simple correlations			
Expenditures per full-time student	0.869		
Average MCAT science score	0.730	0.613	
M.D. candidates per full-time student	−0.651	−0.550	−0.648
Rank (Spearman) correlations			
Expenditures per full-time student	0.866		
Average MCAT science score	0.827	0.684	
M.D. candidates per full-time student	−0.745	−0.629	−0.621

SOURCES: Unpublished data from the AAMC and AMA annual questionnaires. Published data from *Journal of the American Medical Association,* 1966. The data are for the 83 four-year medical schools in active operation in the continental United States in 1965–66.

in conjunction with the faculty's teaching function. The students learn medicine not only in the lecture hall, from the textbook, and in the library, but also at the bedside of the patient.

Hospital Relations

Considerable disquietude on the part of students is associated with the fact that most often they learn at the hospital bedside. There is an increasing pressure upon medical education to arrange learning situations involving patients outside the hospital walls. The argument is that most medical care is rendered to ambulatory patients and does not involve hospitalization. One analysis has pointed out:

It appears that within an average month in Great Britain or the United States, for every 1000 adults (sixteen years of age and over) in the population, about 750 will experience what they recognize and recall as an episode of illness or injury. Two hundred and fifty of the 750 will consult a physician at least once during that month. Nine of the 250 will be hospitalized, five will be referred to another physician, and one will be sent to a university medical center within that month. (White, Williams, & Greenberg, 1961).

It is suggested that a new orientation in medical education would therefore also achieve a greater emphasis on community medicine, social medicine, and preventive medicine. A greater emphasis on the out-of-hospital patient would necessitate the development of arrangements between the medical school and practicing physicians, neighborhood health centers, ambulatory health centers, and so forth.

Today, however, most "bedside" teaching is done in the hospital. As a consequence, the medical school is intimately related to the teaching hospital in both formal and informal ways and in financial arrangements. In some cases there are loose affiliations; in others the arrangements are much tighter, and in a number of cases the teaching hospital is owned and operated by the medical school or university. In all cases, however, the medical school must have a relationship with a teaching hospital (or hospitals) because medical education is structured in ways that require such relationships.

An outline of the relations has been developed in a study by Dr. Cecil Sheps and his associates (1965). This study, based for the most part on 1962 data, found that only a small proportion of hospitals in the United States (497 out of the total of 7,400) were affiliated with medical schools. The study estimated that, at most, 300 hospitals constitute the core for the instruction of undergraduate clinical education. And if only those general hospitals in which medical schools have major affiliations for undergraduate medical education in all four of the principal services—medicine, surgery, obstetrics-gynecology, and pediatrics—are counted, the total is only 89 hospitals in the entire country.[8] While most of the major affiliations of the private schools are with voluntary hospitals, the

[8] A large number of hospitals, it should be pointed out, offer internship and residency programs but are not affiliated with medical schools. In 1968–69 there were 631 teaching hospitals (with 341,000 beds) with affiliations, but there were 781 teaching hospitals (with 427,000 beds) without medical school affiliations. Most interns and residents were associated with affiliated hospitals (34,790 interns and residents of the total of 45,258) (American Medical Association, 1969, p. 17; *Journal of the American Medical Association,* 1969, pp. 1494, 1502).

major affiliations of the public schools are predominantly with government hospitals. Proprietary hospitals are not a significant source of affiliations with American medical schools.

Whatever the form of affiliation, the pattern of ownership and control of the hospital, or the formal or informal working relationship between school and hospital, the facts that many schools have more than one affiliation, that the students and faculty are heavily involved in the operation of the hospital (or some departments), and that the hospital's staff and patients are heavily involved in the teaching responsibilities of the school create problems of quality control, standards, power, responsibility, and decision-making authority. These factors also create complex funding, budgeting, and accounting arrangements. A number of the difficulties and complexities that arise have been documented in the report of the Second Association of American Medical Colleges (AAMC) Administrative Institute, dealing with medical school–teaching hospital relations. Some of the specific financial considerations raised were:

a   Identification and allocation of costs between the medical school and the teaching hospital, e.g., full-time faculty and residents' salaries, outpatient department losses, space for offices and research, and teaching beds.

b   Allocation of income that results from activities of clinical faculty, e.g., from research and research training grants, both direct and indirect costs; from professional services to patients; from professional activity in such units as the diagnostic laboratories, X-ray, anesthesiology, and physical medicine and rehabilitation.

c   The additional cost of running a teaching hospital vis-à-vis the comparable cost of a nonteaching institution, e.g., research beds, increased house staff, increased length of patient stay, and increased number of laboratory procedures ordered (Nourse, 1965, p. 54).

These are the very complications that will also create difficulties in our analysis. Since the teaching hospital is engaged in educational activities, its educational costs should be included in estimating the total costs of medical education. Yet the varying financing arrangements affect the apparent income and expenditures of both the schools and hospitals. In some cases, for example, the salaries of house officers are borne jointly by the hospital and the medical school (raising the problem of apportioning the time devoted to their own education, to the teaching of medical students, and to service). In other cases the school pays a flat, given proportion of the full costs of a resident. In still other situations, salaries are set by negotiations between the hospital administrator and the chairman of the department to which the resident is assigned, and stipends may vary from service to service. In its annual medical school questionnaire, the AAMC asks the schools to report teaching hospital expenditures that directly support regular medical college programs, such as faculty salaries paid by the hospital and rental value of classrooms and other space provided by the hospital. Given the variation in institutional arrangements, it is doubtful that there is great consistency in this reporting among schools.

The task of analysis and cost allocation is also made difficult by complex arrangements within the hospital. Some teaching hospitals make all their beds available for teaching purposes. Others make only a limited number available. Historically, charity patients in wards have provided the predominant teaching material. The rapid increase in third-party payment for medical services has altered that situation considerably. As increasing proportions of patients either pay their bills or have them paid by a third party (insurance carrier, Medicare, Medicaid, and so forth), more and more patients can be considered private patients. This, of course, has required the education of the patients. They have had to be informed that any "invasion of privacy" is more than counterbalanced by the advantages of the teaching environment. When this has been done, they have usually offered much less resistance to the new pattern of medical care than had been anticipated.

Faculty Payment   The strong interrelation of teaching and patient care has necessitated the development of a variety of arrangements for compensating clinical faculty members. This is the faculty that teaches students, primarily in the hospital environment. Thus these faculty members are taking care of patients and are directly or indirectly involved in the transfer of funds that pay for that care. Some of them are active in the affairs of the medical school and view themselves primarily as faculty whose classroom is the hospital. Others view themselves primarily as practicing physicians whose links are to the patients whom they serve and not to the development of the medical school. By title and activity they are part of the academic world of medicine; by values and orientation they are part of the world of the practicing physician. Furthermore, and of great importance in the development of arrangements for compensation, faculty members are aware that the income of an able clinician in private practice is significantly higher than the general level of university salaries. Since much of what the clinical faculty member does is what he would do if he were not a faculty member, that is, since his work does not, as is often argued for the rest of academic activity, represent a "different way of life," it is difficult to assert that the possible differential between the academic salary and the income level the individual might obtain outside the ivy walls is compensated for by psychic income. The clinician is already, even as a faculty member, outside those walls, and the income differentials are usually too large to be fully compensated for by nonmonetary benefits.

Thus the nature of the faculty and of the teaching activity and the level of physician incomes and the salaries offered in the academic world have necessitated the development of special arrangements for the clinical faculty: the development of what has come to be called the *medical service plan.* The particular plan developed depends on such factors as the amount of budgetary support, the number of full-time and part-time faculty members, economic pressures from the local medical community, hospital facilities for private patients, the research orientation of the faculty, the location of the medical school and university, state laws, and federal legislation and regulations.

The various plans developed to compensate clinical faculty members take into account the fact that there are usually considered to be four basic categories of clinical faculty members.

A *strict full-time* faculty member is compensated entirely by salary and has his only office at the medical school or hospital, and his private patients, if any, pay their fees to the medical school or teaching hospital.

The *geographic full-time* faculty member receives a salary, but is permitted to supplement it by fees from private patients. He has his only office at the medical school or affiliated hospital and usually has restrictions placed on the maximum income he can earn. These restrictions are put directly on professional incomes, either as a percentage of the base salary or as a restriction on the sum of salary and supplement, or indirectly, as restrictions on the amount of time the faculty member may allocate to private patient care. Some schools vary their restrictions by faculty rank, allowing senior faculty members greater supplementation, while other schools negotiate restrictions with individual faculty members.

The *part-time* and *volunteer* faculty members are primarily practicing physicians who devote some time to teaching medical students. The former receive monetary remuneration for their time; the latter receive none.

The 1967–68 medical school salary study of the AAMC provides information on the relationship between the salaries paid strict full-time faculty members and those paid geographic full-time faculty members, as well as on the incomes of the latter group. The analysis in Table 7 is limited to the four clinical departments of surgery, internal medicine, pediatrics, and obstetrics-gynecology. The department of pediatrics makes the least use of geographic full-time arrangements; the department of surgery makes the greatest use. Faculty members on the geographic full-time system, as would be expected, receive average salaries which are lower than those for strict full-time faculty members. The ratios of these averages will vary with the department and with the rank of the faculty member. In general, however, they fall between 65 and 90 percent with full professors (and obstetrics and gynecology) at the low end, and associate and assistant professors (and internal medicine and pediatrics) at the higher ratios. The average supplementations of geographic full-time faculty members are inversely related to the ratio of average salaries. They are lowest for assistant professors (and for the department of pediatrics) and highest for full professors (and the department of surgery). Average supplementations range from a low of 12 percent to a high of almost 85 percent.

Part-time faculty members are a significant resource for the education of medical students. In the academic year 1966–67, the 89 medical schools reported that there were 38,331 part-time faculty members (of whom 35,853 were serving in clinical departments). This compared with a total of 19,296 full-time faculty members.[9] But the full significance of these data is difficult to interpret because data on average number of hours worked by

[9] It should be recognized that the distribution of full-time and part-time faculty members is different for clinical and nonclinical departments. There were almost three times as many part-time as full-time faculty members in the clinical departments, while there were over twice as many full-time as part-time faculty members in the basic science departments (*Journal of the American Medical Association,* 1967, p. 750).

Patterns of appointment vary considerably by school. There was, for example, a strong relationship between the ratio of part-time faculty members to full-time faculty members and expenditures per full-time student for the private schools. The ratio for the schools in the quartile of highest per-student expenditures was 1.3, while it was 2.9 for the schools in the quartile of lowest per-student expenditures.

TABLE 7 Ratios of strict and geographic full-time salaries and income of faculty in United States medical schools, by selected departments, 1967–68

Type of ratio and department	Department chairmen	Professor	Associate professor	Assistant professor
Total number reporting strict or geographic full-time salaries				
Surgery	63	196	175	267
Internal medicine	66	326	404	556
Pediatrics	46	123	177	320
Obstetrics-gynecology	41	34	75	112
Ratio of number of strict full-time to total				
Surgery	44.4	52.0	45.7	57.7
Internal medicine	51.5	60.1	64.6	67.1
Pediatrics	63.0	69.9	75.1	74.7
Obstetrics-gynecology	56.1	61.8	53.3	69.6
Ratio of average salary of geographic full-time to average salary of strict full-time*				
Surgery	73.2	64.3	79.3	77.1
Internal medicine	79.9	80.9	85.8	85.0
Pediatrics	83.8	79.8	83.5	87.5
Obstetrics-gynecology	68.2	71.3	76.1	72.3
Ratio of number reporting total income to geographic full-time				
Surgery	65.7	68.1	64.2	54.9
Internal medicine	71.9	63.1	53.1	56.8
Pediatrics	64.7	64.9	56.8	58.0
Obstetrics	66.7	53.8	65.7	58.8
Ratio of average income of geographic full-time to average salary of geographic full-time*				
Surgery	140.7	183.9	142.8	134.2
Internal medicine	116.1	131.7	122.7	118.4
Pediatrics	117.3	120.2	119.4	112.5
Obstetrics-gynecology	156.9	154.1	128.4	133.1

*These are ratios of averages (not averages of individual ratios).
SOURCE: Association of American Medical Colleges, 1967, pp. 4–7, 14–17, 24–27.

part-time faculty members are unavailable. A 1966 survey of the faculty in departments of obstetrics-gynecology (limited in scope and, perhaps, unrepresentative) did, however, indicate that on the average, each part-time faculty member devoted about three hours per week to teaching and absorbed 12.6 percent of the total departmental budgets, while each voluntary faculty member devoted an average of about one-half hour per week to teaching (Association of Professors of Gynecology and Obstetrics, 1967).

The diversity in the ratio of full-time to part-time faculty members is portrayed in Table 8. Several schools had more than five times as many part-time as full-time faculty members, while at the other extreme, some schools used relatively few part-time faculty members. If, as is likely, part-time faculty members are relatively inexpensive per man-hour of teaching, this is obviously true in the case of volunteer faculty members — monetary expenditures of schools which utilize substantial numbers of part-time manpower will understate the true cost of the educational effort and enterprise. It is therefore likely that there is a substantial understatement of the cost of education for the nation.[10]

Of increasing importance, in terms of the activities of faculty members, the environment within which they work, the relationships implied by the environment, and the compensation of faculty members, are group practice plans. These plans, frequently developed as a response to Medicare and/or Medicaid programs and their payment regulations, may be rather substantial enterprises. The gross volume of group practice plans for 10 schools providing financial information in a 1967 survey ranged from $350,000 to $3 million.[11] Of the 72 four-year schools reporting in that survey, 22 schools had a school-wide group practice plan in operation, and an additional 16 schools stated that they were at various stages of development of such a plan. Five of the 22 plans began operation in

TABLE 8
Ratio of full-time to part-time faculty in United States medical schools, 1966–67

Ratio (full-time to part-time faculty)	Number of schools
Under 0.20	4
0.20 to 0.39	27
0.40 to 0.59	20
0.60 to 0.99	14
1.00 to 1.99	6
2.00 to 4.99	5
5.00 and over	5

SOURCES: Unpublished data from the AAMC and AMA annual questionnaires. Published data from *Journal of the American Medical Association*, 1966. The data are for the 83 four-year medical schools in active operation in the continental United States in 1965–66. Two of the 83 schools included in our analysis did not provide this information.

[10] The true cost of faculty services should be measured by the value of forgone activity. The problem of measurement of value and real cost in the educational sector in general is extremely difficult. The medical school is no exception.

[11] These data and the remainder of the material related to group practice plans are taken from Hardy, 1968, pp. 907–911, and from a release by Hardy (n.d.).

1967. Each of these schools stated that Medicare and/or Medicaid had an effect on the creation of the plan. Four other schools had developed (or were developing) an association or group for the purpose of billing Medicare and Medicaid patients.

Given the diversity among medical schools, the differences in arrangements for the distribution of funds collected under the group plans are considerable. While the details of the individual plans are not of special interest in the context of this study, there is perhaps no simpler way to indicate the considerable variation in compensation arrangements among the schools than to list Hardy's summary of answers in response to a survey question asking whether professional earnings went to the individual, to the department, or into the general school budget:

1   All to departments (1 school).

2   Primarily to individuals and/or departments with voluntary contributions to central research and development funds; salaries not tied to rank; no institutional ceilings (2 schools).

3   To general support of school; use determined by dean; everyone on a straight salary (1 school).

4   Fifteen per cent to Medical Sciences Fund to cover deficits in hospital, school, or clinic and for expansion and development; 25 per cent of remainder used as an incentive bonus relating to departmental income; 75 per cent of remainder for academic salaries and benefits; no institutional ceilings (1 school).

5   All for salary support; controlled by clinical department chairmen; no direct relationship of earnings to income; all clinical faculty on a straight salary (6 schools).

6   Same as number 5 except that the part of salary which comes from fees is not guaranteed and must be earned; all clinical faculty on straight salary, but salary not tied to rank (1 school).

7   To individuals up to a ceiling; 25 per cent of the remainder goes to school administration; 75 per cent of the remainder goes to the department (3 schools).

8   Primarily to departments for salaries and expenses; fixed salaries, 10 per cent of balances in departmental funds goes to dean's fund (1 school).

9   To special school account; pays up to one-half of salaries of clinicians; balances used at discretion of the dean in consultation with the clinical faculty (1 school).

10 Fees for consultations go to individuals; other income is divided equally among the department, the school, departmental research, and fringe benefits for earning faculty (1 school) (Hardy, 1968, p. 909).[12]

The extent and distribution of funds through medical service plans can affect the apparent and actual financial condition of the medical school while also affecting the amount of faculty time allocated to patient care. The plan can affect the incentive to submit or collect bills and to keep departmental expenses under close scrutiny (Hunter, 1956, p. 487).

A number of the points raised in the previous sections have significant implications for other parts of the greater university. Many of the features which set the medical school apart from the university relate to its specific orientation to "service." Patient care and service are an important part of the teaching activity and are intimately related to it. This has affected the salary structure in the medical school, the nature of faculty appointments, and so forth. It has also required the development of close relations with the service institution, the hospital. Since it seems to be the case that the entire university is increasingly being drawn into the problems of the community of which it is a part (it has usually viewed itself as apart from the community and must now find a way also to be a part of the community) and may become increasingly involved in service functions, the experience of the medical school may turn out to have broad implications.

Decision Making The decision-making structure in the medical school is affected by the various arrangements for compensating the faculty and for distributing income from group practice arrangements, the various types of faculty positions and proportions of full- and part-time faculty members, the locus of the educational activity, and the demands placed upon the medical school for various kinds of output. The medical school differs from a business firm in that its profits play no role in the determination of its operations (though the behavior of individuals and departments, for example, anesthesiology, radiology, and clinical laboratories, may be affected). However, in many cases the decision makers at the school find that the budget available to them depends, in some measure, on their choice of out-

[12] Eighteen schools are represented in the answers. Responses from four of the schools made income distribution unclear.

puts. Even though they are not maximizing "profits," they may desire to maximize the total budget, and this would, to some degree, affect the choice of outputs.

The total budget, however, is not the only variable that the different decision makers are trying to maximize. The decision-making structures include persons representing the interests of the university, medical school, teaching hospital, faculty, and students. There is no single individual who is *the* decision maker. There is no single goal that is sought or output that is being maximized. The various decision makers represent many different viewpoints and constituencies, and thus there is substantial room for differences and conflict between them.

There are several decision-making structures in the medical schools. Major decisions, dealing with the opening of a medical school and with university funding, are made at the highest level by the trustees and the president and, in the case of state-supported and state-controlled institutions, often by the state legislature. Seventy-two of the 83 four-year medical schools in full operation in 1966 had university affiliations. (This was also true for all 16 schools under development in 1967–68.) Twenty-eight of these schools were located on the general campus of the affiliated university, and 25 were in the same metropolitan area as the general campus. Most of the 18 schools with campuses in different metropolitan areas were public institutions (16 of the 18), and most of them were affiliated with a land-grant institution in a rural location (Blumberg & Clarke, 1967). When the medical school is part of a larger and more extensive medical center (which includes a university hospital and schools of dentistry, pharmacy, nursing, and public health, for example), there has been a tendency, particularly during the last decade, to appoint a vice-president for medical affairs. In 1965 there were 54 institutions with a vice-president for medical affairs or equivalent, and in 38 of these cases the vice-president was a different individual from the dean of the medical school (Seipp, 1967).

The dean of the medical school is the individual charged with the general responsibility for the school's operation. His office is responsible for the allocation of the school's budgeted general funds among the various departments and activities. Deans do not, however, have a high degree of control which they can exercise as they see fit. In part, this restraint arises from the high value the modern university places on discourse and the diffusion of "ownership" among alumni, faculty, students, and the general public, as well as the administration. In the medical school the problem is even more severe because of the school's involvement in service and consequent need to consider its relations with private providers of service—the medical professions. Finally, and perhaps most importantly, in the medical school there is the additional constraint imposed as a result of the receipt of earmarked funds, particularly in the form of research grants to individual faculty members. Earmarked or sponsored funds are usually restricted to the support of specific activities. An increasing and high proportion of the total medical school budget comes from such funds made available to individuals with only *pro forma* involvement by the school and the dean's office. Such funds, though included in the medical school budget, cannot be allocated by the dean. This restricts his ability to institute new programs and to effect change. Thus, as one dean put it at a recent AAMC institute: "Although the net effect of the relative abundance of such funds [research] undoubtedly has been beneficial, it has, to a rather disquieting extent, taken control of the institution's program and its destiny out of the hands of the university administration and given it to the granting agencies" (*Journal of Medical Education,* 1967c, pp. 73–74).

One cannot fail to be impressed with the circumstances in which the dean finds himself: He is important, but he has limited power. He affects morale, he creates a climate of opinion, and he can bring change over time by the force of logic, by cajoling, and by persuasion. He can anticipate pressures for change and can unite individuals behind a banner and standard. He can give a sense of purpose to an institution composed of individuals with diverse interests and loyalties. But he must do most of this outside the confines of his budget. Over time he may be able to add to his budget resources, especially for new programs. But he can do this only slowly. "Instant change" is not one of his options. On the one hand, he must work with the nonclinical faculty, whose support comes in considerable measure from sponsored funds. On the other hand, he must work with the clinical faculty, who are in the hospital (with its own set of constraints) and whose support comes, in considerable measure, from patient care. To effect change in nonclinical priorities is difficult because priorities there are determined by granting agencies. And it is no easier to effect change in the hospital, which often is a free-standing institution.

Thus many a dean who has anticipated the changes that medical practice of the future may entail and who has attempted to redirect his institution's interests to prepare for the future and better meet the needs of the present may be frustrated by his inability to bring about change with the speed that is required. To this frustration is undoubtedly added another dimension: the fact that students fail to recognize the limited power that the dean may have and therefore view shortcomings of the school as directly attributable to the limited commitment of the dean. Curiously, therefore, students often represent a source of power for the dean (though, given the nature of student involvement, this cannot generally be considered an unmixed blessing). It is they who have often spurred constructive change in health care, particularly in outpatient clinics, and who have emphasized the need to admit more students from minority groups and to redirect increased emphasis to education.

In some schools, the most powerful formal decision makers are the faculty members.[13] Full-time faculty members in the medical school work in a different institutional setting from that of faculty members in other parts of the university. The school's dependence on the earnings provided by clinical faculty members (or, alternatively, the fact that the clinician receives major parts of his income from outside the medical school salary) and its additional dependence on the research grants received by individual faculty members have placed the faculty in a position of considerable independence. Nevertheless, because clinicians must have hospital appointments and because research grants are "soft money," a relatively small proportion of faculty members have tenured positions. At a recent AAMC Institute on Administration a vice-president for medical affairs articulated his concern: "There are problems arising from the fact that a substantially larger proportion of medical school personnel are supported by outside sources of income in contrast to the parent institution, resulting in different application of the institution's policies with respect to reappointment and tenure" (*Journal of Medical Education,* 1967c, p. 139).

Faculty power therefore tends to be concentrated in the hands of a relatively few senior faculty members who hold tenured appointments and who tend to be heavily involved in the school's affairs.

[13] In other parts of the university one would write "is the faculty." In a medical school, however, the role of individuals *as individuals* is perhaps more significant than that of the organized faculty. Medical faculties have divided loyalties, interests, and locations and are therefore a much less cohesive group than would be true of groups in other parts of the university. Furthermore, the majority of the medical school faculty are part-time or voluntary faculty.

The bulk of the faculty tend to be more heavily involved with peer groups or with patients. Bethesda (the home of the National Institutes of Health) or the hospital is more familiar and important to them than the dean's office.

The fact that there are few untied resources that can be redirected and that those concerned with the total budget are aware that individual faculty members generate income for the institution and moneys which finance their own salaries creates a difficult situation for the decision makers. Much of the faculty teaches in a setting that is removed physically and in spirit from the medical school itself. The students tend to disappear from the school for their years of clinical training, and interns and residents have no direct involvement with the school as a total institution. A significant proportion of the total student body, the basic science students, are pursuing studies which are considered an appendage to the medical school by some faculty members, and teaching them is considered only a secondary mission by many. All these factors add to the complexities.

Thus it is that individuals who are familiar with the problems faced in American medical education agree that deans do not have the ability to allocate resources as they desire. Deans echo this concern, and a number report that only a very small proportion of their budget can, in any meaningful sense, be considered discretionary. Furthermore, they often indicate that if, for example, they had the same federal support to use as they saw fit, they would not spend it as it is being spent.

While one can sympathize with these deans, an argument can be made that public money should be allocated by the public and its representatives. If the nation has priorities, can it rely on the individual deans to reflect them adequately? On the other hand, it can be argued that innovation can, under many circumstances, be instituted more readily at the "local" level than in a national program that may fail to take account of the diversity that is one of the hallmarks of our institutions. Thus it is argued that national priorities should be set but that each institution should make its own path toward the goal. A balance must be struck, but in the financing of medical education the nation is very far from a balance.

The need to accept restrictive grants that make it possible to use additional faculty members partially for a desired purpose, but at the same time for a less desired one, is prevalent. Combined with the ability of faculty members to determine the allocation of their efforts, their ability to allocate and reallocate scarce resources of the medical school seems limited. This, then, helps reinforce the common cry for additional resources. As in other institutions, it is easier to visualize undertaking new activities by acquiring funds than by reallocating resources from existing to new programs. In part, this may involve a desire to avoid conflict within the school. In part, however, it may be that some deans do not want to assume the additional responsibility for decision making and that some faculty members resist a transfer of authority to the deans and away from their peers such as persons on the National Institutes of Health study groups who currently determine the allocation of NIH research funds to individuals.[14] Furthermore, since many of the existing programs and activities in the medical school are financed by funds which can be used only to a limited extent for purposes other than the specific ones for which they were given, the shift of significant amounts becomes doubly hard to accomplish, if not impossible.

This, then, brings us to the discussion of the sources of medical school funds.

[14] For an excellent discussion of these points see Kidd, 1962, pp. 95–122.

3. Funding Problems and the Evolution of the Financial Structure

FUNDING PROBLEMS
The funding problems we shall examine in this section fall into three main categories. First, there are the problems associated with the changing structure of the medical school finances. Second, there are the problems associated with the increasing demands placed upon the medical schools as perceived and felt by medical school administrators. Finally, there are the problems faced by the less affluent schools which may close or lose their accreditation. Individual schools, and the system in general, face other problems. There are problems associated with the high cost of medical education to the student and the impact that these costs have on the selection of students and on their behavior when they become practicing physicians. Additionally, there are issues associated with the determination of the needed number of medical schools and students and the patterns of financing expansion of enrollment. These problems will be discussed elsewhere in this volume.

Suggestions that American medical schools face financial difficulties have been with us for some time. In 1950, the Surgeon General's Committee on Medical School Grants and Finances (U.S. Federal Security Agency, 1951, p. 52) stated that "shortages of personnel, operating funds, and space have handicapped the majority of schools and in many instances have necessitated curtailment of activities." The financial need for operating support was estimated at $40 million (U.S. Federal Security Agency, 1951, p. 59). Two years later, an article by Darley (1953, p. 11) began with the statement, "Inadequate financing is a threat to the nation's medical schools. Sufficient funds, free of outside control, must be provided if the schools are to continue their progress." He estimated (p. 13) that an additional income of $20 million was needed for instructional purposes. Millett (1952, p. 178), in his general study of financing higher education, stated, "At universities, both public and private, presidents and vice-presidents or deans in charge of academic policy spoke almost unanimously of their concern about the costs of medical education. No other educational program within universities received so much comment or appeared even closely to approach medical education as a major financial worry." He focused his discussion on the high ratio of medical school instructional expenditures to total university instructional expenditures and on the generally high cost of medical education brought about by high faculty salaries and attendant hospital charges.

These comments were made some 15 to 20 years ago. During the intervening years, however, medical school expenditures have risen from about $100 million to over $1 billion. Even taking into account the necessary adjustments for the change in price levels, the medical schools received the $40 million (and more) and their educational funds increased by the $20 million (and more) that earlier were seen as their estimated needs. Yet we still witness a flow of articles on the funding problems of medical schools and on the medical schools' weak financial status.[1]

Difficulties associated with the structure of financial support, assumed to be felt by almost all institutions, relate chiefly to the dichotomy between hard money and soft money and to the restrictions imposed on the uses to which outside funds can be put. The distinction between hard and soft money is generally clear, but what may appear to be soft money to one institution would be considered hard money by another. Generally, the term *hard money* refers to funds which can be depended upon with little risk (and, of course, which are received by the institution rather than by an individual faculty member). *Soft money,* on the other hand, represents funds which may be received for some defined period of time but which cannot be counted on beyond that defined period. Tuition, endowment income, and contractual teaching hospital funds are generally considered hard money.[2] Funds from state government and university transfers are also generally considered hard money, even though there is a degree of uncertainty about the fund-

---

[1] See, for example, "Ailing Medical Schools Face Budget Cut Coup de Grace," 1968, p. A–4; Cohn, 1968, p. B2; and Walsh, 1968, pp. 668–671.

[2] Even these kinds of funds entail elements of risk, but the risk is relatively small. Tuition income can be controlled to some degree by the institution, and endowment income may be greater than the minimum assumed by the institution for adjustment of internal policy (that is, a portion of endowment income can be assumed to be hard, and the remainder then becomes somewhat softer).

ing level for future periods. General research grants and institutional basic improvement grants by the federal government present classification problems—there is some element of certainty regarding their future continuation, but there may be considerable variation in their size, depending upon budgetary conditions and priorities. Project research and training grants generally fall into the soft-money category since they need not be renewed, though they may be.

The difference between hard and soft money, as viewed by the administrator engaged in long-run decision making and planning, is considerable. Since soft money is here today but may be gone tomorrow, it cannot be counted on. Commitments that are based upon such money must be short-term commitments, not to exceed the time period during which the administrator can be relatively certain of the money (that is, the period during which it may be considered hard). Obviously, since risk elements are always present, the probability of having particular funds in the future falls somewhere between 0.0 and 1.0 rather than at one or the other extreme. Administrators, therefore, are always balancing risks. Seldom do they deal in absolutes. It can be argued that in the given year all money, from whatever source received, is hard money and that what is being weighed is the probability that the hard money will also be available as hard money in some subsequent year. Soft money would then be considered money with a low probability of availability in the future (though how low is "low" is a subjective matter).

Schools are generally reluctant to make a long-term commitment based on soft money, for example, grant tenure to an individual whose salary is supported by project grants. They fear that the loss of the grant would place the burden of support on the medical school budget and that they might then not be able to fulfill the commitment. Often, schools attempt to circumvent that difficulty when they are restricted from offering tenure but feel that there is every likelihood that the grant will continue or that other grants will provide future financing. They then attempt to create new categories of faculty appointments that offer the tenure advantages of academic freedom, fringe benefits, and so forth, but do not imply a full commitment for future salary support.

Faculty members, realizing that their relationship with the school is contingent on the continued receipt of funds, must place considerable emphasis on attracting additional grants. In the process they find it increasingly advantageous to associate with their peer groups, to feel a loyalty to them rather than to the school, to let the nature of their salary support affect their allocation of effort, and so forth. The overall goals of the school may well be slighted as key faculty members view their principal responsibility as that of ensuring a financial base for their own empires (however small or large they may be) rather than as having the school as their primary concern. There are also grave implications for academic freedom associated with this method and type of funding. To the extent that faculty members must rely upon government grants made upon application by individuals, that is, by the "principal investigator," and to the extent that the university does not provide tenure, the possibility exists that individuals, even though in a university environment, may be inhibited from stating their views on a variety of matters, particularly those regarding federal programs and policies. Though recent criticism of federal policies by members of university faculties does not suggest that faculty voices are muted because of the source of funding, the possibility that this might be the case is ever present.

Uncertainties associated with the continued receipt of soft money make it extremely difficult for schools to engage in meaningful long-range planning. To the extent that the money is very soft, even short-run planning becomes difficult. The administrator, after all, must plan in terms of specific programs, curricula, and faculty. Even if the size of the total budget can be predicted with some degree of certainty, the lack of knowledge concerning individual grants will make planning most difficult.

Sponsored funds have yet another impact in that they change the relative costs of producing different outputs by permitting medical schools to add more resources if they place their efforts in one direction (say, research) rather than another (say, education). Of course, this expresses the fact that those who provide the funds have a greater demand for one of the products than for another. Unrestricted funds, on the other hand, give the medical school administrator more freedom to guide the institution in the directions that he and other decision makers within the school consider best. This is why unrestricted funds provided by endowment income and gifts and grants are so important to the schools, particularly those schools which are privately controlled. During 1967–68, endowment income and unrestricted grants and gifts provided by foundations, corporations, and private individuals totaled $43.2 million and represented 10.6 percent of the medical school's total expenditures of $409 million for regular operating programs. These same sources also provided $67.0 million in contracts, gifts, and grants for research in 1967–68.[3]

With sponsored funds, decision makers have much less choice in allocating resources as between the broad areas of teaching, service, and research, and they may be forced to utilize resources for specific projects within these broad categories even if they do not consider them most valuable. Yet the most direct and perhaps the most successful way for society as a whole, as well as for specific groups, to indicate its preferences and priorities with respect to the behavior of medical schools is by means of the constraints placed upon the administrator through the financing system. To the extent that medical schools exist to serve the public interest (that, after all, is the basis upon which they seek public support in the first instance), these indications of priorities are most valuable. It is not at all clear that if each school acted in accordance with the priorities which it deemed important, the allocation of resources as a whole would be in the best national interest. "Public" priorities are required, though the medical school along with others should be involved in helping set them. This is the dilemma that we have alluded to earlier. The need is to devise systems of finance which allow the administrator to use his special knowledge and abilities in an optimum fashion but within the broad constraints imposed by society. The need is for "balance."

The second source of difficulty for medical schools, even in the face of rapidly expanding budgets for some of their activities, relates to the demands being placed upon them to undertake yet additional activities. It is frequently said that the major problems facing medicine have been brought about by its successes in developing new technology and knowledge to combat illness and that these have led to rapidly increasing demands upon health personnel. Perhaps it is closer to the truth to say that medicine's successes in expanding knowledge, combined with its relative failure to develop institutions to provide health services in an organized and efficient manner, has led to the major problems facing the medical sector. The

[3] The 1967–68 expenditure data in this chapter are from *Journal of the American Medical Association,* 1969, p. 1486. All overhead funds are treated as expenditures for sponsored programs, rather than for regular operating programs, since they are available only on the receipt of contracts and grants and supposedly only cover part of the costs induced by the sponsored programs.

effective and efficient provision of personal (and community) health services to ambulatory persons remains an underdeveloped area. As a result, and under pressures generated by personal commitment, by students, by the community, and recently by government, there are increasing demands placed upon schools to assume effective leadership in the provision of care. Regional medical program administrators, comprehensive health care planners, and supporters of the Office of Economic Opportunity's Neighborhood Health Centers—these and others are all looking to the medical schools and their faculties and students as the engines and agents of change in the health care system. The medical school is asked to shift its priorities and its funds.

Relatively few people believe that the constraints on the shifting of funds is real and that, though the total budget of the school is large, the "unearmarked" portion of the medical school budget is quite small. It is also true that some medical school administrators shy away from undertaking community projects with funds that are viewed as very soft. They fear involvement in programs which may be underfunded in future periods but which would, nevertheless, have to be continued because of community, student, political, and humanitarian pressures. Thus they fear that ultimately the medical school budget will be unable to sustain the activity and that the school, not Washington, will be subject to criticism. Furthermore, many faculty members are not interested in accepting responsibility for ambulatory health care programs or in providing students with educational opportunities involving "vertical" rather than "horizontal" patients. The role of the administrator is made even more difficult by the fact that the demand for involvement in community ambulatory care projects arises at a time when there is increasing pressure for expansion of the undergraduate medical student body, for more responsibility in the training of interns and residents, and for increases in the quantity and quality of continuing education programs.

It is therefore understandable that many medical school administrators express a need for substantial additional resources as they attempt to respond to the pressures outlined above. Some would prefer that there be no diminution of resources for the programs and activities in which they are now engaged. Others would be satisfied with a reallocation of present funds. Most, however, would agree that the existing funding structure does impede change.

It is not implied that all administrators agree on the importance of community ambulatory care projects or on some of the other priorities outlined above. Several deans have expressed doubts that the medical school's relationship with the ghetto community or the orientation of the faculty provides an optimum environment for successful Neighborhood Health Center activity. They would argue that other institutional frameworks should be developed to allow for better provision of needed health services. Other observers have questioned the ability of medical faculties to provide the quantity of health care services being asked of them, as well as the desirability of their doing so (Page, 1968, p. 261). Nor is it suggested that researchers are prepared to agree to a reallocation of funds. There are those who are convinced that biomedical research holds the answers to major health problems and that the discoveries yet to be made will have the greatest impact on the health status of the nation. Still others would argue that the medical school, like other parts of the university, should reinforce its teaching function, that which it is uniquely equipped to do, and leave more of the research function and activity to independent organizations (Keenan, 1966, p. 7). The school's role, in the eyes of many, is to educate, not to provide service (except perhaps in a research sense—as a means of showing how care can be provided).

Finally, we turn to the third of the problems mentioned earlier: the financial difficulties faced by specific medical schools. For although the total environment of American medical schools may be relatively affluent, not every school is in a favorable financial position.

Substantial variation in the wealth positions of medical schools has always been a feature of our system of higher education,[4] but the fact that there has always been substantial resource disparity does not make the present situation any more palatable to the

----

[4] We have shown that there is substantial variance in the performance on the science section of the MCAT on the part of the entering classes of different schools and that this variance is strongly correlated with the current size of the expenditures of the medical schools. Hutchins has shown that 50 percent of the variance in the caliber of the 1956 freshmen classes could be explained by the variance in the expenditures in a 1910 study (the Flexner report) (Hutchins, 1964, pp. 276–277). The range in total expenditures reported for private schools in that study was from a negligible amount in one school to about $250,000 for another school.

schools that feel undernourished. While no medical school has closed its doors since 1947, a number are convinced that they are on the brink of disaster.[5]

In the recent past, the schools usually listed as being faced to a greater or lesser degree with accreditation or survival problems have been Boston University, Tufts, Marquette, Chicago Medical School, Meharry, Jefferson, Hahnemann, Women's Medical College, Saint Louis University, George Washington University, Georgetown, Creighton, and Loyola Stritch. In fact, most of the 22 schools which received funds under the special improvement grants program of the federal government in the 1968 fiscal year were chosen because they could demonstrate that they were in serious financial straits. These schools, particularly those in the private school category, usually fall into the lowest two quartiles of schools ranked by expenditures per full-time student. The characteristics of those two quartiles can therefore generally be applied to the poor schools. Expenditures per student are relatively small; the ratio of full-time students to full-time faculty members is about 4.8 to 1, as opposed to a ratio of 2.7 to 1 for the higher-expenditure schools; and the ratio of full-time M.D. candidates to full-time faculty members is about 2.5 to 1, as compared with a ratio of 1.1 to 1 for the wealthier schools. In part this disparity is compensated for by the use of part-time faculty members; there are about three times as many part-time as full-time faculty members in the private schools in the quartile with the lowest expenditures per student, but only 1.3 times as many in the highest-expenditure-per-student quartile.

Judgments as to the true severity of the financial crisis facing the poor schools and possible solutions to their problems must be based on analyses of the reasons for their financial problems and of the effects of their relative poverty on their outputs.[6] Correspondence with deans from about one-half of the schools receiving special improvement grants and an examination of published materials

---

[5] In recent years several schools have shifted from private to public status: University of Buffalo School of Medicine (now the State University of New York at Buffalo), California College of Medicine (now part of the University of California system), and Seton Hall College of Medicine and Dentistry (now the New Jersey College of Medicine and Dentistry). Other private schools are increasingly dependent upon state financial support.

[6] Neither of these is easily handled by nonmedical experts since available data and objective studies are limited. It is hoped, however, that the information will assist in understanding the problem.

have enabled us to draw the following broad picture of the poorer schools.

First, it should be noted that all the Jesuit schools—Saint Louis, Georgetown, Creighton, Loyola Stritch, and Marquette—are among the poor schools and that most of the non-university-affiliated schools—Hahnemann, Jefferson, Women's Medical College, Chicago Medical School, Meharry—are also considered to be in difficulty.[7] All these schools place relatively great reliance on tuition and fees as a source of finance. The range of support from this source for the 10 schools is from 9 to 17 percent of total expenditures, with an average of 12.5 percent. ("Rich" private schools get 4 percent of their support from tuition and fees.) Furthermore, several of the poorest schools have found it necessary to use endowment fund capital for operating purposes. According to their reports, the Jesuit schools place relatively great and rapidly increasing demands on their universities. The sums received from the five universities ranged from $267,000 to $1.16 million, with a median of $390,000. Three of the schools had an annual rate of increase in receipt of university funds between 1959 and 1965 that fell between 11 and 27 percent. The rates were even higher for the remaining two schools. One of the Jesuit schools received 79 percent of its moneys as sponsored funds. The fact that it was "poor" while receiving 79 percent in sponsored funds only underlines the paucity of its own and discretionary resources: 21 percent of a small total budget.

Three of the non-university-affiliated schools—Hahnemann, Jefferson, and Women's Medical—are heavily dependent upon grants from the state of Pennsylvania for support and survival. Other poor private schools place substantial demands on the parent university, with one school reporting the receipt of $1.3 million in 1965–66. Demands placed on universities by medical schools are not proportional to the wealth of the universities. Many of the wealthier, strongly endowed universities provide few, if any, dollar resources to their medical schools since they are also strongly endowed and, in addition, receive substantial support from research and training grants.

From the responses to our inquiries, it was clear that the less affluent medical schools feel considerable pressure to participate in the changes taking place in medical education. They want to

[7] New York Medical College is not included in the analysis since it was only recently added to the list of nonaffiliated schools with severe financial problems.

participate in health service programs, they want to change their curricula in order to offer more freedom and more electives to their students, and they want to train more graduate students in the basic sciences and clinical fields. The need for additional full-time faculty in the basic sciences and in clinical subspecialties is felt to be of the highest priority. The schools compared their aggregate ratio of basic science faculty to medical students or the ratio of faculty in a particular department to medical students with the national average of that ratio and used their shortcomings as an indication of need.

Additional and improved clinical and teaching space was also frequently cited as a problem area. One confidential respondent noted: "We are presently using for our outpatient clinic, a building which was completed in the last century and which will during this year be destroyed for the highway system. We have leased a building formerly used as a student nurses residence and made minor modifications so as to continue the outpatient clinic as a teaching resource. . . . Our principal affiliated teaching hospital is composed of significant parts which were constructed in the 1880's and which do not meet present minimum standards."[8]

There is little question that some schools face serious financial and funding problems. Their resources are limited, and they depend heavily on their parent universities and on their students for support. Sometimes unable to compete effectively for research support, they find that they are without resources to build and improve their faculty. Aware that the federal government provides its chief support through research grants, they feel the need to attempt to emulate the schools that receive such support, even if this is not the road that they would wish to travel.[9]

It is understandable that many deans feel the need to emulate programs that are considered the "best" and of high prestige. At the same time, it is not at all clear that the attainment of such a goal,

[8] Letter dated Feb. 21, 1969.

[9] Sponsored funds, even though they often cannot be used as deans might desire, provide the financial underpinnings for many schools. They enable the school to have a larger and, in terms of interests, more broadly diffused faculty. Furthermore, some of the funds pay for teaching services. It is incorrect to assume that research funds are used only for research. They support other activities as well, and medical school officials are aware that a cutback in research funds, without the addition of other funds, would result in financial trauma, not only in the research programs that the funds support, but also in the entire school.

even if feasible, would represent the proper allocation of resources. Since the criteria for the "best" are sometimes narrowly conceived, emulating the best might mean that schools were trying to become like one another, even in their mix of outputs. It is not clear that this is desirable. Perhaps different schools should have different programs — striving to be best at what they do. Nor is it even clear that the best schools are allocating their resources in accordance with national needs. These are complex issues because we are all relatively ignorant of the effect of an increased faculty and improved facilities on the intermediate outputs — teaching, research, and service — and on the final outputs — physicians and other trained educated personnel, patient care outside and inside the hospital, and the benefits of research. A diversity of student mix, output orientation, resources, and other characteristics of medical schools probably is required to achieve an optimum allocation of scarce productive factors to meet local, regional, and national needs.

Yet the variation that exists is extreme, and one can hardly favor funding mechanisms that put some producing units at such a great disadvantage. Some schools, with heavy emphasis on the education of future physicians, are in grave danger at a time when the federal government and others are pressing for the expansion of undergraduate medical student bodies. Yet the significant funds available — growth in these funds has been severely reduced during the past several years — are research funds which are generally allocated to faculty on the basis of research ability. Since most of these higher-ability researchers prefer to work at schools with faculties of similar capabilities and superior facilities, they tend to locate in the "richer" schools (which are also able to offer attractive inducements, such as better students, higher salaries, and more prestige). Thus the wealthier schools receive even more aid from the federal government. This, in turn, makes it possible for them to offer superior educational programs (through their increased ability to obtain nonfederal grants and through their ability to utilize some of the federal moneys for teaching purposes).

There are those who argue that a school's inability to attract federal research grants is virtually conclusive evidence that it is unable to carry on an adequate teaching program. In our view, this argument is specious: (1) The word *adequate* is usually not well defined. Given the needs for physicians in some sections of the country and especially among low-income and minority groups, does one really believe that things would be better if these schools produced no physicians? We rather doubt that this is the case. (2) The federal research budget is not unlimited. Clearly, some scholars are unable to compete effectively for scarce research dollars. This inability, however, is dependent upon the budget allocation for research. With more dollars available, more persons would receive funds. With fewer dollars available, additional persons would fail to receive support. Thus, inability to compete (at a given budget level) indicates little—except in a relative sense—about research capabilities and even less about teaching abilities. (3) While research is intertwined with teaching, it is not clear that the association is such that each unit of teaching of a given quality must be tied to x dollars of research. Indeed, there is ample evidence that even the prestige schools use inputs in varying proportions. It is quite possible that major parts of the research activity are not associated in a significant way with effective training of future practitioners. [10]

None of the problems that we have discussed are insurmountable. None of them are "in the nature of things," to be accepted as "givens" and as something that we must make the best of. Many of them are affected by a variety of factors that are themselves subject to change. All of them are, at least in part, related to the financing pattern that has been developed to support the medical school and some of its activities. Thus it becomes necessary to examine this financing pattern in some detail.

In the remainder of this chapter we shall first discuss the development and evolution of the financing pattern. Then, using available data for the years 1959 and 1965, we shall be able to examine differences which have evolved in funding patterns between groups of schools ranked by expenditures per full-time student. Our analysis will show that although total expenditures (in current dollars) of United States medical schools increased at an annual rate of 14.6 percent between 1947 and 1967, nonsponsored funds in constant dollars (that is, adjusted for inflationary changes in prices)

---

[10] One of the less affluent schools informed us (letter dated Jan. 2, 1969) that its students ranked eleventh of 44 schools in performance on Part 1 of the National Board examinations (Part 1 consists of examinations in anatomy, biochemistry, microbiology, pathology, pharmacology, and physiology). While the school may have admitted more able students, and while a number of other factors might explain this observation, it at least suggests that the relationship between dollars in the total budget and quality of student performance is not as clear as some believe.

increased by only 4.25 percent per annum. Sponsored research funds accounted for more than one-half of the total increase in medical school receipts over the period, and federally sponsored research accounted for almost 85 percent of that growth. These moneys, as the latter part of this chapter will show, were unevenly distributed among schools. They reenforced the differences in total income available to the individual schools.

EVOLUTION OF THE FINANCIAL STRUCTURE In 1947 the 7 two-year and 70 four-year medical schools in the United States had an enrollment of 22,739 students seeking the M.D. degree. By 1967 there were only 5 two-year schools (including one in the developing process), but the number of four-year schools had increased to 88 (excluding one in Puerto Rico and including four developing ones). Enrollment of undergraduate medical students had grown to 34,304,[11] an increase of 51 percent (a compound rate of about 2.1 percent per year). During the same period, expenditures (in current dollars) grew from $72 million to $1.097 billion,[12] an increase of 14.6 percent per year. It is this extremely rapid and substantial growth that leads some observers to conclude that medical schools are "rich," or at least "well funded," and to question the need for additional resources for medical *education*. The rate of growth in expenditures can, however, be quite misleading.

It is true that the growth in total resources available to American medical schools has been substantial during the postwar period (Figure 1). Indeed, the percentage growth in the total expenditures of medical schools between 1947 and 1967 was about double that of the total current fund expenditures for all institutions of higher education. However, medical schools do much more than educate future medical doctors. Much of the increase in expenditures represents the expansion in activities other than the education of medical students. Further, much of the increase is made possible by the availability of funds for the other activities. To understand the significance of the dollar increases in expenditures, it is also necessary to adjust the data to take account of inflation, which had a substantial impact during this period. But it is difficult to assess

[11] This includes 270 part-time and special students (*Journal of the American Medical Association*, 1968, pp. 1995, 2017).

[12] Except where otherwise indicated, expenditures have been adjusted by subtracting one-half of federal teaching and training funds and all federal funds for foreign teaching programs. Expenditures data include the Puerto Rican school.

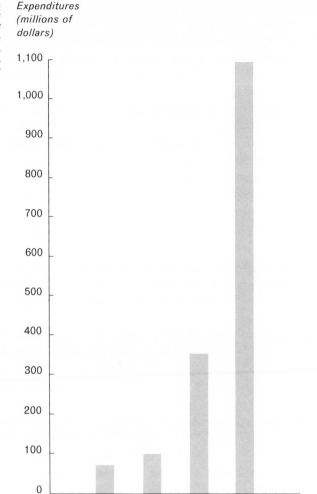

FIGURE 1
Total
expenditures of
United States
medical schools,
selected years,
1947–1967*

Expenditures
(millions of
dollars)

1,100

1,000

900

800

700

600

500

400

300

200

100

0

  1947–48   1951–52   1959–60   1967–68

*See footnote 12.

SOURCES: U.S. Federal Security Agency, Public Health Service, 1951b, pp. 33–36;
Deitrick & Berson, 1953, p. 82; *Journal of the American Medical Association,* 1961,
p. 587, and 1969, p. 1486.

the full impact of inflationary factors because we lack sufficient information on the medical school's "market basket," that is, the relative proportions of the various inputs. While we know that faculty
salaries increased and that the prices of materials, equipment, and
wages of nonfaculty personnel also rose, we do not know the rate
of increase of the various inputs or the weights to attach to each of
them. Nevertheless, it is possible to make some estimates of the

inflationary impact of faculty salaries, the single largest component of the medical school budget.[13]

Basic data taken from the annual faculty salary surveys of the AAMC indicate that during the period 1961–1967, salaries increased at an annual rate of about 6.5 percent for preclinical faculty, and about 5.5 percent for strict full-time clinical faculty. These data suggest that faculty salaries as a whole were increasing at a rate of about 6 percent per year during the period. If this rate had existed during the entire period 1951–1967, the level of faculty salaries would have increased somewhat more than $1\frac{1}{2}$ times over that period.[14] Other available information also indicates that the degree of inflation in faculty salaries was considerable. Deitrick and Berson (1953), for example, have reported that in a survey of 34 schools they found that in 1949–50 the *maximum* salaries for professors, associate professors, and assistant professors in the basic science faculty in tax-supported schools averaged $10,035, $6,747, and $6,007, respectively. By 1967, *average* salaries in these ranks were $20,268, $16,253, and $13,288 (Association of American Medical Colleges, 1967, p. 2).[15]

It is evident that the degree of inflation in faculty salaries accounts for a significant part of the growth in medical school expenditures. When total expenditures in 1967 are deflated, assuming a 6 percent growth in the price of resources used by the medical

[13] We are unable to estimate from available data the proportion of total medical school expenditures that is absorbed by faculty salaries. Undoubtedly this proportion has changed over time. That faculty salaries are a major component of the budget is clear from the study of pediatric departments referred to in Chap. 2. That study indicates that about 50 percent of departmental expenditures (excluding house-staff stipends) were allocated to faculty support in 1966–67. Support personnel accounted for about 25 percent of total expenditures (C. R. Dean Economics, Inc., 1967, p. 1).

[14] Data published by the American Association of University Professors indicate that average salaries for all faculty ranks combined for 36 biennial-survey institutions increased by 5.5 percent per annum during the period 1961–1967. For the period 1951–1967, the level of salaries increased by about 127 percent (1951 data assumed to be at midpoint between 1949 and 1953) ("The Threat of Inflationary Erosion: The Annual Report on the Economic Status of the Profession, 1968–69," 1969, p. 194).

[15] In assessing the implications of these increases for the individual faculty members, it is necessary to adjust the increases downward to take account of cost-of-living increases. The AAUP *Bulletin* (1969) reports that in the period 1939–1968, average salaries for university faculty rose from a base of 100.0 to 370.3. After adjustment for changes in the consumer price index during the same period, the average salaries (adjusted for price changes) rose from a base of 100.0 to 147.9.

schools, their growth rate between 1947 and 1967 is reduced to 8.1 percent. Nevertheless, even after correcting for inflation, there remains a substantial difference between the level of expenditures in earlier periods and the level today. Most of the increase in medical school budgets has been due to an increased use of real resources. The number of full-time faculty members, for example, grew from 3,577 in 1951 to 9,793 in 1960 and 22,163 in 1967. Part-time faculty members numbered 11,971 in 1951, 20,106 in 1960, and about 44,000 in 1967 (see Figure 2).[16] The activities of the schools have been extended; they are doing more things and doing them to a greater degree.

It is also clear that during this period of substantial increase in the real resources available to the medical school, the nature of the institution has undergone significant change. Increased responsibility has been placed on the medical school faculty for the education of interns and residents and students in the basic sciences. While the number of M.D. candidates grew from 26,191 in 1950 to 34,304 in 1967 (a growth of 31 percent), the number of interns grew from 1,786 to 4,309 (141 percent), the number of residents grew from 4,259 to 17,501 (311 percent), and the number of graduate students in the basic sciences grew from 2,720 to 8,785 (223 percent). As the total number of full-time students (including clinical postdoctoral fellows) representing the teaching responsibilities of the faculty increased by 101 percent (about 4.2 percent per annum), the percentage that M.D. candidates were of the total declined from 75 to 49 percent. The responsibilities of the medical school had shifted and had grown (see Figure 3).

The expansion in the number of non-M.D. candidates in the student body was the result of the increased demand for researchers and the increased specialization of physicians. National expenditures on medical and health-related research are estimated to have increased from $161 million in 1950 to $2.28 billion in 1967 (U.S. Department of Health, Education, and Welfare, 1968, p. 5). The medical school was the locus of much of this research effort, in part because it helped create much of the manpower that carries the research forward. Furthermore, the advances in knowledge pro-

[16] It is estimated that full-time faculty provided 60 percent of the total faculty time in 1951. The part-time faculty (and 75 percent of the total faculty) provided the remaining 40 percent (see Diehl, West, & Barclay, 1952, pp. 233–243). The number of part-time faculty in 1967 is our estimate based on the ratio of part-time to full-time faculty in 1966.

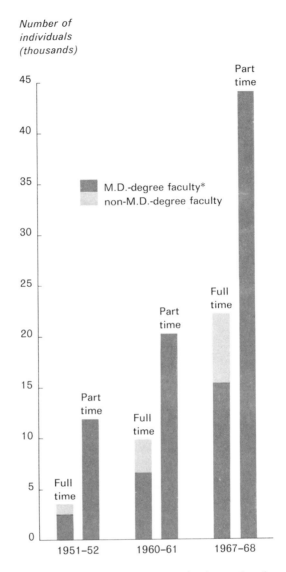

FIGURE 2
Number of
full-time,
part-time, and
M.D.-degree
faculty,
United States
medical schools,
selected years,
1951–1967

*It is assumed that 100 percent of the part-time faculty members have M.D. degrees.
SOURCES: *Journal of the American Medical Association,* 1967, pp. 747, 750; 1968, p. 2008. The number of part-time faculty members in 1967 is an estimate based on the ratio of part-time to full-time faculty in 1966. The number of full-time faculty members with M.D. degrees in 1967 is an estimate based on the proportion of faculty members with M.D. degrees in 1966. In both cases it was assumed that the 1967 ratios were identical with those in 1966. The 1966 data for both estimates are in *Journal of the American Medical Association,* 1967.

FIGURE 3
Teaching
responsibilities
of faculty in
United States
medical schools,
selected years,
1950–1967

Number of
individuals
(thousands)

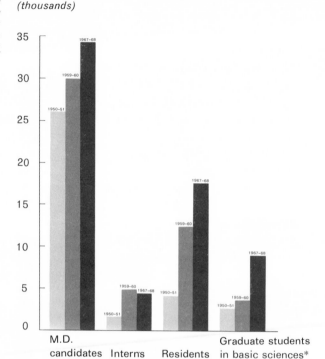

M.D.
candidates   Interns   Residents   Graduate students
in basic sciences*

*Master's, doctoral, and postdoctoral students.
SOURCES: *Journal of the American Medical Association,* 1951, pp. 140, 142;
1960, pp. 1427, 1437, 1441; 1968, p. 2087.

duced by the increased research efforts have been of importance
in expanding the demand for the services of specialists. Thus specialization has grown: In 1950 only about 17 percent of physicians
were certified by specialty boards, but by 1967, 31 percent had
board specialization. Medicine had changed, and so had the medical school (President's Commission on the Health Needs of the
Nation, 1953, pp. 135, 166; Theodore, Sutter, & Haug, 1968,
p. 15).

**CHANGES
IN SOURCES
OF FUNDS**   Much of the increase in medical school expenditures has been associated with the expanding role of the institutions. With this expansion has come a significant change in the sources of funds for the
operation of the medical schools of America. This, of course, should
not be viewed as an "accidental" shift. Indeed, in large measure, it
is the change in the funding pattern that has caused the change in

the medical school. As we pointed out in Chapter 1, the funds that the medical school receives represent the demands of various grantors, and these demands are often for specific outputs rather than for expansion of the activities the medical school decision makers may favor. It may be asked why decision makers should accept funds to carry on activities that do not, in their judgment, have the highest priority. Some of the reasons relate to the enhancement of the prestige of the institution; to the fact that medical school outputs are, as has been pointed out, produced in combination, and thus expansion of activity A carries with it some spin-off benefit to activity B; and to the fact that some proportion of the funds that are received for expansion of a particular activity can, under some circumstances, be used to support other purposes. Other reasons are related to the multiplicity of decision makers and allied institutions making up the medical school–teaching hospital complex; to the independence of faculty members and the fact that funds are, in essense, granted to the individual rather than to the school; and to the fact that while medical school decision makers may not favor certain outputs (in a priority sense), neither do they oppose them. In any case, however, expansion in expenditures has been financed by funds from new constituencies and new sources for a different mix of activities (see Table 9).

In 1947–48, state and city appropriations and university transfers, taken together, provided the largest source of funds for medical schools, totaling $25 million and accounting for 34 percent of all funds received by the schools. By 1967 the amount provided by state and local governments and by university transfers had grown to $187.3 million, but this accounted for only 18 percent of total medical school income. Growth in the absolute amount of income from unrestricted endowment funds (from $6.7 million to $29.6 million) and in tuition and fees (from $12.1 million to $48.3 million) was also insufficient to keep pace with the total expansion of the medical school. Thus unrestricted endowment income, which represented 9 percent of total income in 1947, accounted for only 3 percent in 1967, and tuition and fees income dropped from 17 percent of total income to only 4 percent over the same period. But if these sources were declining as a percentage of total income, other sources had to be increasing.

The single most important factor in the increase was financial support of research. Between 1947 and 1959, when medical school expenditures were growing at the rate of about 14 percent per year, sponsored research funds (including overhead) grew from $17.1

TABLE 9 *United States medical school funds by source, selected years, 1947–1967**

Source	Amount (in millions)			Percentage of total		
	1947–48	*1959–60*	*1967–68*	*1947–48*	*1959–60*	*1967–68*
Tuition and fees	$12.1	$ 25.8	$ 48.3	17	7	4
Sponsored research	17.1	134.4	473.3	24	38	43
Federal	8.0	92.2	389.6	11	26	36
Nonfederal	9.1	42.2	83.7	13	12	8
Endowment (unrestricted)	6.7	18.7	29.6	9	5	3
State and local plus	25.0	60.9	159.4	34	17	15
university transfers		18.0	27.9		5	3
Training grants plus	6.9	21.4	93.7	10	6	9
other gifts and grants		17.0	53.8		5	5
Teaching hospital		18.5	36.7		5	3
Medical service funds		10.9	48.0		3	4
Overhead	†	16.2	82.5		5	8
Other	4.7‡	12.7	44.0	6	4	4
TOTAL§	72.5¶	354.5	1097.4	100	100	100

*See footnote 12.

†Included in sponsored research. Not separately available.

‡Includes $1.9 million for separately organized postgraduate education.

§Figures are rounded and will not necessarily add to totals.

¶Excludes $36.5 million of income received from hospital and clinical activities. The basis for this income was poorly defined and the income has been generally excluded in the studies of the movement of medical school income.

SOURCES: U.S. Federal Security Agency, Public Health Service, 1951 b, pp. 33–36; *Journal of the American Medical Association,* 1961, p. 587, and 1969, p. 1486.

million to $150.6 million (about 20 percent per year). This trend continued into the 1960s. During the period 1959–1967, when total funds expended increased at a compound growth rate of 15 percent per annum, sponsored research and overhead funds increased to $555.8 million (about 18 percent per annum). Thus sponsored research and overhead funds accounted for 24 percent of all funds received in 1947, 43 percent in 1959, and 51 percent in 1967. Most of this increase was due to the very rapid and large expansion in federally sponsored research activities. In 1947 these had totaled $8 million. By 1959 they had grown to $108.4 million, and by 1967 they had reached $464.1 million.[17] By 1967 federally sponsored re-

[17] We included the total amount of overhead ($16.2 million) in federally sponsored research in 1959 since no separation was made between overhead for federal and nonfederal grants and contracts. However, only overhead for federal contracts and grants ($74.5 million) was included in federally sponsored research for 1967. The latter figure is from *Journal of the American Medical Association,* 1969, p. 1486. As noted in Table 9, overhead data for 1947 are not separately available.

search funds were the single largest source of income to the medical school and accounted for 42 percent of all receipts (having grown from 11 percent in 1947).

Growth of sponsored research funds thus accounted for more than one-half of the total increase in medical school receipts between 1947 and 1967, and federally sponsored research funding accounted for almost 85 percent of that growth. The medical schools were receiving more dollars from every source, but in general, the other sources were declining in relative importance. Federally supported research was becoming preeminent.

This, it must be noted, has affected the decision-making authority in the medical school. Sponsored funds which are reflected in the total medical school expenditures and receipts are most often granted to the individual faculty member, to the "principal investigator," and not to the school—even though the institution must be the formal recipient of the funds. Indeed, the school receives the "overhead" only to the extent that the investigator requests funding, and both school and investigator are aware of this fact. Though some schools claim that the overhead is insufficient and that they lose money on each grant and contract, the contract or grant is taken as given (that is, as long as there is a seller's market, the school cannot resist faculty members' seeking grants if it desires to retain them on the faculty). The overhead, even if insufficient, does cut the losses which would otherwise be incurred. In 1967–68, almost one-half of the full-time faculty received some salary support from research and training grants provided by the federal government, and 16.5 percent received 100 percent federal support. Fifty-five percent of the funds expended by the medical school fell into the sponsored-fund category with associated restrictions on the object of expenditure, and this percentage rises to 63 percent if overhead on contracts and grants is included in the sponsored-funds category (*Journal of the American Medical Association,* 1968, p. 2010 and 1969, p. 1486). That this situation has grave implications for decision making in the medical school is clear.

The substantial growth in sponsored research funds was accompanied by a much more modest growth in nonsponsored funds. Indeed, as one examines the reported affluence of medical schools, one finds that, at least in terms of growth of discretionary funds, the affluence appears somewhat illusory. It is true that during the 20-year period (1947 to 1967) nonsponsored funds grew by about 12 percent per year. But much of this growth does not represent a growth in real resources. If we assume a 6 percent rate of inflation in the prices of medical school inputs, the growth (adjusted for price changes) in available resources of a nonsponsored type is cut down to about 4.25 percent per year. Thus one can understand why deans of medical schools speak of poverty in the midst of plenty and of shortages in the midst of affluence.

One of the effects induced by the change in the sources of funding is the change in the educational focus of the medical school as more nonclinical and research-oriented faculty members are attracted. One observer has noted that "A ten- to twenty- or forty-fold increase in a school's research budget alters the composition of that school's faculty, and modifies the educational climate, by changing the kind of model presented to the student, and by creating an atmosphere in which the importance of research is emphasized, at the expense of other school activities" (Caughey, 1964, p. 430).[18]

Sponsored research funds are associated with a number of the medical school characteristics that were examined in Chapter 2. In considering these associations and relationships, it is important to recognize that the sponsored research funds are not equally distributed among all the medical schools. There is considerable variation in the receipt of the funds, and these variations are associated with the school characteristics examined earlier. Table 10 presents data on the ratio of sponsored research (excluding overhead) to total expenditures for the various quartiles for public and private schools separately, with quartile rankings determined by the index being used (for example, ratio of medical students to full-time students, MCAT scores, average total expenditures per full-time student, and average total expenditures). We can readily see that for each of the indices examined, private schools have a higher ratio of sponsored research to total expenditures than equivalent quartiles of public schools. Furthermore, we find that

1 In general, the ratio of medical students to full-time students varies inversely with the ratio of sponsored research to total expenditures. This is as would be expected, since the sponsored research funds are important in helping support activities that attract non-M.D. candidates to the student body.

2 MCAT scores and the sponsored research ratio are positively re-

---

[18] The relationship between dollars spent for research and other similar variables and the changing characteristics and goals of students has been examined (see Hutchins, 1962, pp. 67–82).

lated. This is also true if one examines average total expenditures per full-time student and average total expenditures. The schools that spend more in total and more per student, as well as the schools with a more able student body, are the schools that have higher ratios of sponsored research to total expenditures.

Though it is clear from Table 10 that there is considerable variation in the ratio of sponsored research to total expenditures and that the range is large, the ratio is fairly high for every quartile of schools. In no case does sponsored research represent less than one-third of the total expenditures, and in a number of cases it represents over 50 percent.

Yet another way of seeing the role that sponsored research plays in medical school expenditures (and the impact that it has in association with other characteristics) is to examine the dollar expenditure less sponsored research per full-time student. In the tables presented in Chapter 2, average total expenditures per full-time student were related to quartile groupings by selected characteristics. Average total expenditures, of course, are significantly reduced when sponsored research funds are subtracted. In order to see the significance that is attached to this subtraction, the reader should consult Table 11, which presents the data for expenditures less sponsored research per full-time student and, in parentheses, the data for expenditures without the subtraction.[19]

The increase in research funds available to the medical schools has altered these institutions in ways that cannot be revealed by economic data alone. There have been changes in the climate of the schools, in their view of their purposes, in their ability to implement curricular changes, in decision-making structures and power relationships, in the aspirations of the student bodies, and so forth. Some of the changes were consciously sought (for example, building the scientific base for medicine), some were by-products (for example, research funds came to represent the financial underpinning and foundation of the schools), and some were unfortunate (for example, schools without a research emphasis or capability found it difficult to attract funds for their other activities). For the moment it must suffice to note that there has been a revolution in the sources

---

[19] As has been noted earlier, expenditure figures do not represent the cost of educating the M.D. candidate.

TABLE 10	Quartile averages			
Characteristic used for ranking	Public schools			
	Highest	Second	Third	Lowest
Ratio of M.D. candidates to full-time students†	0.360	0.316	0.395	0.457
MCAT science score	0.429	0.383	0.371	0.373
Total expenditures per full-time student	0.427	0.418	0.340	0.370

TABLE 10 *Quartile averages of ratio of sponsored research funds to total expenditures of United States medical schools, grouped in order of value of selected characteristics, 1965–66**

*See pp. 62–76 for an explanation of the quartile groupings.

† The quartile rankings are not "inverted" (see Table 1), as would be the case if we wanted to show the association between the high-expenditure, high-expenditure-per-student, and high MCAT science score schools and the schools with low ratios of medical students to full-time students.

of medical school funds and in the uses to which they could be put. That a revolution in funding is accompanied by substantial and significant changes in the institutions involved is clear. It is not the economist's parochialism that leads to the view that changes in the economic structure of an institution will be accompanied by changes in the institution itself.

QUARTILE ANALYSIS

The annual medical school financial reports that are collected by the Association of American Medical Colleges and the American Medical Association permit us to make quartile analyses of the financial

Characteristic used for ranking	Quartile averages			
	Public			
	Highest	Second	Third	Lowest
Total expenditures per full-time student	$ 9,700 (16,900) [6,867]	$ 7,400 (12,700) [5,602]	$ 6,600 (10,000) [5,432]	$ 5,000 (7,900) [3,782]
MCAT science score	8,000 (13,900)	6,700 (10,900)	7,300 (11,600)	6,400 (10,300)
Ratio of M.D. candidates to full-time students†	5,700 (8,800)	7,900 (11,500)	7,200 (11,800)	7,800 (14,300)

TABLE 11 *Quartile averages of expenditures per full-time student of United States medical schools, without and with sponsored research funds,* grouped in order of value of selected characteristics, 1965–66*

*Excluding overhead. Data in parentheses represent expenditures (including sponsored research) per full-time student as taken from Chap. 2. Data in brackets represent expenditures per full-time student if total sponsored funds including overhead are subtracted from expenditures.

† The quartile rankings are not "inverted" (see Table 1), as would be the case if we

Quartile averages			
Private schools			
Highest	*Second*	*Third*	*Lowest*
0.381	0.491	0.567	0.509
0.555	0.506	0.470	0.400
0.555	0.498	0.455	0.409

SOURCES: Unpublished data from the AAMC and AMA annual questionnaires. Published data from *Journal of the American Medical Association,* 1966. Overhead on contracts and grants is excluded from sponsored research expenditures.

structure of American medical schools for 1965–66 (and to compare some of the financial sources available to the different quartiles of schools in 1965 with those available in 1959). We are thus able to examine the quartile distribution of sponsored funds, the shift in sources of funding (1959 to 1965), and the relative dependence of the schools in a given quartile on the various sources.

Operating Funds In 1965, private schools (with 48 percent of the M.D. candidates, 53 percent of the interns, 51 percent of the residents, and 49 percent of the graduate students in the basic sciences) received 59 percent of all federal teaching, training, research, and overhead

Quartile averages			
Private			
Highest	*Second*	*Third*	*Lowest*
$ 9,400	$ 7,400	$ 5,300	$ 4,300
(21,100)	(14,700)	(9,800)	(7,300)
[4,460]	[4,960]	[3,692]	[3,188]
7,600	8,300	4,600	6,100
(17,000)	(16,800)	(8,600)	(10,200)
5,200	6,300	6,300	8,600
(8,300)	(12,400)	(14,500)	(17,500)

wanted to show the association between the high-expenditure, high-expenditure-per-student, and high MCAT science score schools and the schools with low ratios of medical students to full-time students.

SOURCES: Unpublished data from the AAMC and AMA annual questionnaires. Published data from *Journal of the American Medical Association,* 1966.

funds granted to medical schools.[20]

Within the private school group, however, there was considerable variation in the receipt of such funds. The private school quartile with the highest expenditure per student received 47 percent of the federal funds granted to all private medical schools. The lowest-expenditure private school quartile received 11 percent of the federal funds granted to private institutions. An examination of Figure 4 shows that private schools receive relatively more federal teaching and training funds, federal research funds, overhead on federal grants and contracts, other research and training funds, tuition and fees, and general university funds than the public institutions. The latter receive the vast bulk of state appropriations and share about equally in the receipts from medical service funds and moneys from teaching hospitals and clinics. It is also noteworthy that the two highest-expenditure private institution quartiles and the highest public group received considerably greater support from medical service funds—funds provided from the payments for the services of the clinical faculty—than the other quartiles. These 30 schools (out of the total of 83 schools) received about 80 percent of the total medical service funds.

Figure 4 indicates the percentage of funds from each of the sources that the school quartiles received in 1965–66.[21] It is clear that the schools do not share equally in the moneys from these sources. The fact that schools share unequally does not mean that the patterns of financing within each of the quartiles differ. In theory, schools could share to the same unequal extent in all sources, and thus their *pattern* of financing would be the same, although some schools would have considerably greater resources than others. Also, some inequalities may be less significant than others in affecting the pattern of financing since some sources provide small money amounts relative to other sources. Therefore, the relative importance of the funds supplied by the sources of sup-

---

[20] Overhead accounted for about one-eighth of the federal funds received by private schools in 1965. In 1959 private schools received 61 percent of all federal funds.

[21] Because the number of public and private schools (and thus the number in the quartiles) changed between 1959 and 1965, it is impossible to compare the percentage distribution of moneys to each quartile in 1959 with that in 1965. Figure 4 is therefore limited to the latter year. Rough estimates suggest that there was relatively little change in the distributions over the period 1959–1965.

FIGURE 4
Percentage allocation of funds of United States medical schools by sources of support for schools grouped in order of expenditures per full-time student, 1965–66*

Public school quartiles   *Private school quartiles*

Federal teaching and training grants

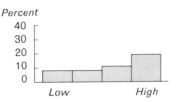
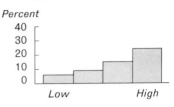

Federal research grants

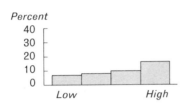
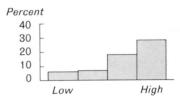

Overhead on federal grants and contracts

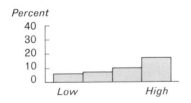
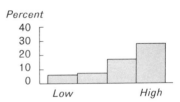

Total federal funds

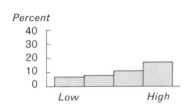
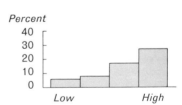

Other research and training grants

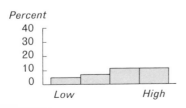
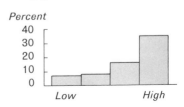

FIGURE 4
(continued)

Public school quartiles   Private school quartiles

Tuition and fees

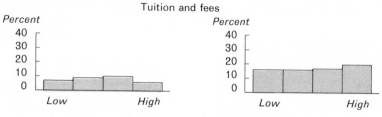

Medical service funds

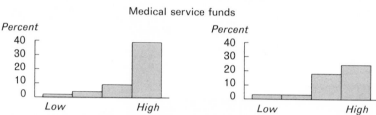

General university funds

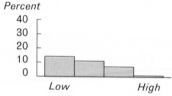
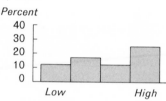

State appropriations

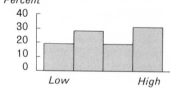
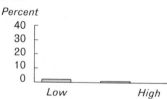

Teaching hospitals and clinic fees

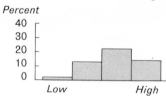
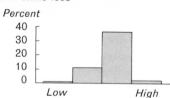

*The percentages do not add to 100 because miscellaneous sources of support are not shown.

SOURCES: Unpublished data from the AAMC and AMA annual questionnaires. Published data from *Journal of the American Medical Association*, 1966.

port is significant. That information, for 1959–60 and 1965–66, is presented in Figure 5.[22]

During the period 1959–1965, total expenditures in current dollars for the 36 public and 42 private medical schools analyzed increased at a rate of about 15 percent per year. Federal funds increased at a rate of almost 23 percent per year, while funds from most other major sources increased at a rate of about 10 percent per annum. As a result of this differential growth, federal funds (including overhead), which represented 34 percent of all receipts in 1959, rose to 50 percent by 1965. Most of this increase was due to the growth in federal *research* funds. By 1965 federal research funds (including overhead) accounted for 39 percent of the receipts of public institutions and 48 percent of the receipts of private schools (having increased from 26 percent and 34 percent, respectively, in 1959).[23]

The support structure that the various schools are dependent upon differs. Public institutions derive about 45 percent of their support from federal sources; private institutions receive about 55 percent of their support from these sources. Public institutions also derive less relative support from nonfederal research and training grants (about 10 percent for the public institutions, as compared with 15 percent for the private medical schools). General university

---

[22] The distinction between the two concepts is important in understanding Figs. 4 and 5. In the former case we divide each source of funds among the schools, and in the latter we see what percentage of the total funds of a school comes from each of the sources. The former concept might say that school *A* receives 90 percent of all federal and 30 percent of the state funds, while *B* receives 10 percent of the federal and 70 percent of the state funds. The latter concept might say that of all the funds *A* receives, 86 percent are federal and 14 percent are state and that of *B's* funds, 22 percent are federal and 78 percent are state.

[23] The two studies of clinical specialties referred to in Chap. 2 also have developed data on sources of funds received for departmental expenditures. The study of obstetrics-gynecology departments reported that general medical school funds and research grants each provided approximately 27 percent of departmental incomes. Substantial additional support was provided by hospitals and by income from private practice. The pediatric study reported that 49 percent of departmental funds were obtained from research and research training grants. Nineteen percent were provided by the medical school and an additional 18 percent were obtained from hospitals. Over half of the hospital funds represented the payment of stipends to interns and residents. Research and training grants provided 61 percent of the funds in the largest pediatric departments (those with expenditures of over $1.3 million per annum) (C. R. Dean Economics, Inc., 1967, pp. 1, 3).

FIGURE 5
*Percentage
allocation
of support of
United States
medical schools,
for schools
grouped
in order of
expenditures
per full-time
student,
1959–60 and
1965–66**

1959-60

1965-66

All schools
Percent

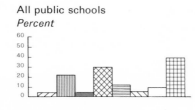

All schools
Percent

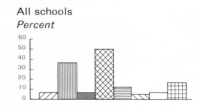

All public schools
Percent

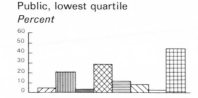

All public schools
Percent

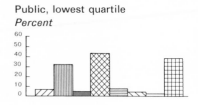

Public, lowest quartile
Percent

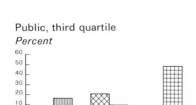

Public, lowest quartile
Percent

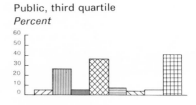

Public, third quartile
Percent

Public, third quartile
Percent

Public, second quartile
Percent

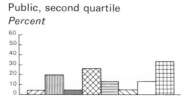

Public, second quartile
Percent

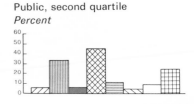

1959-60

1965-66

Public, highest quartile
Percent

Public, highest quartile
Percent

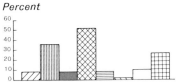

All private schools
Percent

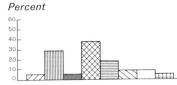

All private schools
Percent

Private, lowest quartile
Percent

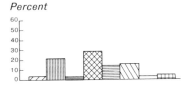

Private, lowest quartile
Percent

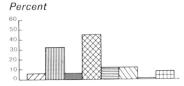

Private, third quartile
Percent

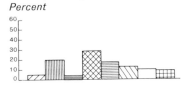

Private, third quartile
Percent

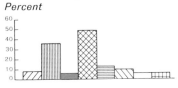

Private, second quartile
Percent

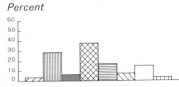

Private, second quartile
Percent

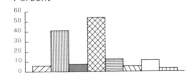

FIGURE 5
(continued)

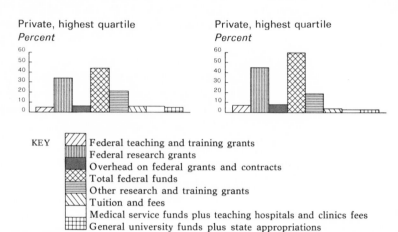

1959-60

1965-66

Private, highest quartile
Percent

Private, highest quartile
Percent

KEY

Federal teaching and training grants
Federal research grants
Overhead on federal grants and contracts
Total federal funds
Other research and training grants
Tuition and fees
Medical service funds plus teaching hospitals and clinics fees
General university funds plus state appropriations

*The percentages do not add to 100 because miscellaneous sources of support are not shown. Total research may not equal the sum of the components because of rounding.

SOURCES: Unpublished data from the AAMC and AMA annual questionnaires. Published data from *Journal of the American Medical Association,* 1961, p. 587; 1969, p. 1486.

funds and state appropriations fill the gap: they are a minor source of support for the private schools (representing about 5 percent of total support), while they are the second most important source of support for the public institutions and represent 31 percent of total receipts.

Figure 5 also shows the differences in the structure of support for the four quartiles of private and the four quartiles of public institutions (with quartile rankings based upon expenditures per full-time student). Federal and other research and training grants provide 57 percent of the support for the lowest-expenditure (per full-time student) private schools and 79 percent of the support for the highest-expenditure schools. The support is less and the range is smaller among the public institutions (varying from 45 percent for the second-lowest-expenditure schools to 59 percent for the highest).

As previously noted, the presentation of data by quartiles is useful in providing summary measures, and yet it carries with it the necessary cost of obscuring (because of the averaging process) some of the variation. Since individual schools may (and do) face particular financial problems, we have provided an analysis of the relative dependence on different sources of funds (in 1959 and 1965) of the individual institutions (Table 12). Here the wide variation in sources of support becomes most evident; for example, 16 schools (5 public and 11 private) received over 60 percent of their support from federal sources, and yet 4 schools received less than 25 percent of their support from these funds. Here, too, we can see the shift in sources of support between 1959 and 1965; for example, while 14 of the private schools received over 15 percent of their support from tuition and fees in 1959, this was true for only 2 schools by 1965; while only 6 schools received over 50 percent of their support from federal funds in 1959, this was true for 35 schools by 1965 (yet even then 4 schools, as noted, received less than 25 percent of their support from federal funds). We shall find that the rapid and significant growth of federal funding had important effects but that schools did not share in the funding equally. Therefore, the particular situation that some schools are in as a result of the structure of their support must be recognized. The problems faced by some schools are made more difficult because, on the average, other schools are in a stronger position.

Data for 1959–60 and 1965–66 also make possible a comparison of public and private school quartiles in terms of four characteristics for those periods. In Table 13 public and private schools are ranked by quartiles for the following characteristics: average total expenditures per school, average expenditures per full-time student, MCAT scores, and ratio of undergraduate medical students to full-time students. Over the six-year period all groups substantially increased their average total expenditures and their average expenditures per full-time student. The percentage increases for all quartiles were of about the same order of magnitude. All groups except public, third quartile, showed declines in the ratio of M.D. candidates to all full-time students, with the greatest declines coming in the two private school quartiles with the lowest ratios in 1959. MCAT science scores increased for all groups, generally by about 20 points.

Capital Funds   Medical schools, like other public and nonprofit institutions (including universities), have treated capital expenditures separately from their operating expenses. Depreciation charges are not included in their operating statements, and separate funding of major building and equipment expenditures is obtained from federal and state governments, private philanthropy and foundation grants, and borrowing. The total amount of capital expenditure has been

TABLE 12 *Relative dependence of individual United States medical schools on selected sources of support, 1959-60 and 1965-66*

Percentage class	Federal teaching and training grants 1959-60	1965-66	Federal research grants 1959-60	1965-66	Total federal funds* 1959-60	1965-66
Public schools						
0-4	19	7				
5-9	16	28	1			
10-14	1	6	8	1	3	
15-19			7	2	3	1
20-24			10	6	7	1
25-29			4	10	6	2
30-34			1	7	8	6
35-39			4	6	3	6
40-44				6	2	7
45-49				3	3	5
50-54			1			5
55-59						3
60 and over					1	5
Private schools						
0-4	22	10				
5-9	20	24				
10-14		8	7		1	
15-19			5	2	3	
20-24			6	2	7	2
25-29			8	4	4	
30-34			9	8	7	3
35-39			3	7	7	4
40-44			3	8	3	4
45-49			1	5	5	7
50-54				6	5	2
55-59						9
60 and over						11

*Includes overhead.

SOURCE: Unpublished data from the AAMC and AMA annual questionnaires. Published data from *Journal of the American Medical Association,* 1961, p. 587; 1969, p. 1486.

substantial. It has averaged about $100 million per year since 1960–61 (see Figure 6), equal to about 13 percent of expenses for current operations over the same period.

The AAMC has surveyed medical schools in an effort to ascertain detailed information on capital construction and the sources and uses of funds. These data are not completely accurate because buildings, like personnel, are used for multiple purposes, such as both research and teaching, and because the accounting and book-keeping systems of many medical schools are grossly inadequate and their records are not comparable with those of other schools. Nonetheless, the AAMC findings, together with information on

Other research and training grants		Tuition and fees		General university funds		State appropriations	
1959-60	1965-66	1959-60	1965-66	1959-60	1965-66	1959-60	1965-66
3	5	13	31	17	35	3	2
16	24	20	8	5	2		
7	9	2	1	9		3	3
6	2	1		4	2	1	4
3	1			1	1	4	7
					1	3	4
1						7	8
						2	2
						2	2
						2	4
						3	3
						3	1
						3	1
2	2	2	9	27	26	40	40
4	13	19	19	6	8		1
14	12	7	12	5	3		
8	9	8	2	2	3	1	
10	4	3		1	2		1
2	1	3					
2				1			
	1					1	

individual schools, do provide considerable insight into funding patterns.

According to the AAMC surveys, $2.46 billion was spent on medical school construction (including the cost of fixed equipment) completed between 1948–49 and 1967–68. Almost 30 percent of these expenditures were incurred in the last seven years. Between 1948–49 and 1959–60, 63 percent of the construction completed was allocated to medical service facilities (teaching hospitals owned or controlled by the university), and 34 percent to research and teaching facilities. These distributions changed radically in the decade of the 1960s. In the period 1960–1965, only 21 percent of

TABLE 13
Comparison
of quartile
averages for
expenditures
and student
composition of
United States
medical schools,
1959–60 and
1965–66,
grouped
according
to rank in
1965–66

Type of school and quartile[a]	Total expenditures per school (in millions)		Total expenditures per full-time student	
	1959–60	*1965–66*	*1959–60*	*1965–66*
Public				
Highest	$7.0[c]	$16.0	$9,322	$16,890
Second	3.9[e]	9.6	6,953[e]	12,723
Third	3.3	7.5	5,207[c]	9,965
Lowest	1.9[c]	4.2[d]	4,381[e]	7,901[d]
Private				
Highest	8.0	20.3	11,059	21,079
Second	5.4	12.1	8,608	14,663
Third	3.3	6.8	5,509	9,767
Lowest	2.2[f]	4.0[f]	4,060[f]	7,335[f]

[a] Except as noted, each quartile contains 10 schools.

[b] The quartile rankings are "inverted" in order to show the association between the high-expenditure, high-expenditure-per-student, and high MCAT science score schools and the schools with low ratios of medical students to full-time students.

[c] Eight schools.

the expenditures were reported allocated to medical service facilities, 51 percent to research, and 18 percent to teaching facilities. In the two-year period 1966–1968, medical service facilities absorbed 18 percent of the construction funds, research facilities absorbed 36 percent, and teaching facilities absorbed 38 percent. Thus, in the earliest period medical service facilities absorbed an average of $90 million annually, while research and training facilities together received about $48 million per annum. Between 1960–61 and 1965–66, medical service facilities received only $15 million per annum, research facility construction absorbed $35 million per annum, and teaching facilities received about $12 million per annum. In the last two-year period, total construction expanded significantly, with the sharpest increase occurring for teaching facilities. Teaching facilities received $59 million per annum, research received $57 million and medical service facilities received $29 million.

It is possible to gather some evidence from a variety of diverse sources regarding the providers of funds for this construction. One estimate is that the federal government provided 13 percent of the construction expenditures by medical schools and their affiliated hospitals between 1948 and 1959 (Powers, Darley, & Oppermann, 1960, pp. 108–119).[24] Almost $1 billion of the total construction

[24] Federal support made up 15 percent of the capital expenditures for teaching and research facilities, 14 percent of construction of medical school–owned hospitals, and 12 percent of construction of affiliated hospitals. These data include both facilities completed and those for which construction had begun.

MCAT science score		Ratio of M.D. candidates to full-time students[b]	
1959-60	*1965-66*	*1959-60*	*1965-66*
555[d]	577	0.44[c]	0.39
525[c]	547	0.62	0.53
498[c]	525	0.57[c]	0.58
479	493[d]	0.70[e]	0.67[d]
594	618	0.47	0.34
553	579	0.55	0.42
522	559	0.62	0.54
486[f]	504[f]	0.72[f]	0.70[f]

[d] Eleven schools.
[e] Nine schools.
[f] Twelve schools.

SOURCES: Unpublished data from the AAMC and AMA annual questionnaires. Published data from *Journal of the American Medical Association,* 1960, 1966.

undertaken during this period involved federal matching funds, with an aggregate matching ratio of $3.33 for each $1 of federal funds. The federal government financed 22 percent of the educational and research facility construction undertaken by private schools and about 10 percent of that undertaken by public institutions. Conversely, it supported 17 percent of construction expenditures on hospitals owned or operated by public institutions (and 16 percent of expenditures by hospitals affiliated with public institutions) and only 9 percent of the construction expenditures by hospitals owned or operated by private schools (and 10 percent of the construction of affiliated hospitals).

In 1966–67 and 1967–68 the federal share in construction increased markedly, from 28 percent in the first year to 44 percent in the second. State shares fell from 32 to 21 percent, and the private share fell from 17 to 14 percent. The university share remained at about 17 percent. Thus, as with operating expenses, the federal share is becoming dominant. Whatever the image that the public may have, or that those connected with the schools themselves may have, in general American medical schools are now financed in large part by the federal government and are increasingly dependent upon that source of funds with whatever restrictions that brings. It should be remembered, however, that most often the federal government does not support the medical school per se, but rather particular activities within the school (research, as we have seen, receives relatively more support than education). Thus, this dependency is not without its own problems and difficulties. The situation

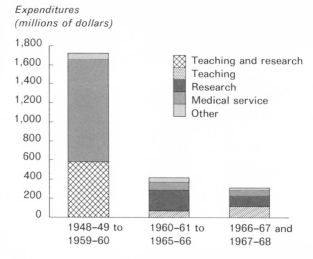

Expenditures
(millions of dollars)

1,800

1,600 — ⊠ Teaching and research

1,400 — ▨ Teaching

1,200 — ■ Research

1,000 — ▬ Medical service

800 — ▢ Other

600

400

200

0

| 1948–49 to | 1960–61 to | 1966–67 and |
| 1959–60 | 1965–66 | 1967–68 |

*Expenditure data include fixed equipment.
SOURCES: *Datagrams,* 1967, table 1; *Journal of the American Medical Association,*
1968, p. 1997, and 1967, p. 734.

is particularly difficult, as has been pointed out, for those schools
which receive few research dollars and thus are unable to utilize
research funds to support some of their educational activities.
The lack of other substantial sources of funds from the federal government has therefore placed them in a particularly vulnerable
position.

Though the major financing for construction comes from the
federal government, the role of the private sector is not insignificant,
especially for some schools. Smythe has indicated that in his study
of the funding of 16 newly developing schools (14 of them owned
and operated by states), 9 received substantial private support.
Five schools received between $0.5 million and $1.5 million, and
two schools received between $3 million and $6 million as grants
from foundations, major gifts from individuals, resources of trustees of the institutions, and capital raised in private gift campaigns.
Two schools (one of them state-owned) have been initiated with
private gifts in excess of $10 million (Smythe, 1967, pp. 991–
1004).[25]

[25] Private sources provided 16.5 percent ($54.6 million) of all funds provided for
construction of medical school buildings in 1966 and 13.7 percent ($48.0 mil-
lion) of all such funds in 1967. These funds have a multiplicative effect in that
they help the schools to meet matching requirements of public programs.

4. The Medical Student: M.D. Candidate, Intern, and Resident

In order to understand medical students' abilities to provide funds for the operation of medical schools, we must examine the financial considerations involved in the decision to become a physician and the impact of the costs of attending medical school on career decisions. These costs affect the socioeconomic characteristics of the M.D. candidate and lead to a biased distribution of these characteristics in the current medical student body. Their impact is considerable. Any examination of the role that student payments play in providing funds for medical schools cannot ignore the impact that such costs have on the socioeconomic mix of students.

Medical students (M.D. candidates, interns, and residents) provide only about 5 percent of the total income of medical schools. Nonetheless, they bear the major portion of the costs of medical *education.* This contrast arises because (1) a substantial portion of the total expenditures of medical schools supports the production of outputs other than medical education and (2) "opportunity costs," that is, income that the student might have been earning were he not attending medical school or participating in the internship and residency training programs, must be included in the computation of the costs of medical education.[1] These costs to the student are considerable and have an impact on the decisions of potential applicants to medical school and on the behavior of persons who complete their medical training and enter practice. The scenario that some write would go something like this: High costs of medical education bar many able but needy students from

[1] If the opportunity costs are measured by the median earnings of males with at least four years of college (adjusted to age of attendance at medical school), they represent 93 percent of the personal costs of medical education (in 1966) for the M.D. candidates attending public medical schools and 83 percent for those in private schools. Opportunity costs represent the total cost for the intern and resident.

the field. Thus physicians are drawn largely from one stratum of our society. This stratum does not fully understand the medical and other problems of the low-income or minority groups. Such physicians, therefore, do not serve those persons adequately. Furthermore, having gone into debt during their long period of education and being older than others beginning to earn incomes when they finally enter medical practice, they exact high fees. Thus, it is argued, a significant change in the pattern of financing medical education and in its costs would bring many benefits to the nation: physicians drawn from lower-income groups, fewer financial difficulties for medical students, and more socially responsible behavior on the part of new physicians.

The financial considerations involved in the decision to become a physician, the impact of medical school costs on career decisions, the selectivity of medical schools, and the sources students use to finance their medical education are discussed here as background for assessing the implications of some of the medical student assistance proposals that are part of the current debate on the future financing of medical education.

Many questions about the impact of financial considerations and constraints on the decision to apply to medical school cannot be answered with available data. We shall discuss what data should be weighed by potential applicants to medical school who consider economic matters. No one knows, however, to what extent such matters are in fact considered or, if they are, what data are utilized. We cannot provide a model of behavior because we do not have the data to do so. Yet information available will help in answering some of the questions concerning applicant behavior, student finances, and the implications and possible consequences of the costs of medical education.

THE DECISION TO APPLY In the 1966–67 academic year 345,000 males and 239,000 females received bachelor's and first professional degrees from American colleges and universities. It has been estimated that about 8.5 percent of these were first professional degrees. During the same period there were 18,724 applicants (16,773 male and 1,951 female) for the 1967 entering class into American medical schools (Jarecky, Johnson, & Mattson, 1968, pp. 1216–1217). Obviously, demand for admission into medical school is limited. Only a small proportion of all students who might consider themselves eligible and a small proportion of all students who, on the basis of their academic records, are eligible actually apply.

The absolute number of students who apply for medical school has varied considerably over time (and among schools). There were 15,791 applicants for admission to the class entering medical school in 1957. This number declined gradually to 14,381 for the 1961 class, climbed to 19,168 for the 1964 class, and, as noted above, dropped to 18,724 for the 1967 first-year class. During this period there was a significant change in the size of the population (B.A. recipients) from which most medical students are drawn, the number of medical school openings available, and other educational indices (see Table 14 and Figure 7).[2] During the last decade the percentage of applicants entering medical school has varied between 47.2 and 60.4 percent, tending to about 50 percent in recent years.

Over the same years the number of applications filed per applicant has also increased, from about 3.9 to 5.0. Thus, the total number of applications filed and processed has grown from about 61,000 a decade ago to about 93,000 (*Journal of the American Medical Association,* Nov. 1968, p. 2013) for the 1967–68 academic year (though fluctuating in the intervening years). The increase in the average number of applications per applicant has meant that, in general, individual schools have had an increasingly large pool of applicants from which to draw. It has also meant that applicants admitted to a particular school were more likely to be admitted to other schools as well.

There has been considerable variation among the individual schools in the number of applications received. For example, for the academic year 1966–67, the number of applications (and applicants) per available space in the individual schools ranged from 2 to 22. Similarly, the range in the average number of applications submitted by each school's applicants was from 1.7 to 11.3

[2] In 1966, 86 percent of M.D. candidates who entered medical school had received at least the bachelor's degree. The number of bachelor's degree recipients, therefore, is only a proxy for the population from which applications are drawn. The start of a major upturn in the number of bachelor's degree recipients occurred in the 1967–68 school year when an estimated 401,000 males received bachelor's and first professional degrees (see Table 14, second footnote). This compared with 318,000 males in 1964–65. The U.S. Office of Education (1968, p. 31) estimates that 493,000 males will receive the bachelor's and first professional degrees in 1974–75.

TABLE 14
Medical school applicants and openings, and bachelor's, Ph.D., and M.D. degrees conferred, United States, 1947–1967

| | | | Degrees conferred | |
| | | | Male bachelor's | |
Year	Applicants to medical school	Medical school openings*	degree plus first professional degree†	Bachelor's degrees in science†,‡
1947–1948	18,829	6,512	175,456	
1948–1949	24,242	6,973	264,168	29,961
1949–1950	24,434	7,150	328,841	37,185
1950–1951	22,279	7,254	279,343	30,980
1951–1952	19,920	7,663	225,981	28,062
1952–1953	16,763	7,778	200,820	24,517
1953–1954	14,678	7,756	187,500	23,336
1954–1955	14,538	7,878	183,602	23,600
1955–1956	14,937	7,969	198,615	28,898
1956–1957	15,917	8,263	221,650	32,348
1957–1958	15,791	8,302	241,560	35,684
1958–1959	15,170	8,366	253,488	39,638
1959–1960	14,952	8,512	254,063	43,149
1960–1961	14,397	8,560	254,216	44,789
1961–1962	14,381	8,682	260,531	47,518
1962–1963	15,847	8,959	273,169	51,615
1963–1964	17,668	9,063	298,046	59,031
1964–1965	19,168	9,043	317,669	62,889
1965–1966	18,703	9,012	328,853	64,113
1966–1967	18,250	9,123	345,000¶	69,610¶
1967–1968	18,724	9,702	401,000¶	83,950¶

*Applicants accepted.

† Data on bachelor's degree recipients are not separately available. First professional degrees, which in general include (1) bachelor's degrees requiring five or more years of work and (2) master's or doctor's degrees in professional fields which have not been preceded by a professional degree in the same field, constituted about 8.5 percent of total bachelor's and first professional degrees in 1964–65.

‡ Includes mathematics and the biological and physical sciences in general, but the coverage increased in comprehensiveness as the years progressed.

(Mattson, Johnson, & Sedlacek, 1968, pp. 10–11). In general, private medical schools have more applicants per available spot than public schools (Table 15).

Since the probability of acceptance differs among the individual medical schools, the choice of a medical school will be in part

Ph.D.'s in science‡	*M.D.'s*	*Ratios of applicants to openings*	*Ratios of applicants to male bachelor's (lagged)§*	*Ratios of applicants to bachelor's in science (lagged)§*	*Ratios of M.D.'s to Ph.D.'s in science*
	5,543	2.891			
1,410	5,094	3.477	0.138		3.61
1,790	5,553	3.417	0.092	0.82	3.10
2,059	6,135	3.071	0.068	0.60	2.98
2,690	6,080	2.600	0.071	0.64	2.26
2,921	6,668	2.155	0.074	0.60	2.28
2,990	6,861	1.892	0.073	0.60	2.29
2,957	6,977	1.845	0.078	0.62	2.36
2,927	6,845	1.874	0.081	0.63	2.34
3,026	6,796	1.926	0.080	0.55	2.25
3,027	6,861	1.902	0.071	0.49	2.27
3,139	6,860	1.813	0.063	0.43	2.19
3,346	7,081	1.757	0.059	0.38	2.12
3,528	6,994	1.682	0.057	0.33	1.98
3,856	7,168	1.656	0.057	0.32	1.86
4,325	7,264	1.769	0.061	0.33	1.68
4,676	7,336	1.949	0.065	0.34	1.57
5,445	7,409	2.120	0.064	0.32	1.36
5,943	7,574	2.075	0.059	0.30	1.27
6,440¶	7,743	2.000	0.055	0.28	1.20
7,210¶	7,973	1.930	0.054	0.27	1.11

§ The previous year's bachelor's degree recipients are used.

¶ Estimated.

SOURCES: Columns 1, 2, and 6: *Journal of the American Medical Association,* 1968, pp. 2013, 2017. Columns 3 through 5: 1947–48 to 1954–55, Bureau of the Census, *Statistical Abstract of the United States,* various issues; thereafter, U.S. Office of Education, 1966, pp. 27, 31, 35; 1968, pp. 31, 34, 38.

dependent upon the individual's subjective estimate of the probability that he will be accepted. This subjective estimate will initially influence his decision regarding career choice and is not entirely a function of his estimate of his academic ability or his actual performance, for he may feel that in admitting students

FIGURE 7　*Medical school applicants and openings, and bachelor's and Ph.D. degrees in science conferred, United States, 1947–1967*

Number
(thousands)

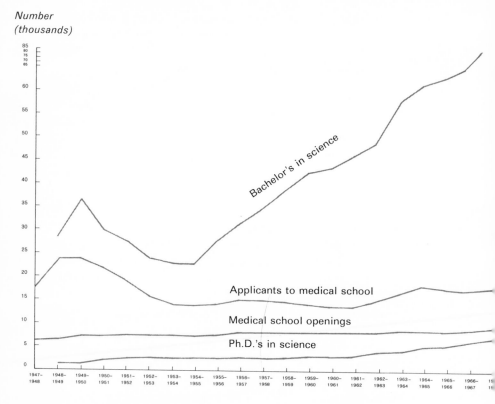

medical schools judge applicants by a number of factors — such as sex, race, economic status, ethnic origin, and religion — other than academic ability.

Furthermore, the individual's impression about the relationship between his own academic performance and academic requirements for entrance into medical school will depend on his state of residence. As noted earlier, the ability levels of students in the various medical schools is substantially different. A potential applicant of a given ability level who is considering applying to a state-supported institution with a very restrictive residency requirement will have a subjective probability of acceptance greater than that of a potential applicant of the same ability who is considering applying to private schools that have fewer residency restrictions (and a larger pool of applicants from which to draw) or public schools which lie outside his home state and which may either be open to all students on an equal basis or discriminate against out-of-state applicants.

Little is known about the motivations and decisions of potential applicants to medical schools, but some patterns are clear. Many make early decisions concerning career orientation. Others, while postponing their decision until relatively late in their college career, have had various relevant alternatives "in the back of their minds" for some time. Some have weighed a number of options, of which medicine was one, while others have not included a career as a physician as an option. Some who are attracted to medicine feel that they cannot continue in school (for financial or family reasons) for the number of years required. Others may wonder whether medical practice will be as attractive in the future as it may seem today. Some may doubt that they can successfully complete the medical curriculum, while others may find other fields more stimulating and exciting. Some may prefer to reduce the probability of service in the armed forces. Others may prefer income in the immediate future to an even larger income at a later point in time. These are some of the factors that potential applicants weigh as they consider pursuing courses as undergraduates that will prepare them for medical school.

Given all these considerations, the role that economic factors play in the decision-making process is not clear. Medical school educators sometimes suggest that the motivation to be a physician is the critical element and that this motivation does not involve assessments of present costs or future income. Yet they are among the first to argue that present costs are excessive in that they bar some (motivated) students from attending medical school and that physician incomes are not irrelevant to the practice, location, and a number of other decisions that practitioners make. It is most improbable that the costs of education and the income of physicians are irrelevant to the decision to pursue medicine. To some extent students are aware of both of these factors. Balancing them may be a complex task since the costs come in the near future and the income appears much later in time, but they are not ignored. Medical school applicants are like other students who make career decisions. No other occupational choice, however, has as strong a father-son determination as medicine. A study of entering college freshmen in 1961 indicated that 43.64 percent of the sons of physicians intended to become physicians (Werts, 1965). This may mean

TABLE 15 Applicants per new entrants in United States medical schools, by quartile averages for schools grouped in order of expenditures per full-time student, 1959–1961 and 1965–1967	*Type of school and quartile*	*1959–60 and 1960–61*	*1965–66 and 1966–67*
	Public		
	Highest	4.75	8.34
	Second	5.95	8.65
	Third	4.18	7.09
	Lowest	2.90	4.78
	Private		
	Highest	11.20	12.81
	Second	11.13	15.27
	Third	8.86	12.70
	Lowest	8.48	13.08

SOURCES: *Journal of Medical Education,* 1961, pp. 298–299; 1962, pp. 1206–1207; 1967a, pp. 34–35; 1968a, pp. 10–11.

that economic factors play a smaller role in the considerations of this group of individuals (representing 13.7 percent of the freshmen who intended to become physicians). Alternatively, however, it may mean that this group has more and better economic (as well as other) information upon which to base its decisions. If medicine were not economically rewarding, the first point could be argued with greater conviction. The fact that it is economically rewarding obscures the role that economics plays in the decision.

As the student decides to seek additional formal education, he is probably doing so in part for consumption and in part for investment reasons. After all, people pursue additional education partly because they enjoy it and would do so even without additional monetary returns. It is also likely, however, that the willingness to obtain more education and the price that individuals are willing to pay for it are related to their expectations of future increases in income (as well as nonmonetary benefits). Although we cannot assess the relative importance of the consumption and the investment aspects at various levels of education and in various disciplines, it is probable that the consumption aspects are greater in undergraduate college education than in graduate and professional education. We do know that the costs of the latter are greater, in largest measure because of increases in the forgone-income component of costs. The medical student must typically complete four years of undergraduate medical education, one year of internship, two or more years of residency training, and probably two years of service in the armed forces prior to entering the desired aspect of the practice of his profession. Except for the two years in the armed forces, his income is substantially below that of others of equal age and ability who entered the labor market with a first degree. His willingness to bear these high costs may be due in large measure to his expectation concerning future income, that is, to the investment aspect of his education.

Very little research has been undertaken to ascertain the kinds and quality of information that individuals acquire on their possible future incomes relative to costs of potential entrance into an occupation. This is most unfortunate because it is the individually *perceived* rather than the *actual* income and costs that affect decisions. Yet we know little about these perceptions. However, it seems probable that the broad outlines of the monetary costs and returns are known. Furthermore, if the individual is industrious, he can obtain published information on incomes which he can use in reaching a decision. A brief review of the kinds of data the prospective candidate might consider is illuminating.

Two series of incomes of physicians for selected years during the post-World War period are presented in Table 16. The Social Security Administration has published the most complete and consistent series, based on Internal Revenue Service (IRS) data on self-employed physicians. The fortnightly journal *Medical Economics* has also published survey data for nine postwar years. These two bodies of data differ in several respects. The *Medical Economics* survey reports median net income of self-employed physicians under age 65 who have been in practice throughout the entire year. In contrast, the IRS statistics use means of the net profit from self-employment practice only and do not include any income received in the form of salary, dividends, interests, rents, etc. All physicians who earned any income from private fee practice—interns and residents, partially retired physicians, and those with full-time salaried positions—were within the population sampled. These differences in the definition of the population account for a substantial part of the variation in the levels of the two series after 1947. They are only partially offset by the fact that mean income is generally higher than the median.[3]

In order to obtain a clearer picture of the real increases in physician incomes, we also present income in constant dollars for the time series. Both series show that since 1951, physician incomes (in real dollars) have grown at an annual rate of about 4.5 percent. However, while the IRS data showed a real growth rate of 4.3

[3] This discussion is based on the thorough analysis of the differences in the two series presented in Louis S. Reed, 1968, pp. 37–41.

TABLE 16 *Trends in United States physician incomes, 1947–1967*

Year	Current dollars		Constant dollars (1957–1959 = 100)*	
	Medical Economics surveys (median net income)	Internal Revenue Service data (net profit)	Medical Economics surveys	Internal Revenue Service data
1947	8,744	9,055	11,239	11,639
1951	13,150	11,706†	14,530	12,935
1953		13,181		14,143
1955	16,017	15,162†	17,167	16,251
1956		15,768		16,650
1957		16,781		17,123
1958		17,992		17,867
1959	22,100	19,093	21,773	18,811
1960		19,519		18,932
1961		20,337		19,517
1962	24,300	21,354	23,055	20,260
1963	25,050	22,438	23,477	21,029
1964	28,380	23,806	26,253	22,022
1965	28,960	25,446	26,351	23,154
1966	32,170	27,155	28,444	24,010
1967	34,744‡		29,874	

*Derived by deflating current dollars data by the corresponding consumer price index. *Economic Report of the President,* February, 1968, p. 261.
† Extrapolated. Internal Revenue Service data are not available for 1951 and 1955.
‡ The exact figure was not reported, but in *Medical Economics* (1968c) it was stated that incomes in 1967 were about 8 percent higher than those in 1966.
SOURCE: Reed, 1968, pp. 31, 39.

percent for the period 1962–1966, the *Medical Economics* series indicated a real growth rate of 5.4 percent.

These trend figures relate to the past. They may, however, give a measure of reassurance to the prospective applicant concerning possible future trends (unless drastic events affect either the demand for, or the supply of, medical services). Further reassurance may be offered by the *Medical Economics* prediction of physician incomes in 1978: "All things considered, the median net of all private M.D.s under 65 will probably rise an average of 5.4 per cent in each of the next 10 years. That's a lower rate of gain than in the past, based on the assumption that more restraint will be exercised in raising fees. Conservatively, then, the typical private M.D. under age 65 will net a projected $65,000 before income taxes in 1978" (*Medical Economics,* 1968b, p. 99).[4]

In addition to information on the general trend in physician earnings, the prospective applicant may also be influenced by the expected time stream of physician incomes (that is, the income of physicians as related to age). The data indicate that after a few years of private practice, physician incomes (by age) level off and remain relatively stable up to the age of 60. In 1966, when the median income of physicians was $32,170, the income of those with only one to five years of practice was $28,380 (*Medical Economics,* 1967, pp. 63, 71). Thus, the aggregate trend in incomes should apply to earnings at all ages.

Another factor which may affect decisions is the perceived variability of income, particularly if the prospective applicant feels he will have to go into debt in order to finance the completion of his medical education. The standard deviation will not provide adequate information if the distribution is skewed (as the distribution of physician incomes is). A better measure is the proportion of physicians whose earnings are under a specified level and over a specified high level. In 1966, according to the *Medical Economics* survey, only 3 percent of physicians in full-time private practice earned less than $10,000, and 15 percent earned less than $20,000. On the other hand, 30 percent earned $40,000 or more, and 15 percent earned $50,000 or more (*Medical Economics,* 1967, p. 68).

Finally, it is possible that the prospective applicant to medical school may implicitly derive considerable information concerning his future income by noting the relative wealth position of physicians as compared with that of other earners. *Medical Economics* has surveyed the asset position of physicians, and the results are not likely to discourage a prospective applicant. Excluding the cash value of life insurance, physicians in their thirties had median assets of $38,600; those in their forties had median assets of

[4] In a survey of 10,000 randomly chosen male students in the Boston area and 1,000 at the University of Massachusetts in Amherst, Richard B. Freeman examined income expectations of individuals planning careers in various fields. He concluded: "It is quite surprising to find that the occupation for which changes in incomes are most *under*estimated is medicine. The expectations of change of prospective doctors or dentists are far below what can be expected on the basis of 1950–1960 changes in income" (1967, pp. 8–19).

$85,100; those in their fifties had median assets of $134,400; and those in their sixties had median assets of $176,200.[5]

While fully comparable data are not available on the asset holdings of the general population for the same year, the Federal Reserve Board did survey the financial assets of the general public as of December 31, 1962. The median assets for families with the head under age 35, aged 35 to 44, aged 45 to 54, and aged 55 to 64 were $1,032, $6,931, $10,847, and $13,129, respectively (Projector & Weiss, 1966, p. 30, table 8).[6]

If the prospective applicant is to assess the net benefits which would accrue to him as a result of his investment in medical education, he would need some idea of the incomes from alternative occupations which he might pursue. Table 17 presents data on incomes for males with bachelor's degrees and for engineers, dentists, and Ph.D.'s in the sciences. A study of the median incomes of alternative occupations in conjunction with an examination of the age distributions provides useful information on the income differentials which might be expected if a medical career is chosen.

Future incomes, of course, are only a part of the total picture. The high position on the income ladder is purchased at a price. The costs include tuition (and charges) as well as forgone income during the years in which the individual pursues his medical education.

The weighted average tuition for public medical schools was $640 in 1966 (increasing from $378 in 1949 and $519 in 1959). For private schools tuition was $1,610 in 1966 (increasing from $716 in 1949 and $1,147 in 1959).[7] It is true that scholarship aid that offsets these charges is available in many cases. The pro-

[5] From *Medical Economics*, Financial Survey, 1967, *Medical Economics*, Apr. 29, 1968, p. 93. Most of the value was accounted for by savings accounts, equity in home and office, other real estate, and stocks and bonds.

[6] Of course, some consideration must be given to the fact that physicians must purchase their own insurance and retirement benefits or accumulate assets to protect themselves against contingencies such as disability or retirement, which other earners and many professionals who are salaried receive as fringe benefits and which are not usually included in surveys of income.

[7] The data are for the public and private schools analyzed in Chaps. 2 and 3. The weights for public schools were the number of resident freshmen attending the various schools and the resident tuition. Private schools were weighted by the total number of medical students attending the various schools. For the few private schools with different rates, the resident tuition was used (one school in 1949 and two in 1959 and 1966).

spective applicant may, however, have little information about scholarship aid and even less about the probability that he would receive aid, as he considers the cost of attending medical school.

In addition to tuition and other associated costs the prospective applicant may consider his forgone earnings. These opportunity costs are considerable. Since most medical students have high abilities, they could well be earning over $10,000 a year (at 1966 income levels) during the four-year period of medical school attendance and even more during the years of internship and residency (stipends received during internship and residency must, however, be considered). These opportunity costs are so significant that we estimate that in 1966, the ratio of forgone earnings to total medical school costs for the student was 0.83 for those attending private schools and 0.93 for those attending public schools (increases from 0.76 and 0.86, respectively, in 1949).[8]

Tuition charges and other substantial expenses associated with attending medical school represent large "out-of-pocket" expenses to the potential applicant. The part they play in the career decision may be out of proportion to their effect on the total cost (including opportunity costs) of receiving a medical education. This is due to the fact that individuals wishing to invest in themselves face serious difficulties in attracting funds for that purpose if they have not accumulated savings (or if they are not subsidized by their families). There is, as is true of higher education in general, an imperfect market for human investment purposes, in part because the individual cannot use himself as collateral. Thus, even if the individual can pay the opportunity costs by maintaining a lower level of consumption than he would if he were working, he may have considerable difficulty in attracting funds through the private capital market to pay tuition and the other costs associated with attendance at medical school. The implication can be illustrated by a brief example: Assume that there are two individuals. Both have $2,000

[8] If the relevant alternative were to do graduate work in another field, then the stream of opportunity costs would be different. To date, graduate students in other fields have a greater probability of receiving stipends and for larger amounts than medical students. The length of the education is also different: The graduate student in the sciences can receive his Ph.D. in four or five years after receipt of the B.A., as compared with the seven- to eight-year period generally required by medical students. Finally, the probabilities of entering the armed services differ: Under present regulations an individual is subject to the draft upon receipt of the B.A., at an earlier period and at lower pay than the potential M.D.

TABLE 17
Median incomes for selected levels of educational attainment, 1960–1967, and for selected fields, by age group, 1966 or 1967

A. By educational attainment

Year	Four-year college	Doctor of philosophy degree (science)	Doctor's degree in biology	Degree in dentistry — Internal Revenue Service data[a]
1960	$7,261[d]	$10,000	$ 9,000	$11,868
1962		11,000	10,000	13,711
1964	8,430	12,000	11,200	15,359
1966	9,728	13,200	12,500	18,140
1967				

B. By degrees or field and age

	Age group (years)	
	25–34	35–44
Bachelor's degree (1966)	$ 8,687	$11,108
Science (1966)[e]	10,500	13,500
Biology (1966)[e]	9,600	12,500
Dentist (1967)[e,f]	20,600	25,100
Engineer (1967)[g]		
Bachelor	11,670	15,140
Doctor of philosophy	15,360	19,310
Medical degree (1966)[h]	28,380	35,230

[a] Net profit.

[b] Mean net income.

[c] 1967 was the first year that the National Society of Professional Engineers collected income data by degree. However, the trend is suggested by the movement in salaries for the median grade associated with each degree level. (Grades were applied in the study according to duties and responsibilities.) The grade level for bachelor's degree recipients was 5; for the Ph.D.'s, 7.

	Median income	
	Grade 5	Grade 7
1962	$11,120	$16,880
1964	11,800	17,730
1967	13,580	20,280

The data are from National Society of Professional Engineers, 1968, p. 53.

in savings, and neither can work while attending school. In one case tuition paid is zero and opportunity costs are $7,000. In the other case tuition is $2,000 and opportunity costs are $5,000. Though the total costs are identical in both cases, the first individual is able to use his $2,000 in savings for subsistence (though his consumption would be considerably reduced below what it would have been with earnings of $7,000). In the case of the second individual, however—and in the absence of an adequate capital

American Dental Association data[b]	Engineering[c] (median income)	
	Bachelor's degree	Doctor's degree
$16,025[d]		
19,839		
24,740	$13,960	$19,310

45–54	55–64
$11,646	$10,840
15,600	16,000
14,950	16,000
24,200	18,150
17,160	16,350
22,130	20,810
34,320	30,730

[d] 1961 data.

[e] Since the age distribution was in ranges of five years, we averaged two classes to get our numbers, except in the first class (25 to 34), where we went three-quarters of the distance between the first two published classes.

[f] Based on American Dental Association data (see part A above).

[g] Estimated from data based on year of entry into the profession.

[h] For 1 to 5 years of practice, 6 to 10 years, 11 to 20 years, and 21 to 30 years, respectively.

SOURCES: U.S. Bureau of the Census, 1963, p. 31, 1965, p. 39, 1967, pp. 39, 40; Freeman, 1967, table 4.2; National Science Foundation, 1966, p. 113, 1968, p. 91, and unpublished data from the NSF; Reed, 1968, p. 88; "1968 Survey of Dental Practice," 1969, pp. 343, 346; National Society of Professional Engineers, 1968, pp. 19, 47; *Medical Economics,* 1967, p. 71.

market—if the $2,000 in savings is used to pay the tuition charges, nothing remains for subsistence. The fact that, on the average, medical education may appear to be a "good" investment does not imply that prospective applicants can take advantage of the investment, even if they desire to do so. Good investments also require that the individual have the wherewithal to invest or that the capital market be better developed than it is in the field of education.

Just as there has been relatively little research on the perceived income and costs that the medical student weighs in his career decision, so too there has been relatively little research on how individuals weight costs and incomes that occur in different years, that is, how they take account of the fact that both incomes and costs (including opportunity costs) come in a stream over a long period of time but that the period when costs exceed income occurs in the nearer future. Economists, however, combine costs and benefits related to occupational choice into an index that calculates the internal rate of return. The internal rate of return is that rate of interest which equates the discounted value of the flow of income over a period of time with the discounted value of the flow of costs over the same time period; that is, it computes the rate of return that equates the time stream of benefits with the time stream of costs.

The calculation of internal rates of return has been made under several assumptions, using bachelor's degree salaries and science Ph.D. incomes as the alternative cost streams. When using the bachelor's degree income stream, 10 percent was added to the projected median income to take account of the superior ability of those individuals who might be considering application to medical school. In order to compute the internal rate of return, one must estimate the time stream of cost and income which the prospective applicant might use in his decision making. The basic assumptions which differentiate the various computations and the computational procedures are discussed in detail in Appendix C.

The rates of return computed with the bachelor's degree alternative and the cost of public medical school fall between 15.1 percent and 18.4 percent (see Appendix C, Table C-3). The return using private school costs of medical education would be about 0.7 percentage points lower. The rates of return fall between 22.6 percent and 23.9 percent for the Ph.D. alternative. In this case the difference between public school and private school costs would reduce the rate of return by about 0.3 percentage points. These computations appear to be comparable to those presented by

[9] These rates of return are higher than those which others have computed for investment in attaining a bachelor's degree. Becker (1964, p. 128) found an internal rate of return of about 13 percent for the 1949 cohort of white males and 14.8 percent in 1958 for all males. Borland and Yett (pp. 16, 20) found the rates of return to be 12.7 for all males who had completed four or more years of college in 1949 and 14.8 percent for those who had completed four or more years of college in 1959.

Sloan (1968, p. 164).[9] Using the bachelor's degree alternative for 1966, he found an internal rate of return of 18.2 percent. Whether or not the current monetary returns are strong enough to attract an individual to apply to medical school would depend upon many other factors, but it is clear that the returns are relatively high.

All these considerations and a host of nonmonetary ones may be relevant to the individual's decision to undertake the long educational and training period involved in medicine. The demand for medical education may be related to the individual's parental income, pressure, and influence; his family status (whether he is married and the number of children); the private costs of medical education; his expectations concerning his future income as a physician and the income he would receive in feasible alternative professions; his rate of time preference (the relative value placed upon present and future income and consumption); his assessment of the probability of being accepted into medical school and of successfully completing the medical curriculum; the nonmonetary benefits and costs associated with being a physician as compared with those he could expect in the alternative careers he might consider; cultural and attitudinal considerations; and so forth. It would be extremely advantageous to be able to estimate an aggregate demand function for medical education. If one could assess the relative importance of a variety of factors, one could then estimate the impact of changes in those variables which are subject to alteration by public policy decisions. However, the data to estimate such a cross-sectional function are not available.[10] Nevertheless, some data on the characteristics of potential applicants are available that help provide information on the decision to attend medical school and on the characteristics of those who consider applying to medical school.

Characteristics of Medical School Applicants There is a body of literature that provides a variety of information on the characteristics of potential applicants, actual applicants, and students in American medical schools. Until recently, however, the information was gathered largely through studies made exclusively from the perspective of medical education. Most of the studies placed the primary, and often the sole, emphasis on the

---

[10] Sloan (1968, pp. 68–93) studied the factors that affect the aggregate number of applicants to United States medical schools. He used time-series data and employed multiple regression analysis and several estimation techniques to find the coefficients for his parameters.

student or the applicant and tended to overlook the undergraduate who considered medicine as a career and, at some point in his education, decided not to apply to medical school. In part, of course, the reason for this omission was that the population that included potential applicants was much larger than that of actual applicants. The costs of undertaking studies of potential applicants (in the absence of a broader interest in undergraduate students in general) would therefore have been quite high.

Recently, as a result of more widespread interest in college-educated youth, in the loss of talent, and in the characteristics of those who seek undergraduate and graduate education, major studies (including some of a longitudinal nature) have been undertaken. The data on actual and potential applicants are now available as part of much broader studies undertaken by groups outside the field of medical education itself.[11] We shall review the findings of four such studies: Project Talent, National Merit Scholarship Corporation, the National Opinion Research Center, and the American Council on Education.[12]

In 1966, the American Council on Education (ACE) conducted its annual survey of freshmen who entered college that fall. A study sample of 289 representative freshmen premedical students and 2,646 preprofessional freshmen (including the premedical students) was compared with the total of 206,865 freshmen in the 1966 entering classes of some 250 undergraduate colleges and universities. In a paper that discussed the characteristics of individuals in these three groups, Johnson (1968) found:

In general, the data indicate that the premedical students entering college tend to be not only better scholars than most of their classmates but also to have excelled in previous extracurricular accomplishments, including varsity athletics and leadership positions. More of them also place high value on service to others and have a high degree of both intellectual and social self-confidence. Although more of the premedical students come

---

[11] The studies of a less general context remain extremely valuable since they often provide even more detailed information (although on a more restricted population). Medical educators and organizations are involved in the studies undertaken by other groups, either in helping design the studies or in analyzing the findings for medical applicants in greater detail than is usually done in the more general studies.

[12] On occasion we may refer to other studies and findings. Our decision to limit ourselves in this section is based on the fact that it is not our intention to provide more than a background review.

from higher socio-economic backgrounds than their average classmate, a wide variation in backgrounds is represented. It is also noteworthy that more of the premedical students tend to be enrolled in colleges which they characterize as being intellectual and liberal in nature but which are also characterized by great pressure for good grades and by having a student body of generally high academic calibre. Thus, it is suggested that any perceived lack in today's premedical students may be as much a function of the undergraduate college environment in which they find themselves as of any basic failing in the students themselves.[13]

Table 18 presents some of the American Council on Education findings as excerpted from Johnson's analysis. About 4.9 percent of all freshmen, 13.2 percent of professional aspirants, and 80.1 percent of physician aspirants planned to obtain an M.D., D.D.S., or D.V.M. degree. The reason why only 80 (rather than 100) percent of the physician aspirant group intended to obtain medical degrees is that the group included all those who listed medicine as the first of their three choices of "probable career occupation," but some felt that for academic, financial, or other reasons they would in fact not obtain the desired academic degree. If the approximately 20 percent who fell into that category—aspiring but not planning to receive a medical degree—were excluded from the data, the academic and financial differentials between the various groups would increase. The 4.9 percent of all freshmen who considered medicine to be the field of probable occupation is equivalent to about 66,000 in absolute numbers (based on ACE estimates of the total freshmen population in Astin, Panos, & Creager, 1967, p. A6). Since, in recent years, there have been about 19,000 applicants to medical school (and about 9,000 to 10,000 admissions), it is clear that expectations are revised substantially during the four undergraduate years.

Another major survey that yields data on potential medical school applicants was conducted by the National Merit Scholarship Corporation. This study, undertaken in the fall of 1961, included 127,212 entering freshmen in 248 colleges and universities. As in the ACE study, there are numerous findings, only a small portion of which can be summarized here:

[13] The perceived lack to which Johnson refers appears to be related to the complaint that he reports is voiced by several premedical advisers and undergraduate college admissions officers. They allege that many of the premedical students are "grade grubbing, overly competitive, self-centered, and the like."

TABLE 18 *Comparison of characteristics of freshmen physician aspirants with total freshmen preprofessional aspirants and total freshmen, 1966**

Characteristics†	Total freshmen (N= 206,865)	Preprofessional aspirants‡ (N= 2,646)	Physician aspirants (N= 289)
Percent planning to obtain M.D., D.D.S., or D.V.M. degree	4.9	13.2	80.1
Percent with A— or better averages in high school	15.4	17.6	35.9
Percent with C+ or lower averages in high school	30.5	30.0	13.2
Aspiration (percent)			
To be very well off financially	43.8	55.8	46.5
To help others in difficulty	68.5	59.8	78.9
To join Peace Corps or VISTA	21.0	13.8	26.9
To contribute to scientific theory	13.3	25.9	38.9
Trait self-rating (percent above average)			
Academic ability	57.4	46.8	48.3
Drive to achieve	56.8	62.9	77.9
Understanding of others	60.1	47.4	52.8
Parents' education (percent)			
Father, college degree or more	26.6	30.3	45.3
Mother, college degree or more	18.0	19.4	28.9
Percent male	54.3	89.3	82.4
Percent with parental income			
Under $10,000	53.7	48.9	37.4
$10,000–15,000	25.2	26.4	26.8
$15,000–$20,000	9.4	10.7	12.7
$20,000–$30,000	7.0	7.4	10.8
$30,000 or more	4.7	6.5	12.3

*Based on a representative sample of the entering class in approximately 250 undergraduate colleges and universities in the United States in 1966.

† In calculating percentages, the denominators were the number of students in each group as defined in the column headings.

‡ Includes the 289 premedical students.

SOURCE: Johnson, 1968.

1 Freshmen males underchose[14] the career of physician when their fathers were farmers, manual laborers, semiskilled workers, skilled workers, foremen, and technical workers. They overchose when

[14] *Underchoose* refers to a case in which the percentage choosing a career is statistically significantly smaller than would be expected on the basis of the percentage of fathers engaged in the particular occupation. For example, 3.07 percent of the males were sons of physicians. If the career of physician were selected randomly with respect to father's occupation, 3.07 percent of those in each career choice would be sons of physicians. Therefore, underchoosing means that the actual percentage is statistically smaller than 3.07 percent. Overchoosing means that it is statistically larger than 3.07 percent.

their fathers were businessmen and particularly so when they were physicians. As previously noted, the percentage of all fathers who were physicians and whose sons chose the same career was 43.6 percent. No other occupational choice exhibited so strong a father-son determination (Werts, 1965, table 1).

2   The distribution of high school grades for males who aspired to be physicians was significantly higher than that of entering freshmen. Students with a high school grade average of B+ or better were overrepresented, while those with an average of B— or lower were underrepresented (Werts, 1966b, table 3).

3   Thirty thousand of the 127,000 freshmen studied in the fall of 1961 were followed up one year later to study career-decision changes. Of the 1,576 students whose career choice was physician in 1961, 73 percent had identical career choices at the end of the freshman year. There had been 424 "defectors," that is, students who changed their career decision away from physician. Additionally, however, there had been 502 "recruits"—students who changed their career decision to physician during the freshman year. The defectors had fathers whose educational level was statistically significantly lower than that of the "loyalists." As measured both by high school grades and college freshman grades, the loyalists were more able than the defectors. Sons of physicians were less likely to change their career decision to be physicians than sons of nonphysicians. In general, students who were unlike the majority of the other students who wanted to become physicians were more likely to change their career plans to another field (Werts, 1966a, pp. 2–8).

4   Confirmation of the "holding power" of medicine is evident from analysis of career decisions of male winners of National Merit Scholarships. In the five-year period 1956–1960, 7.4 percent of male National Merit Scholars (approximately the top 1 percent in academic ability of high school juniors in each state) designated medicine as their career choice upon entering college, and 8.2 percent actually entered the field. Fully 60.4 percent of those whose initial preference was medicine remained in the field (and 6.1 percent changed to biological sciences). Of all those whose final decision was medicine, 54.3 percent had made that career their initial choice (an additional 15.6 percent had come into it from the biological sciences) (Watley, 1968, pp. 5, 9).

5   Since 1957, the percentage of National Merit Scholarship finalists who indicate an interest in a career in medicine has been increasing, but (also since 1957) the percentage who choose the field of premedicine in college has been declining (Watley & Nichols, 1969, p. 5).

A third study to be reviewed is the National Opinion Research Center (NORC) study of June, 1961 graduates from 135 colleges and universities. In this study about 3 percent of the graduates listed medicine as their anticipated career field.[15] By requesting information from the graduating seniors regarding their occupational plans when they were freshmen, it was possible to compare the characteristics of seniors and freshmen who chose medicine as a career and to study the characteristics of the freshmen who defected from medicine as well as those of the freshmen who were recruited to medicine. Using an elaborate procedure to adjust college grade-point averages to take account of the selectivity of the college, Davis designed an academic performance index (API).[16] He found that 42.1 percent of those who aspired to a career in medicine were in the top fifth of the index, an additional 42.4 percent were above average, and only 15.5 percent were in the bottom half. The only graduate fields that attracted a higher percentage of students in the highest quintile category were English (43.9 percent) and physics (42.3 percent), but they had 19.0 percent and 29.1 percent, respectively, in the bottom half (Davis, 1964). He also found that 69.7 percent of those who planned on medicine as a career fell into the high-socioeconomic-status category, a figure considerably higher than that found in other sciences and surpassed only by the percentage of those indicating an interest in law (p. 164).

Davis also concluded that in contrast to the findings of the National Merit studies, which were based on a one-year follow-up, graduates show a strong movement out of medicine during the four years of college. Fifty-six percent of those freshmen who had opted for a career in medicine had abandoned the field at the time

[15] About 85 percent of the eligible graduates completed the questionnaire, providing a sample of 33,982 graduates (see Davis, 1964, 1965).

[16] This study is of particular interest because of the adjustment to take account of the selectivity of the undergraduate college. In many cases, measures of academic performance do not take account of this factor and therefore lead to somewhat ambiguous findings.

of graduation, while medicine recruited 1 percent of the individuals originally outside the field, giving a net decline of 43 percent in the number of students who aspired to be physicians (Davis, 1965, pp. 19–21). Davis summarized the dynamics of choice during college as follows:

1 API has a very strong effect. Regardless of values, two-thirds or more of the low API men abandon medicine, and regardless of values, half or more than half of the high API men retain their freshmen preferences for medicine. Similarly, recruits to medicine are more often high API than low . . . this API effect produces a striking increase in the API level of aspiring physicians from the freshman to the senior year.

2 Within each API group, medicine recruits and retains people-oriented men.

3 Although it was unrelated to a freshman choice of medicine "original and creative" as an occupational value has a negative relationship with a choice of medicine made during college. Particularly striking is the swathe this value cuts through a group otherwise high on choice of medicine, the high API men who are people-oriented. For those in this group who do not endorse originality the defection rate is 21 percent, but the loss among those who want opportunities to be original and creative is 46 percent (Davis, 1965, pp. 19–21, 170–175).[17]

The final study to be reviewed briefly is an analysis undertaken by the American Medical Association of data derived from Project Talent, a nationwide testing program designed to obtain information on student aptitudes and abilities (as well as on other characteristics). Results for tests taken in 1960 by high school seniors were obtained for four groups of students: (1) 158 students who at that time had selected medicine as a career and who subsequently attended medical school; (2) 123 students who selected a career other than medicine, but subsequently attended medical school; (3) 1,668 students who selected medicine as a career, but did not attend medical school (including students who did not apply to medical school as well as those who applied but were not accepted); and (4) students who were in the upper 20 percent of the senior high school class on the General Academic Achievement Test (given by Project Talent).

---

[17] It should be noted that when API is accounted for, the index of socioeconomic status had little effect on defecting among freshmen choosing medicine. See Table 3.8d (Davis, 1965, p. 169).

When the various groups were compared, the following two results of particular interest were noted:

1 Medical students who had initially opted for medicine had higher mean scores on leadership and on the socioeconomic index than the students who opted for medicine but failed to attend medical school. They also had superior grades in high school.

2 Medical students who had originally selected medicine as a career had approximately the same mean scores as high-ability seniors in six tests that are considered important in measuring ability. Students who had initially selected medicine but were not enrolled in medical school had significantly lower mean scores than the high-ability seniors in all six tests.[18]

These four major studies indicate that medical school applicants are among the ablest students, come from families of high socioeconomic background, and, in a high proportion of cases, make their career choices well in advance of applying to medical school.[19] These studies provide data on characteristics of students who at some time had chosen medicine as their career interest. Unfortunately, therefore, many of the relationships are based upon samples of self-selected students and exclude students who might have been interested in medicine but never included it as one of the options open to them (perhaps because of academic reasons, financial considerations, and so forth).[20]

[18] The six tests are general aptitude, technical composite, scientific aptitude, English, math, and total information (see "Factors Affecting Choice of Medicine as a Career by High School Students in Project Talent," 1967).

[19] The evidence that those who change their choice from medicine are not as able students as those who continue in medicine is supported by a study of 44 Harvard College premedical students who did not apply to medical school. The data in the study indicate that 18 of these students, all with a favorable image of the physician, failed to achieve high grades in premedical science courses; 8 with high grades indicated that they considered the physician an "inferior scientist"; 8 with high science grades perceived the physician as a "nonhumanitarian person"; and 8 had the same image of the physician as well as low science grades. Thus 26 of the 44 students (59 percent) had low academic performance in science courses (see Funkenstein, 1961, pp. 924–933).

Corroboration of the "early decision" is provided in two studies made of University of Pennsylvania medical students in the 1950s. Those studies indicated that about 44 percent of the students had made a decision to enter medical school even prior to beginning college (see Rogoff, 1957, pp. 109–129; Thielens, 1957, pp. 131–152).

[20] Funkenstein (1961) found that none of the premedical students failed to apply to medical school because of financial considerations. This, however, may be

Useful as the description of characteristics is, it does not provide information that can be used to estimate the aggregate demand function for medical education. Taken by itself it is not sufficient to judge the impact of alternative policies on the number of applicants or on the characteristics of those who would apply. The clues that the aggregate analysis provides and that the examination of characteristics of applicants and potential applicants offers, supplemented by additional material on medical students and the ways in which they finance medical education will, however, assist us in our endeavor.

THE MEDICAL STUDENT Entrants to medical school are not drawn in equal proportions from all the institutions of higher education. This is not surprising, given early career choices and the relationship between academic ability, career choices, and financial status. For admission to the 1964–65 first-year medical school class, 25 undergraduate colleges or universities provided 4,672 (or 24 percent) of the applicants and 2,497 (or 29 percent) of the first-time enrolled students. The total acceptance rate for these 25 institutions was 53.4 percent, compared with an acceptance rate of 47.2 percent for all applicants in that year. The reason, therefore, why these institutions, with 34,189 male graduates whose acceptance rate was not unduly high, contributed so many applicants and entrants lies in the fact that they had a much higher application rate per graduate than other schools. Some 13.7 percent of their male graduates applied to medical school. The rest of higher education contributed only 14,496 applicants, though having 263,857 male graduates (an applicant-per-graduate percentage of 5.5). Similarly, 7.3 percent of the male graduates of these 25 schools were entrants to medical schools, while for the rest of higher education the percentage was only 2.5.[21] Since our earlier data indicated that, in many cases, students who aspire to become physicians make career decisions

---

due to the fact that only those who are able to finance medical school education become premedical students. College entrants are most probably aware of the high costs involved in attending medical school. In his sample, Funkenstein did find one student with low grades who was dissuaded from applying to medical school because he realized that he would not receive a scholarship.

[21] While the 8,571 first-year admissions were drawn from 741 different colleges and universities, 90 percent of the entering class came from 42 percent of these institutions, and 75 percent came from 21 percent (see *Journal of Medical Education,* 1967a, p. 83).

even before entering undergraduate colleges, it is likely that the choice of undergraduate college is not random but is related to career plans, academic ability, and financial status.[22]

Similarly, entrants to medical school are not drawn in equal proportion from all income classes. During the 1967–68 school year, the National Institutes of Health, in cooperation with the Association of American Medical Colleges, collected data concerning medical students and their socioeconomic characteristics (Crocker & Smith, 1970). These data showed that a disproportionately large number of medical students come from high-income families. Though only 34 percent of all American families reported incomes over $10,000 in 1967, 63 percent of all medical students reported that they came from families with incomes over $10,000. Conversely, though 25 percent of all American families earned less than $5,000, only 9 percent of medical students came from such families.[23]

It is clear that the distribution by income of medical students

[22] Eight of these twenty-five schools were also among the twenty-five schools with the highest percentage of applicants accepted for admission. Five schools ranked among the first twenty-five on three measures: number of medical school entrants, percentage of male graduates entering medical school, and percentage of applicants receiving medical school acceptances (see *Journal of Medical Education,* 1967a, p. 83; 1967b, p. 181).

[23] The proportion of all individuals in the relevant age groups (about 22 to 26 years old) who come from such families is not known. However, it is likely that the parents of persons aged 22 to 26 are in the 45-to-54 age bracket. About 48 percent of families with heads in that age group had incomes greater than $10,000 in 1967, and about 15 percent had incomes of less than $5,000 (see U.S. Bureau of the Census, 1969, pp. 32–35).

A survey conducted by the American Council on Education of freshmen undergraduates entering 51 universities in 1967 requested information on the income of the students' parents. According to the weighted national norms computed from these data, 58.3 percent of freshmen men who knew their parents' income stated that the income was greater than $10,000, while only 11.6 percent stated that their parents' income was less than $6,000 (Panos, Astin, & Creager, 1967, p. 17).

Reliable data on the parental income of other graduate students are not available. However, fields other than medicine probably allow for much greater participation by students with lower parental incomes than occurs in medicine, for the following reasons: (1) the wider variability in educational attainment associated with the ability to pursue other graduate work (if indeed students from lower-income families exhibit lesser educational ability as measured by the factors with which graduate schools are concerned), (2) the possibility of pursuing part-time studies and earning outside income simultaneously (not easily done in medicine), and (3) the ability to obtain substantial support through stipends.

is significantly different from that of the general population and overrepresents the higher-income groups. The direction of change in the overrepresentation of the higher-income groups over time is difficult to interpret. We present the relevant information in Table 19.

The distribution of medical students according to their fathers' education also shows considerable difference from the overall distribution of males by education. The 1967 National Institutes of Health study found that 51 percent of medical students had fathers who had completed college (or who had gone beyond). This compared with 12.5 percent of all family heads 25 years of age and over who had completed four or more years of college in 1967. More importantly, it compared with 34.7 percent of freshmen men entering universities in 1967 whose fathers had obtained that much education (Panos et al., 1967, p. 16; U.S. Bureau of the Census, 1967, p. 28). In general, these data are similar to the data reported earlier in this chapter on potential applicants and would appear to bear out the conclusion that the medical student population is different from the total student population (and from the total population in the relevant age group). It comes from a particular (and small) part of American society.

Even though it is clear that, on the average, medical students come from the highest socioeconomic groups, there is considerable variation in the socioeconomic status of students attending the various medical schools. Using data available for freshmen from the 1967 National Institutes of Health–Association of American Medical Colleges study, we have examined the distribution of parental income, father's education, and father's occupation for the eight groups of schools ranked by expenditures per student in 1965–66.[24] An examination of the data in Table 20 shows the variations. At the one extreme are the lowest-expenditure public institutions, with 40 percent of the freshmen from families with incomes under $10,000. At the other extreme are the highest-expenditure private institutions, with only 24 percent of freshmen from families in that income class. Similarly, in public institutions in the quartile with lowest expenditures per student, 45 percent of the freshmen came from families where the father had completed

[24] Each school with a response rate of 50 percent or greater was included and given a weight in accordance with the size of its freshman class. If the response rate was less than 50 percent, the school was dropped from the analysis.

TABLE 19
Comparison of
parental
income of
medical
students with
income of
United States
families with
head aged
45 to 54, 1959,
1963, and 1967

Type of family and	Percentage distribution*		
income class	1959†	1963	1967
Income of parents of medical school students			
Less than $5,000	15	15	9
$5,000–$9,999	40	36	28
$10,000–$14,999 ⎱	45	20	22
$15,000 and over ⎰		29	41
Income of United States families with head aged 45 to 54			
Less than $5,000	36.2	26.4	15.3
$5,000–$9,999	45.9	44.7	37.1
$10,000–$14,999	13.8	20.1	28.4
$15,000 and over	4.3	8.9	19.3
Median income	$6,137	$7,415	$9,676

*Percentages may not add to 100 because of rounding.
†Seniors only.
SOURCES: Whiting, Powers, & Darley, 1961, p. 755; Altenderfer & West, 1965, p. 9. Unpublished data from the 1967 NIH-AAMC survey of medical students and U.S. Bureau of the Census, 1961, p. 25; 1964, p. 22; 1969, p. 33.

college or gone beyond, while this was true for 65 percent of the freshmen in high-expenditure private schools. Tuition levels, of course, are considerably different for the public schools and the private institutions, but it is likely that other factors also play an important part in determining the characteristics of the students attending the various schools. Among these factors are academic achievement, undergraduate school attendance, and performance on the MCAT.

Medical students come from the highest part of the socioeconomic spectrum. They are also among the highest-ability students (as measured by academic performance in undergraduate studies). Again, however, there is significant variation in the ability levels of students among the various schools. (Data on MCAT scores for schools grouped in quartiles by various measures were presented in Chapter 2.) There appear to be two different findings regarding the trend in the ability level of medical students. In general, the movement of MCAT scores during the past 15 years appears to indicate substantial improvement in the abilities of entering medical students. At the same time, the decline in the proportion of entering students who had A averages in college seems to indicate that the medical schools are getting a smaller proportion of the highest-quality students. The mean MCAT science score for accepted applicants into medical school rose from 525 in 1952–53 to 565 in 1967–68. The verbal ability score rose from

522 to 554, the quantitative ability score from 526 to 596, and the general information score from 519 to 566.[25] Nonetheless, in 1952–53, 18 percent of first-year medical students had achieved an A average in college, while in 1966–67, this percentage had dropped to 14 percent—the percent with a C average also dropped (*Journal of the American Medical Association,* Nov. 17, 1962, p. 748 and 1968, p. 2014).

These two apparently contradictory observations can easily be reconciled. It is very likely that the ability levels of students in the schools from which medical schools draw the bulk of their students have increased over the past 15 years. Thus, even though other fields of graduate study have become increasingly attractive to the best students from these highest-ability student bodies, the capability of medical students has also improved.

Financing and the Adequacy of Student Aid

The student who enters medical school has most often already completed four years of undergraduate higher education. He still faces a long period in which there will be substantial financial outlays and large forgone earnings. The most recent data on expenses faced by the M.D. candidate and his family pertain to the 1967–68 school year (Crocker & Smith, 1970). The average annual expenses reported amounted to $4,394 (including tuition, fees, books, personal maintenance, lodging, family expenses, and so forth). School expenses averaged $1,003 for students attending public schools and $1,956 for students attending private schools. They accounted for 25 percent and 40 percent of the student's total expenses, respectively.[26] The total expense varied with the marital status of the student, the size of his family, the control of the medical school (public or private), and the student's year in medical school (see Table 21).[27]

[25] The mean scores of rejected applicants showed the following changes: science, from 457 in 1952–53 to 485 in 1967–68; verbal, from 465 to 496; quantitative, from 459 to 514; and general information, from 467 to 514 (*Journal of the American Medical Association,* 1968, p. 2015).

[26] Tuition charges, which are the largest proportion of these expenses, have been rising rapidly, particularly at private schools. Between the 1957 and 1967 school years, the median tuition charges for resident students at public schools increased by 42 percent, while the median tuition charges at private schools increased by 91 percent.

[27] Expenditures for board and lodging and for other items (accounting for 39 percent and 26 percent of total expenditures, respectively) would have been required even if the individual were not a student.

TABLE 20
Percentage distribution of freshmen in United States medical schools by socioeconomic status; quartile averages for schools grouped in order of expenditures per full-time student, 1967–68*

A. Parental income

	Below $5,000	$5,000–5,999	$6,000–6,999	$7,000–9,999
Public				
Highest	(10) 9.0	4.5	5.0	17.7
Second	(9)10.0	4.0	5.1	17.7
Third	(9) 6.2	5.4	5.9	18.6
Lowest	(10)10.1	5.3	5.8	19.5
Private				
Highest	(8) 4.5	3.9	3.3	12.6
Second	(10) 7.2	3.4	4.3	13.0
Third	(9) 7.9	5.4	3.9	14.4
Lowest	(7) 7.2	5.1	5.2	17.3

B. Father's education

	Eighth grade or less	Some high school	Completed high school	Some technical training
Public				
Highest	(10) 6.2	4.9	20.4	5.7
Second	(9) 7.7	8.6	17.1	5.4
Third	(9) 8.0	7.8	19.8	5.8
Lowest	(10) 8.8	5.4	17.6	5.8
Private				
Highest	(8) 4.6	4.6	12.8	2.9
Second	(10) 4.4	6.0	15.7	3.5
Third	(9) 6.6	6.6	16.4	5.5
Lowest	(7) 7.6	8.2	17.5	4.3

C. Father's occupation

	M.D.	Other professional	Owner of business	Clerical
Public				
Highest	(10)12.7	34.8	23.5	3.9
Second	(9)13.1	32.6	22.1	4.1
Third	(9) 9.2	31.3	25.4	4.6
Lowest	(10)13.4	31.9	20.6	3.6
Private				
Highest	(8)16.8	38.2	25.6	2.3
Second	(10)20.0	34.0	24.4	3.6
Third	(9)15.3	33.9	24.7	3.0
Lowest	(7)16.9	30.0	27.6	4.8

*Each school with 50 percent or more response was inflated to the size of its freshman class. If the response was less than 50 percent, the school was dropped out. The number of schools included in each group is in parentheses.

Medical students financed their education with funds from a variety of sources. The 1967–68 study reports that four out of five students used funds from their own savings and earnings to provide

$10,000– 14,999	$15,000– 19,999	$20,000– 24,999	$25,000 and over
23.0	12.0	10.3	18.4
22.4	15.5	8.8	16.6
27.8	12.1	9.8	14.1
22.9	11.8	7.8	16.8
22.5	16.4	10.4	26.4
22.0	14.1	9.8	26.2
23.4	13.2	9.5	22.3
21.7	13.2	6.3	24.1

Some college	Completed college	Graduate school or professional
14.7	17.3	30.8
12.6	14.1	34.4
15.5	15.1	28.0
16.9	13.5	31.9
10.2	19.7	45.4
10.5	18.8	41.0
14.8	15.4	34.5
11.9	15.2	35.2

Sales	Skilled laborer	Unskilled laborer	Farmer
4.7	10.8	4.4	5.4
7.6	12.6	3.6	4.4
6.8	13.6	5.1	4.0
7.4	13.8	5.2	4.3
6.1	6.9	2.3	1.7
6.2	7.5	3.2	1.1
6.9	12.2	3.1	1.1
4.8	9.0	5.3	1.6

SOURCE: Raw data from the 1967 NIH-AAMC survey of medical students.

part of the required financing. However, the majority found medical school so demanding (or job opportunities so limited) that only 23 percent reported that they were employed during the cur-

TABLE 21 *Average annual expenses of students in United States medical schools, by marital status and school class, 1967–68*

Type of school and marital status	Average annual expenses				
		Medical school class			
	All classes*	Freshman	Sophomore	Junior	Senior
All schools, total†	$4,394	$3,817	$4,291	$4,617	$4,954
Single	3,421	3,336	3,422	3,488	3,533
Married	5,777	5,512	5,827	5,764	5,871
No children	5,727	5,446	5,758	5,704	5,859
One child	5,730	5,383	5,699	5,828	5,796
Two or more children	6,310	6,498	6,874	6,203	6,089
Public schools, total†	3,982	3,335	3,909	4,204	4,610
Single	2,832	2,741	2,889	2,838	2,951
Married	5,345	5,018	5,416	5,334	5,462
No children	5,258	4,945	5,325	5,221	5,411
One child	5,342	4,964	5,270	5,424	5,460
Two or more children	5,995	5,969	6,527	6,012	5,744
Private schools, total†	4,839	4,346	4,708	5,062	5,314
Single	3,963	3,921	3,927	4,054	3,995
Married	6,357	6,290	6,404	6,332	6,375
No children	6,305	6,210	6,331	6,272	6,356
One child	6,376	6,214	6,362	6,552	6,317
Two or more children	6,869	7,222	7,642	6,606	6,633

*"All schools" and "private schools" include data for students in the first year of the five-year program at Stanford.

† Includes data for students who were widowed, divorced, or separated, which is not shown separately or in any of the categories.

SOURCE: Crocker & Smith, 1970.

rent school term. The average annual amount utilized from their own earnings and savings (for the students using those sources) was $1,392. Gifts and loans from the students' families, spouses' earnings, loans from outside the family, and nonrefundable grants filled the gap between the students' own funds and their expenses. Sixty-five percent of the students received some support from their parents. In addition, 80 percent of the wives of the medical students contributed to the family income.

Aggregate data on grants and loans to students for the 1967–68 school year are available from the 1967 AMA-AAMC annual questionnaire, which requested each medical school to provide information on the student aid programs which it administered. Funds provided directly to the student—without going through the school —are not included. According to the responses, 57.4 percent of public medical school students borrowed an average of about $1,015, and 53.0 percent of private medical school students borrowed an average of $1,140, while 24.9 percent of public medical school students received grants averaging $700, and 34.1 percent of private medical school students received grants averaging $975. In total, the medical schools administered $20.3 million in loans and $8.7 million in grants — an average of $590 in loans and $250 in grants per enrolled student.[28] About 75 percent of the loan funds and about 36 percent of the nonrefundable grants were provided under the 1965 amendments to the federal Health Professions Educational Assistance Act.[29] This represents a substantial change from the immediately preceding years. For instance, in the 1964–65 school year, federal funds accounted for approximately 45 percent of the funds borrowed by medical students, as did the sum of AMA-ERF and school funds. In the 1966–67 school year, federal funds supported only 23 percent of the value of grants.[30]

Student aid funds were not equally divided among schools. This was particularly true of grants which are provided, to a great extent, out of resources of the individual schools. The 10 privately controlled schools with the highest expenditures per full-time student (in 1966) administered $2.17 million in grants in 1967–68 while responsible for 3,668 students ($592 per student), while the 12

[28] *Journal of the American Medical Association,* 1968, p. 2017. In 1957–58, the medical schools administered $1.3 million in student loans and $1.5 million in scholarships. By the academic year 1963–64, these figures had increased to $5.6 million in loans and $3.9 million in scholarships (*Journal of the American Medical Association,* 1964, p. 614).

[29] This program will be discussed in detail in Chap. 6. Other sources of loans are school funds, the American Medical Association Education and Research Foundation (AMA-ERF) loan program, and a number of miscellaneous programs. The AMA-ERF program provides guarantees for long-term bank loans which must be repaid in monthly installments over a period of up to 10 years' duration starting four months after completing full-time training. The interest rate, which is closely tied to general credit conditions, is $6\frac{1}{2}$ percent during in-school and deferment periods and $7\frac{1}{2}$ percent during the repayment period, and the maximum amount which can be borrowed is $750 ($1,500 between 1966 and 1969). School funds support most of the nonfederal grants, frequently through the use of tuition-remission grants.

[30] Grants under the Health Professions Educational Assistance amendments of 1965 were being gradually phased in until 1969, thus accounting for the relative increase in federal aid in 1967 over 1966. The original legislation provided funds for fiscal year 1967 based on the number of first-year students; for fiscal 1968, based on the number of first-year and second-year students; for fiscal 1969, based on the number of first-year and second-year students; and for fiscal 1970, based on all students. (*Students* refers to full-time students.)

privately controlled schools with the lowest expenditures per full-time student administered only $867,000, though responsible for 4,829 students ($180 per student)—this in spite of the fact that the students in low-expenditure schools came from families with considerably lower incomes than those of students at the high-expenditure schools.[31]

Data made available from the 1967 NIH-AAMC survey have enabled us to undertake a more detailed analysis of the availability of, and demand for, student aid. This analysis is useful in judging the adequacy of current programs.

Table 22 presents information on the demand for grants by students in public and private institutions, in various parental income categories, and by marital status. We find that:

1 In general, and as would be expected, as income rises, the percentage of students who request grants declines.

2 The percentage of students who request grants is higher in the private schools than in the public institutions. Private institutions are more expensive, and the amount of financial assistance required is therefore greater. On the other hand, parental incomes of students in private schools tend to be higher. The demand for funds may be due to the fact that these institutions have more grant funds available.

3 The percentage of students who request grants is highest for single students. Though these students have the least family responsibilities, their need for grants is probably related to the fact that there are no other earners in the family.

4 On the average, about 90 percent of the students who requested grants had received them at the time of the survey.

5 Though students do not necessarily receive as much as they request, the total amount granted is generally over 75 percent of the total amount requested (including requests not granted). This percentage tends to be higher for private than for public institutions.

6 The average amount requested is higher in private than in public institutions. For single students the amounts requested decline

[31] The data in this paragraph were taken from *Journal of the American Medical Association,* 1968, pp. 1994–1995, and from an analysis of unpublished data.

as income rises. For married students, where the ability of the wife to work is an additional variable and where the ages of the children may influence earning power, the average amount requested does not show as clear a relationship to income.

7 The average amount received, as a percentage of the average amount requested, is quite high, tending to be over 85 percent in general. The percentage is about the same for private and public institutions.

It is clear that financial aid in the form of grants is an important source of money for the financing of medical education. Many students request such aid, a high proportion receive it, and the amount that they receive is a high percentage of the amount requested. Thus, for example, 77 percent of the single students in private schools with parental incomes under $5,000 request aid, 97 percent of those who request it receive aid, and they receive 92 percent of the average amount requested. As a result, 71 percent of the students in that income category are receiving aid, averaging $1,432 per grantee (and about $1,011 per student).

Nor are grants the only source of assistance. Students also request (and receive) loan funds. Table 23 presents data for loans (using the same classification scheme that is used in Table 22). Again it is clear that the dollar amounts requested and received in the form of loans are significant.[32] For example, in private schools, single students with family incomes under $5,000 (the group just discussed) receive significant loans in addition to the grants they obtain. Sixty-six percent of them receive loans (71 percent receive grants), and on the average, they receive almost as much as they request: almost $1,500. In general, a somewhat higher percentage of private than of public school students request loans. Furthermore, a higher percentage of those who request loans receive them in the private schools. Additionally, private school students request and receive larger amounts on the average than public school students. It is also worth noting that single students from families with incomes under $5,000 request fewer loan dollars (on the average) than students in other income categories. In part this may be due to the fact that they tend to receive more in grants,

---

[32] These data are for freshmen, and the period of education in medical school is a long and extended one. The loans can therefore be expected to increase significantly over that period.

	Percent of freshmen	Percent of those
TABLE 22 *Type of school,*	*with parents in this*	*who requested*
Requests and receipt of grants by freshmen in United States medical schools, by marital status* and parental income, 1967–68 *marital status, and parental income class*	*income class who requested grants*	*grants who received grants*
Public schools		
Single		
Under $5,000	71	92
$5,000–9,999	54	95
$10,000–14,999	33	91
$15,000–19,999	23	88
$20,000 and over	15	90
Married (0 or 1 child)		
Under $5,000	47	98
$5,000–9,000	45	93
$10,000–14,999	28	87
$15,000–19,999	16	75
$20,000 and over	16	89
Private schools		
Single		
Under $5,000	73	97
$5,000–9,000	67	96
$10,000–14,000	50	95
$15,000–19,999	34	95
$20,000 and over	18	94
Married (0 or 1 child)		
Under $5,000	57	100
$5,000–9,999	45	92
$10,000–14,999	45	91
$15,000–19,999	40	82
$20,000 and over	14	86

*"Single" includes separated, widowed, and divorced. Data are available but not presented for the very small number of married students with two or more children.
SOURCE: Raw data from the 1967 NIH-AAMC survey of medical students.

but it may also be due to a significant aversion among persons who are at the bottom of the income ladder toward borrowing large amounts. This phenomenon may also be a function of the fact that higher-income students who request and receive loans seem to be concentrated in a relatively few schools.

In Table 24 we have brought together information on loans and grants since both are sources for financing students' medical education. This table indicates (for the freshmen who responded) that:

1 A majority of students from families with incomes under $10,000 receive grants. The proportion of recipients and the average amount received are

Total grants received as percentage of total number requested	Average amount requested	Average amount received	Average amount received as percentage of average amount requested
79	$1,123	$ 968	86
88	974	905	93
81	762	678	89
79	843	760	90
77	705	598	85
87	1,238	1,108	90
80	892	769	86
75	939	807	86
64	1,293	1,111	86
79	828	733	89
89	1,558	1,432	92
86	1,512	1,344	89
85	1,302	1,162	89
84	1,268	1,113	88
82	1,195	1,050	88
92	1,305	1,206	92
87	1,424	1,351	95
76	1,298	1,086	84
63	1,438	1,098	76
85	1,231	1,225	99

somewhat greater in the private schools than in the publicly controlled schools.

2 Students from families with incomes from $10,000 to $19,999 are relatively more dependent on loans than students from lower-income groups.

3 Single students from families with incomes below $10,000 utilize about $1,800 in student aid if they are attending private schools and about $1,100 if they are attending public schools.

Perhaps the best indication of the financial burdens felt by medical students from families in different income classes is provided by the total debt accrued in financing their medical education.

TABLE 23
Requests and receipt of loans by freshmen in United States medical schools, by marital status* and parental income, 1967–68

Type of school, marital status, and parental income class	Percent of freshmen with parents in this income class who requested loans	Percent of those who requested loans who received loans
Public schools		
Single		
Under $5,000	64	91
$5,000–9,999	60	90
$10,000–14,999	47	91
$15,000–19,999	35	89
$20,000 and over	12	82
Married (0 or 1 child)		
Under $5,000	55	94
$5,000–9,000	57	93
$10,000–14,999	47	90
$15,000–19,999	35	74
$20,000 and over	19	88
Private schools		
Single		
Under $5,000	69	96
$5,000–9,000	65	95
$10,000–14,999	62	94
$15,000–19,999	38	92
$20,000 and over	13	86
Married (0 or 1 child)		
Under $5,000	73	86
$5,000–9,000	66	92
$10,000–14,999	48	92
$15,000–19,999	44	94
$20,000 and over	22	85

*"Single" includes separated, widowed, and divorced. Data are available but not presented for the very small number of married students with two or more children.
SOURCE: Raw data from the 1967 NIH-AAMC survey of medical students.

Fifty-three percent of the seniors in 1967 who responded to the NIH-AAMC questionnaire reported debts. These averaged $4,328 (Table 25). The proportion of students with debts varied from 78 percent of seniors with parental incomes below $5,000 to 24 percent of those whose families had incomes above $20,000. The average debts were $4,965 and $3,839 (for students with debts) in these two groups, respectively. It can be argued that these debts are manageable, given the earnings prospects of physicians. Yet it must be remembered that the senior, about to receive his doctorate in medicine, is still far removed from his relatively high earning years. He must complete his internship and residency,

Total loans received as percentage of total number requested	Average amount requested	Average amount received	Average amount received as percentage of average amount requested
80	$1,200	$1,050	88
75	1,326	1,099	83
76	1,391	1,156	83
75	1,435	1,221	85
67	1,569	1,281	82
78	1,715	1,421	83
78	1,416	1,191	84
76	1,465	1,241	85
61	1,603	1,316	82
73	1,394	1,166	84
90	1,573	1,476	94
82	1,575	1,360	86
78	1,646	1,365	83
79	1,641	1,417	86
74	1,555	1,329	85
63	1,687	1,228	73
80	1,637	1,425	87
78	1,661	1,405	85
81	1,504	1,296	86
63	1,539	1,143	74

and he faces his armed forces obligation. Furthermore, he will not enter practice without additional capital investment in office and equipment. Given these factors, and the fact that he is in an age group where others are beginning to acquire equity (housing, consumer durables), it is small wonder that he feels the economic pressures and does not find these relieved by the knowledge that over the longer span his rate of return on his investment in medical education will be high.

ATTRITION   More medical students begin their M.D. education than receive the degree; that is, there are dropouts. Since this attrition adds to

Type of school, marital status, and parental income class	Percent of freshmen with parents in this income class who received grants	Average grant per grantee
TABLE 24 Total student aid received by freshmen in United States medical schools, by marital status* and parental income, 1967-1968		

Type of school, marital status, and parental income class	Percent of freshmen with parents in this income class who received grants	Average grant per grantee
Public schools		
Single		
Under $5,000	65	$ 968
$5,000-9,999	51	905
$10,000-14,999	30	678
$15,000-19,999	20	760
$20,000 and over	14	598
Married (0 or 1 child)		
Under $5,000	46	1,108
$5,000-9,999	42	769
$10,000-14,999	25	807
$15,000-19,999	12	1,111
$20,000 and over	14	733
Private schools		
Single		
Under $5,000	71	1,432
$5,000-9,999	64	1,344
$10,000-14,999	47	1,162
$15,000-19,999	32	1,113
$20,000 and over	17	1,050
Married		
Under $5,000	57	1,206
$5,000-9,999	41	1,351
$10,000-14,999	41	1,086
$15,000-19,999	33	1,098
$20,000 and over	12	1,225

*"Single" includes separated, widowed, and divorced. Data are available but not presented for the very small number of students with two or more children.

SOURCE: Raw data from the 1967 NIH-AAMC survey of medical students.

the costs of producing the final product, the doctor of medicine, and can be affected by the financial pressures placed on the student, it is worthwhile to review briefly some of the dimensions of the attrition problem.

The most extensive study of this phenomenon indicated that about 9 percent of the students entering from 1949 through 1958 failed to receive the M.D. degree (Johnson & Hutchins, 1966, p. 20).[33] The rate of attrition increased from 7 percent from those

[33] The authors point out the difference in dropout rates for most other professions such as law (40 percent), nursing (44 percent), engineering (51 percent), and theology (15 to 20 percent). The attrition in dental school is similar to that in medical school.

Percent of freshmen with parents in this income class who received loans	Average loan per borrower	Average grant per student	Average loan per student	Average total grants and loans
58	$1,050	$ 634	$612	$1,246
54	1,099	459	591	1,050
43	1,156	200	497	697
31	1,221	152	382	534
10	1,281	82	128	210
52	1,421	511	734	1,245
53	1,191	322	628	950
43	1,241	199	528	727
26	1,316	133	342	475
16	1,166	103	191	294
66	1,476	1,011	981	1,992
62	1,360	864	884	1,748
58	1,365	552	793	1,345
35	1,417	358	489	847
11	1,329	179	145	324
63	1,228	683	778	1,461
61	1,425	522	863	1,385
45	1,405	441	626	1,067
41	1,296	361	537	898
19	1,143	144	217	361

admitted in 1950 to an estimated high of nearly 11 percent for those who entered in 1961. The 9 percent attrition rate for the classes entering over the 1949–1958 period represented 6,556 individual student dropouts. It would have taken about eight additional schools to have produced this number of physicians over the 10-year period. Thus, the cost of this attrition to society is high. We shall briefly summarize the findings that are relevant to our analysis:

1 Of all students who entered from 1949 to 1958, 16 per cent of the females failed to graduate as compared with 8 per cent of the males. Although the proportion of academic dropouts was quite similar (5 per cent for men

Type of school, marital status, and parental income	Number reporting income	Number with debt	Percent with debt	Average debt
Public schools				
Single				
Under $5,000	65	48	74	$4,821
$5,000-9,999	211	142	67	4,696
$10,000-14,999	173	93	54	3,786
$15,000-19,999	103	43	42	3,406
$20,000 and over	194	36	19	3,739
TOTAL	746	362	49	4,231
Married (0 or 1 child)				
Under $5,000	112	86	77	3,702
$5,000-9,999	383	284	74	3,729
$10,000-14,999	304	173	57	3,926
$15,000-19,999	148	74	50	3,570
$20,000 and over	302	92	30	3,019
TOTAL	1,249	709	57	3,665
Private schools				
Single				
Under $5,000	68	55	81	5,638
$5,000-9,999	216	165	76	5,147
$10,000-14,999	197	118	60	4,166
$15,000-19,999	114	45	39	4,188
$20,000 and over	333	60	18	4,072
TOTAL	928	443	48	4,703
Married (0 or 1 child)				
Under $5,000	72	54	75	4,605
$5,000-9,999	288	218	76	4,466
$10,000-14,999	243	157	65	3,819
$15,000-19,999	137	66	48	3,563
$20,000 and over	377	91	24	3,486
TOTAL	1,117	586	52	4,052
All schools*				
Under $5,000	362	283	78	4,965
$5,000-9,999	1,200	891	74	4,616
$10,000-14,999	967	578	60	4,068
$15,000-19,999	524	245	47	3,757
$20,000 and over	1,259	300	24	3,839
TOTAL	4,312	2,297	53	4,328

TABLE 25 Debt of seniors in United States medical schools, by marital status and parental income

*Public and private combined for all students: single, married with children, and married without children. Includes 328 students who were married and had two or more children.

SOURCE: Raw data from the 1967 NIH-AAMC survey of medical students.

and 7 per cent for women), there were almost 2.5 times as many non-academic dropouts among the women as among the men (8 per cent vs. 3 per cent) (Johnson & Hutchins, 1966, pp. 44–45).

2   Academic dropouts [who accounted for 59 per cent of those who left school] have relatively lower scores on all 4 MCAT subtests, particularly on Quantitative Ability (482) and Science Achievement (470). The nonacademic dropouts score substantially higher than the academic dropouts and the graduates perform at an even higher level on all 4 sections of the Test. Of particular interest is the contrast between the average science score of 532 for those who graduated and that of only 470 for those who were in academic difficulty when they left medical school (Johnson & Hutchins, 1966, pp. 49–50).[34]

3   In general, the family backgrounds of students making regular and irregular progress during 1961–62 are quite similar. For example, both groups come from relatively high socioeconomic levels (approximately 50 per cent have fathers in professional, semiprofessional or managerial occupations. . . .) (Johnson & Hutchins, 1966, p. 45).

4   Almost 60 per cent of both successful and unsuccessful freshmen medical students reported no educational debts and only 6 per cent reported debts of 3,000 dollars or more (Johnson & Hutchins, 1966, p. 46).

5   Only 3.5 per cent of students dropped for academic reasons [during 1961–62] had A averages in their premedical work. Of those who left for nonacademic reasons, 14.1 per cent had premedical averages of A; this compares with the successful medical students, 13.7 per cent of whom had A averages in their preprofessional studies.

   Conversely, almost 30 per cent of the academic dropouts had C averages in college compared with 19 per cent of the nonacademic dropouts, and only 16 per cent of students who made regular progress in medical school (Johnson & Hutchins, 1966, p. 51).

Data on attrition indicate that apparent ability levels are of importance in affecting the completion rate of individual medical students. Some medical educators have related the increased attrition during the past 15 years to the decline in the number of medical students entering medical school with superior premedical education grades. However, the relationship between MCAT scores

---

[34] An expectancy table of the science achievement subtest is presented to show this relationship. Table 26 indicates the number of chances in 100 that students with a given MCAT score will make a particular type of progress during their medical school careers.

	Chances in 100 that student will make progress indicated		
Range of science score	Total M.D.	On-time M.D.	Delayed M.D.
750–799	96	91	3
700–749	96	90	3
650–699	95	90	3
600–649	95	90	2
550–599	94	90	1
500–549	93	88	1
450–499	90	84	1
400–449	87	80	1
350–399	82	73	1
300–349	75	63	1
250–299	63	52	2
200–249	68	68	0
Test not taken	88	82	1

TABLE 26 Expectancy table for medical school progress based on science achievement scores on the MCAT, 1949–1958 entrants to United States schools

*Number corrected by authors.

SOURCE: Johnson & Hutchins, 1966, p. 164.

and grade-point averages within individual schools has usually been shown to be significant but not very great.[35]

While it is true that the percentage of students who drop out of medical education is relatively low, nonetheless the number of students who are "lost" is not insignificant. Furthermore, one would expect the percentage to be low, given the self-selection process involved in applying to medical school, the commitment required of the person who wants to become a physician, and the care exercised in admitting students to medical school. Given a tight aggregate supply of medical school places (and a rationing of

[35] The data developed by Johnson and Hutchins, cited above, can be combined with the material on schools grouped by quartiles in terms of average total expenditures per full-time student (in 1966). Public institutions exhibit little variation in attrition rates (highest quartile, 10 percent; second highest 10 percent; third highest, 9 percent; and lowest, 11 percent). Private schools have a lower attrition rate (highest, 5 percent; second highest, 7 percent; third highest, 9 percent; and lowest, 8 percent). Even when the schools are grouped by MCAT score, we find substantially the same pattern: the public school rates are 10, 10, 10, and 11 percent, while the private school rates are 5, 8, 7, and 9 percent. As would be expected, the variation of dropouts among individual schools is much greater, ranging from 3.6 percent for one school during the period 1949–1958 to 17.1 percent for another school (Johnson & Hutchins, 1966, pp. 165–166).

Repeat M.D.	Academic dropout	Nonacademic dropout	Total dropout
1	1	3*	4
3	1	3	4
2	2	3	5
3	2	3	5
3	3	3	6
4	4	3	7
5	6	4	10
6	9	4	13
8	12	6	18
11	19	6	25
9	26	11	37
0	19	13	32
5	6	6	12

admissions on a quality basis), the attrition rate can be expected to be modest. Perhaps it can be lowered from its recent level. The stakes, in terms of absolute numbers, are high. Attrition, however, is not the focus of our interest (except as one element of cost). We have examined it in order to provide the reader with some feel for the dimensions of the problem. Most medical students do, in fact, graduate with the M.D. degree. They move on to internship (and, generally, to residency) and face additional costs in that part of their medical education.

INTERNSHIP AND RESIDENCY The medical student who graduates from medical school has not completed his education when he receives the M.D. degree. He must still serve his internship and, given the increasing proportion of specialists, will very likely serve a residency of two or more years as well. During this time he will still be undergoing formal education and in most cases will be doing so in a hospital that is affiliated with a medical school. The medical school (or a department of it) therefore has a degree of responsibility for the educational program. It is this phenomenon that helps account for the fact that a high proportion of students in medical school are interns and residents and that the number of such students has been increasing significantly. In 1953–54, medical schools were responsible for the education of 7,400 interns and residents. By 1966–67, this number had grown to 20,200.[36]

The period of internship and residency is relevant to our analysis for two reasons. First, the prospective entrant to medical school must take account of the period of internship and residency as he considers medicine as a career choice. His decision may be significantly affected by the costs and benefits of this extension of the period of education. This also means that as one discusses policy measures to assist some (or all) students to meet the costs of medical education, one cannot (and should not) focus exclusively on the period before receipt of the M.D. degree. Second, medical school and teaching hospital resources are allocated to the intern and resident, and at the same time, the intern and resident make resources available to the school and hospital: the intern, and particularly the resident, is a teacher as well as a student, and he is also a provider of care to patients.

This tripartite role of the intern and resident makes analysis of the financing of their training even more complex than analysis of the M.D. candidate's financing. The distribution of costs and benefits related to this training is diffuse and imperfectly measured. The real costs of graduate medical training can be related to the faculty time absorbed, the extra capital required, and the added cost elements the intern and resident introduce into the provision of services. It is asserted that such added costs are introduced by unnecessary laboratory procedures ordered by trainees and by longer lengths of stay brought about by this inexpertness. A 1966 study of short-term general hospitals participating in the Professional Activity Study of the Commission on Professional and Hospital Activities showed that similar patients (that is, with

[36] In the annual education issue of the *Journal of the American Medical Association* two conflicting numbers of interns and residents are presented. The number used above, 20,000 (excluding Puerto Rico), was presented in the table of the estimated total teaching responsibilities of medical school faculties (see *Journal of the American Medical Association,* 1967, p. 815). Yet there were 27,307 internships and residencies reported filled in hospitals with medical school affiliation (*Journal of the American Medical Association,* 1967, pp. 773, 766). This difference can be explained partially by the fact that hospitals and medical schools interpret the affiliation relationship differently and partially by the fact that all interns and residents at affiliated hospitals need not be the responsibility of a medical school faculty. An additional 14,850 interns and resident positions were reported filled at hospitals with no medical school affiliation.

length of stay adjusted for patient mix) remained 10 percent longer in teaching hospitals than in nonteaching hospitals. This might be explained by the more complicated cases seen at teaching hospitals (that is, the patient-mix adjustment was not fully adequate) (Commission on Professional and Hospital Activities, 1968, p. 3). A recent study of seven medical centers has shown that average operating costs related to intern and resident education (based on medical school faculty effort allocation) were between $5,300 and $9,100 per intern and resident (in addition there must be provision of extra physical space for teaching purposes) (T. J. Campbell, 1969, p. 29, 30). On the other hand, it is claimed that teaching hospitals provide superior-quality care and that the productivity of the attending physicians is considerably increased because of the availability of the house staff. Transformation of these factors into a rational financing system has proved difficult.

According to a survey conducted by the American Medical Association's Council on Medical Education and Hospitals in 1960, house-officer training programs are supported by hospital charges, assessments levied on the attending staff, endowments and grants, and income from third-party medical care plans (see "Compensation of Interns and Residents," 1962, p. 460).[37] Medical schools and the federal government (mainly through its support of Veterans Administration and Public Health Service hospitals) also support these programs. Third-party plans and private patients pay for the training programs through increased hospital per-diem charges rather than by paying directly for the services provided by the house staff.[38] There have been attempts within the American Medical Association to formalize financial support of graduate medical education through the collection of fees for their services from patients and third parties, but such proposals have not been accepted by the Association's House of Delegates.[39]

A study in a large university hospital in the late 1950s indicated that on the average, residents spend only about a quarter of their

[37]Several econometric studies have indicated a significant relationship between graduate medical education training programs and the average costs of hospital care, which are usually the base for hospital charges (see Berry, 1968, p. 15; Ingbar & Taylor, 1968, p. 54).

[38] Blue Cross does not officially accept cost of training programs as allowable cost, but cost accounting procedures at hospitals are such that it apparently does bear some of the burden (see Kaitz, 1968, pp. 36–37).

[39] For an excellent discussion of these matters, see Hepner, 1964.

working time away from patient service (*Physicians for a Growing America,* 1959, p. 35). A pilot study of program costs at the Yale–New Haven Hospital in the mid-1960s was in general agreement with that finding. The 140 interns and residents who completed a report of the distribution of their time for a one-week period spent an average of 58.8 hours in patient care activity out of an average total time of 79.4 hours (Carroll, 1969, p. 76).[40] Undoubtedly both the intern and the resident have been paid considerably less than the value of their marginal productivity, with the surplus shared by the patient, third parties, the attending physician, the hospital, and the medical school. An exceedingly low stipend will not only affect the behavior of the future physician but also lead to inefficient use of the intern and resident and to an excess demand for their services. They will be used to perform activities that less able personnel could do (Clute, 1963, pp. 434–435).

In the last several years payments to interns and residents have increased at a fairly rapid rate. In 1965–66, the mean stipend for interns was about $3,800. Two years later it had risen to $4,950. During the same period the mean annual stipend for first-year residents rose from $3,930 to $5,040. It must be remembered, however, that these are the stipends received by individuals who have had four years of college and four years of medical school (and in the case of residents, who have served their internship period as well) (*Journal of the American Medical Association,* 1968, p. 2037).[41] These stipends are low in relation to the amount of education already obtained by interns and residents, the age of the individuals, the incomes received by others of the same age group or educational level, and the family responsibilities of the

[40] The rest of their time was distributed to professional development (including study), 12.7 hours; teaching, 3.8 hours; research, 3.0 hours; and unallocated time. These distributions varied among the different services and among the interns and residents. For instance, the interns in medicine and pediatrics averaged 97 total hours with 81 hours allocated to patient care, 10.3 hours to professional development, and 4.9 hours to teaching, as compared with the residents in medicine and pediatrics, who averaged 75 total hours with 56 hours allocated to patient care, 11.4 hours to professional development, and 6.7 hours to teaching (Carroll, 1969, p. 81).

[41] A survey conducted by *Hospital Physician* showed that the median annual stipend for fourth-year residents, that is, individuals of about age 30 with 12 years of education and training beyond high school, was $6,700 (Haidak, 1968, p. 41). The data cited do not include any allowances for room and board.

interns and residents. The stipends are also low if one considers the activities in which the intern and residents are engaged, for although they are students and are learning, it is also true that they are "producing." They are responsible for a considerable proportion of the patient care that is rendered in hospitals and for much of the teaching of undergraduate medical students on hospital wards.

The relationship of the internship to undergraduate medical education, on the one hand, and to residency training, on the other, is a source of concern to many medical educators. There are numerous suggestions that the undergraduate medical education and the year of internship could be combined into a four-year program. Alternatively, there are those who feel that the internship can be merged, at least in part, with the residency. Changes of this kind would substantially affect the costs of medical education.

The numerous comments that are made concerning the high costs of medical education (which oftentimes refer to the four years of medical school and which seldom take account of "opportunity costs") and their relationship to the future behavior of physicians and to the kinds of persons attracted into medicine can, perhaps, be made even more effectively in relation to the low earnings of interns and residents. A greater recognition of the importance of forgone income and of the long period of education and training after completion of the four years of undergraduate medical school (the long period of time before the physician enters into income-producing practice) would help focus attention on the problems associated with internship and residency training.

The financial problems associated with the internship and residency period may, as we have indicated, affect the initial career decision regarding the field of medicine. Though there is little that the individual prospective physician can do to shorten the education period required to obtain the M.D. degree, he can shorten the period between the receipt of the degree and his entry into independent practice by his decision regarding specialization or general practice (and by his decision regarding which of a number of possible specialties to select). While factors in addition to economic considerations are involved, there is evidence that economic considerations are important and that they influence the length of training beyond the M.D. and the career choices of the physician. These relationships were examined in an extensive study of a sample of 1950 and 1954 graduates from 12 medical schools (Lyden, Geiger, & Peterson, 1968). It was found that debt at graduation was associated with the choice of type of internship. Rotating internships, in which an intern rotates among various types of practice, were associated with more frequent large debts, while straight internships, such as medicine or surgery, showed an opposite association. Further, those respondents who indicated that they had curtailed their training below what they had desired most often indicated that they were deterred for economic reasons. Family financial support played a most important role in making long residency training possible: in 80 percent of the cases those with four or more years of residency had parental support for the major portion of their educational costs. This was true for only 50 percent of those with no residency training.

SUMMARY The factors that influence the number and characteristics of applicants and students are many, but two seem of particular importance: (1) the emphasis on high achievement as measured by academic performance and tests and (2) financial considerations. Regarding the former, it is clear that the person admitted to medical school has passed through a number of screening devices at various points in his academic career and, further, that his ability to get through any particular screen was in part a function of how successfully he passed through some earlier screen; that is, there is a cumulative nature to the selection and admission process. Persons from poor families who receive lower-quality elementary and secondary education have greater difficulty in being admitted to college (and if admitted are more likely to attend poorer-quality educational institutions). Thus their chances of subsequently being admitted to medical school are reduced, and since they may perceive these probabilities accurately, they will fail to take those programs which would prepare them to apply or to achieve a superior score on the MCAT. To overcome these obstacles medical schools are offering special motivational and substantive programs to youth in college, but not yet in the senior years. These efforts are worthwhile, but they will have to be pushed back even earlier in the educational continuum because of the timing of the medical career decision and because those who attend college are already a select part of the socioeconomic spectrum. Our purpose in mentioning this earlier barrier (and others even earlier in the life of the child could be noted) is to point out that while medical schools must do what they can do to improve the situation, others —perhaps under pressure from medical educators or in concert with them—will necessarily be involved if, as they must, solutions are to be found.

Entrance into the study of medicine is influenced by financial considerations. These, too, involve more than the problems associated with the four years that are spent in medical school in the process of obtaining the M.D. degree. Poverty is seldom associated with the broadening of horizons that decision makers in educational institutions seem to feel is important. The environment of poverty does not contribute to better performance on tests that educational institutions deem relevant (for example, tests of general knowledge about things of great interest to upper-middle-class America). Financial considerations have other important impacts as well. The opportunity costs for studying while in high school may require that the individual in a low-income family substitute work for study, thus perhaps reducing academic performance and the probability of college acceptance. In addition, of course, the chance of attending college is lessened by the need to meet out-of-pocket costs and by the opportunity costs involved in such attendance. The student from a low-income family may have to go to work to help support his family and will have considerable difficulty in borrowing funds to finance his college expenses. Even if admitted to college, he may have to substitute work for study and perhaps, as a result, reduce the level of his academic performance. Thus, he may lower his probability of acceptance into a medical school that puts a premium on previous academic accomplishment as an indicator of academic potential and future academic performance and whose admissions committee does not accept "effort" as a partial substitute for "accomplishment." Finally, of course, the student must face the considerable expenses involved in attending medical school and the very significant opportunity costs that stretch over a relatively long period of time.

Economic considerations enter into the period preceding medical school and restrict arrival at the entry point to a select group. The same kinds of considerations enter into the period of further training following medical education. The number affected in their choice between, say, surgery and general practice may be less than the number who are barred from medicine in the first place. Perhaps the degree of economic discrimination involved in the former is much less significant than in the latter. This, however, does not make it less worthy of attention.

Even if the present system of financing does not place an undue burden on students in medical school, it precludes others from attending. The fact that physicians' incomes are high does not enable low-income students to pay today's costs. It is surely likely that if high-ability students were found exclusively in families with low incomes, a very different system of financing medical education would have developed in order to make it possible for the nation to have enough well-qualified physicians. Thus the fact that medical schools apparently can find sufficient numbers of able nonpoor students has helped perpetuate a system which does not take sufficient account of the needs of the less affluent.

That greater opportunities are open to those with greater financial resources is not a surprising finding. In spite of the emphasis on equality of opportunity in American society, few would claim that the goal of equality has been reached. The fact that opportunity is restricted is well known and acknowledged, but it need not be accepted. Economic constraints may have important and undesirable impacts on the kinds and quality of physicians that American medical education produces, on the kinds of practice into which these physicians enter, on their sets of values and behavior patterns, and thus on the medical care system itself. Even if there were no undesirable effects on medicine (and we believe that there are), rationing of educational opportunity to those who have the private means to increase their range of opportunity and the number of choices open to them violates expressed American ideals.

Since medical education is a long and continuous process, there are many points at which intervention is possible. Furthermore, the economics of medical education and those of medical practice are not divorced from each other. Consideration of the income of physicians in practice is not irrelevant to the consideration of the sources of possible financing of the education of the future physician. For, just as there are questions of equity regarding the opportunity that some may have to study medicine (as a function of their or their parents' income), so too are there questions of equity among medical students and all other students and between persons who will enter into a financially rewarding practice and the rest of society. What must be sought is a mechanism that balances a variety of considerations with as few unfavorable "side effects" as possible.

It is possible to summarize briefly the kinds of considerations, objectives, and constraints that must be faced in alternative financing mechanisms (in doing so we shall also be able to provide a summary of some of the material discussed in this chapter):

1 The rate of return in the medical profession, even given the high costs attached to medical education and the significant opportunity costs, compares favorably with rates of return in other occupations.

2 Opportunity costs—the forgone income—make up the largest part of the costs to the individual.

3 Students in medical schools come in disproportionate numbers from the upper socioeconomic groups in our society. While this results from a number of factors, financial considerations are not unimportant.

4 Though the rate of return in the medical profession is high, the student's problem of financing medical education is a real one since the period of education and training is long and the returns come much later than in other fields. This problem is made more severe by the fact that the capital market, here as in most of higher education, is inadequate. The problem in other fields is often to make the field more attractive by increasing future incomes or reducing present costs. The problem in medicine, however, appears to be different.

5 While significant financial assistance is available to students in the form of both grants and loans, this assistance may be inadequate when account is taken of opportunity costs. Furthermore, the decision to make medicine a career tends to come at a relatively early stage in the educational spectrum, and students may be unaware of the amount of possible aid at the time that they are making their career decisions.[42]

[42] We have focused on income as a key factor and have discussed the problem of financing medical education that students from low-income families face. The reader may wonder why we have not discussed the problem of minority representation, particularly by Negroes, in medical school bodies. It is our view that there are special problems that blacks face in American medical education and that medical schools must address themselves to these problems more

Before examining alternatives for the financing of medical education, it will be necessary to discuss the role and possible roles of the federal government and of state governments, for the problem of financing is not that of the student alone; it is one that the medical school and society share as well. The money paid by students is a part of the revenues of the schools and amounted to $48 million dollars in 1967–68 (more than 4 percent of total expenditures in 1967 and about 10 percent of the total unsponsored funds). The difference between students' payments (whatever they might be in the future) and the full costs of medical education must come from other sources. The next two chapters will examine the role that government plays at the present time in the financing of medical education. Only when those discussions are completed will we be able to assess the possible alternatives and their implications.

vigorously. Many of the criteria by which students are selected may be irrelevant or deserve much less weight (as is suggested by the fact that medical schools are not producing a homogeneous product). We believe, however, that a change in admissions policies without a change in the pattern of financing medical education would probably not be sufficient to alter significantly the racial distribution of students. The larger the number of low-income students admitted to medical schools, the larger the number of dollars needed for assistance. The nature of the assistance mechanism will not depend upon whether the low-income student is white or black.

5. Public Expenditures: The States

In examining the role of state governments in medical education, we begin with a general discussion of the rationale for public expenditures. Later sections will analyze the relationships that help explain the level of assistance the various states provide to medical education. Our analysis will show that population size is of primary importance in explaining the variations in the amounts different states provide for medical education. Nonetheless, there is substantial variation in the extent of support relative to population size and to personal income. The extent of support is explained partially by differences in the number of freshman places in privately controlled schools, the propensity for public expenditures in the state, and the rate of growth in the state's population. We shall also find that (1) the number of recent medical school graduates practicing in a state is not very sensitive to the number of graduates from schools in that state (new physicians tend to locate in states with substantial population growth); (2) the number of medical school entrants who are residents of a particular state does not increase proportionately to the expansion of freshman places in public medical schools in the state; and (3) citizens of the state may derive a significant direct benefit from public medical schools because of the training programs for house staff. The relationships found would lead the states to take insufficient account of the public demand for medical education. As a result, there is likely to be underinvestment by the states in medical education.

THE RATIONALE FOR PUBLIC EXPENDITURES Government intervention into particular sectors of the economy can be defended on a number of grounds. First, in the absence of government intervention, production of various goods and services may be less than optimum. This suboptimal production results from the failure to account properly for "externalities" (Bator, 1965, pp. 118–133; Heller, 1965, pp. 154–156.)

The concept of externality has been of primary importance in advancing the analysis of public expenditures during the past decade. It refers to benefits or costs over and above those which accrue directly to individuals participating in an exchange transaction. An individual's purchase and planting of a tree, for example, can provide benefits to his neighbors as well as himself. Frequently, the failure to take account of the existence of these external benefits (or costs) will lead to the production of smaller (or greater) quantities of the good in question, rather than to the production of socially optimum quantities. Health education involves both health and education, each of which is frequently cited as an area where externalities exist. Most often, however, the externalities related to health are cited as being of primary importance in providing a rationale for public support of medical education.

Externalities in health production can be divided into two categories. The first encompasses activities undertaken in the public health sector. Immunization of an individual against certain communicable diseases can reduce the probability that other individuals will contract the diseases. The second category encompasses those cases in which an individual includes the health of others in his preference function and would therefore be willing to pay in order that the health of other individuals might be improved through the receipt of health care.[1] The existence of those externalities in health indicates the need for community intervention to induce the production of a greater quantity of services than would be forthcoming if only individual preferences were allowed for.

Other factors in addition to the externalities connected with the provision of health care also provide a rationale for public support of medical education. One of these factors is the probable existence of a difference between individual and social rates of time preference.[2] As was shown in the previous chapter, a substantial portion of the cost of medical education is accounted for by the forgone production of the student, which in turn is represented by

[1] Two recent doctoral dissertations have presented detailed discussions of this concept of externality (see Lindsay, 1968; Pauly, 1967).

[2] Rates of time preference refer to relative valuation of present and future consumption. A relatively high rate of time preference indicates a relatively high valuation of current consumption.

his forgone income. The student may be less willing to forgo present income and the associated consumption in order to increase his future income than society, as a whole, would be willing to forgo present production in order to have more highly valued production in the future. Thus, public bodies may find it desirable to pay a portion of the costs of medical education in order that the present value of the stream of forgone income to students might approach the present value of the stream of forgone production to society (when each of these is discounted by the relevant rates of time preference).

An additional justification for public subsidization of medical education is related to the relatively long period of time required to train physicians and effect major changes in the number of physicians. Given the long period of education required for physicians, expected movements of supply and demand in the future are of considerable importance in determining the optimum number of physicians to be trained today. It is possible that projections of conditions in the future made by public bodies will be more accurate (and less conservative) than individuals' forecasts. Since the desire of individuals to pay for the costs of their education will be related to their own projections of future incomes, the public may wish to subsidize individuals' educations in order to equate expected public and private returns.

A fourth factor that may lead to subsidization of medical education is the uncertain and emergency nature of much of the provision of health services. The existence of hospitals and the availability of physicians provide protection to those individuals who are fortunate enough not to need facilities and physicians as well as to those who do. Under a system without insurance, it would be difficult to determine the extent of the demand for the "standby" availability of medical facilities and personnel by those individuals who do not use them over a given period of time. The availability of insurance does permit the communication of this demand, at least to some extent, but an alternative is to express it through public subsidization of the building of facilities as well as the training of those who provide services.[3]

---

[3] See Sloan, 1968, pp. 154–155, for a discussion of this factor. That substantial fluctuations in the aggregate level of demand for physician services do exist and can be troublesome has been demonstrated during epidemics (for example, flu), when many people are unable to get medical care. While the provision of an

In addition to the efficiency conditions already considered, public intervention may be desired in order to subsidize the education of some students so that the opportunities for medical education are made more equal for individuals from different socioeconomic backgrounds. The purpose of the subsidy would be to reduce the effects of present individual or parental income on the demand for medical education. This would still leave variation in the demand for medical education due to differences in cultural attitudes and inequalities in academic capabilities, some of which are related to socioeconomic standing. It would, however, remove the inequities related to variations in the ability to finance medical education due to differentials in parental income.

Finally, public intervention can be based on the need to overcome capital-market imperfections. Such imperfections present obstacles to borrowing by medical students. They are introduced by the fact that borrowers cannot offer their future earnings as security on loans. The lack of collateral will lead to higher interest rates, fewer loans, and discrimination among loan applicants on the basis of parental income. Actions to improve capital markets may be called for.

Whatever the rationale, public intervention may be undertaken either by the states or by the national government. The level of intervention can have a substantial effect on the total public aid forthcoming and, because of differing tax structures, on the distribution of the burden among individuals within different income classes. The most appropriate level of government intervention will depend, in part, on the degree to which external effects cross state borders and on the degree to which it is felt appropriate that the federal government overcome the effects of differences in the wealth of the states on their support of medical education. All levels of government, however, will be faced with the problem of allocating constrained budgets among a variety of competing ends. The decision to allocate funds to medical education by the governmental units requires that (at the minimum) the health benefits their population is expected to receive from these expenditures be compared with the benefits expected from other possible public expenditures in the health area—on hospitals, on research, and on financing the purchases of services. On a more general level, the

---

excess capacity of physician services for extreme fluctuations may cost more than society would be willing to pay, the cost of some excess capacity might be supported.

expenditures on medical education must compete with demands from other areas of public interest—general education, housing, and so forth.

If intervention is called for and undertaken, it can proceed through actions involving either demand or supply. If public intervention operates on the demand side, the effects would at first be, in part, reflected in higher prices for, and (in part) increased production of, health services. The distribution between price increase and quantity increase would be dependent upon the short-run responsiveness of the quantity supplied to increased prices and upon the price elasticity of demand.[4] It is likely that the higher price would induce some underemployed factors of production to increase their provision of services. In the longer run, it would be expected that the higher price of services, having led to higher incomes, would induce more individuals to desire to enter the professions connected with the health services. This, one would hope, would lead educational institutions to increase the number of applicants accepted for training. In turn, this would, in time, lead to a shift in the supply schedule. Thus, over time, the quantity of health services supplied would increase toward the optimum level.

Alternatively, efforts could be made to shift the supply schedules for health services in a more direct fashion. In the short run it may be very difficult to add substantially to the number of health personnel. Yet it might be possible even in the short run to increase productivity of existing personnel (and thus to increase the supply of services) by introducing incentives to providers of health services. In the long run, community efforts to shift supply schedules by increasing the number of health personnel might be successful in reaching the optimum quantity of health services. Subsidies can be used to induce potential medical students to apply to medical school and encourage medical schools to expand enrollments. If market pressures work in the health industry, the increased quantity of services supplied may result in a reduction in the price of services.

The differences in these two approaches is portrayed graphically in Figure 8. In the upper portion, the demand curve is shifted from D to D' through public subsidy of the purchase of health care

[4] We shall frequently refer to "elasticity" in this chapter. Elasticity denotes the degree of responsiveness of one variable to changes in another variable. When considering finite changes, it can be defined as the percentage change in the dependent variable divided by the percentage change in the independent variable. For example, demand is price-elastic if a given percentage increase (or decrease) in price induces a larger percentage decrease (or increase) in the quantity demanded.

services. The immediate effect is to increase prices from P_1 to P_2 and to increase the quantity of services provided from Q_1 to Q_2. This increase in the price of services and the resultant increase in incomes may eventually lead to an increase in the stock of health personnel which shifts the supply schedule to S', the price to P_3, and the quantity to Q_3.[5] If the subsidy is provided to, or concentrated on, a particular socioeconomic group, that group will attempt to bid additional services away from other groups. The short-run emphasis, thus, is on the redistribution of existing supply. In the lower section of Figure 8, the supply curve is shifted from S to S' through public subsidy of the training of health personnel. The price falls from P_1 to P_2, and the quantity increases from Q_1 to Q_2. This form of intervention does not directly affect the distribution of the provision of health services. It operates to increase supply, but only over the long run. As a result, it is likely that a combination of the two forms of intervention is socially optimum.

FIGURE 8
Expansion of community demand for health services through subsidy of demand and services

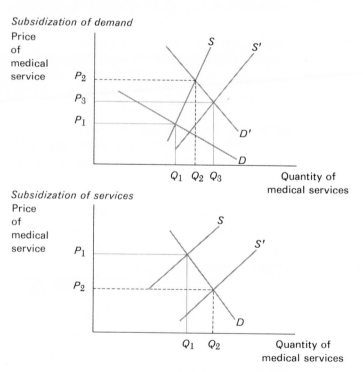

Subsidization of demand

Subsidization of services

---

[5] Realistically, current institutional arrangements do not lead to confidence that medical schools would respond to increased applications by expanding their freshman openings.

The introduction or expansion of direct state support of medical education and medical schools has most often been discussed on the basis of three major goals or objectives.[6] First and foremost are considerations dealing with the adequacy of the number of practicing physicians expected to be available to provide services within the state at some future date. Second, a desire is frequently expressed that the number of medical school openings be increased in order to provide greater opportunity for medical education for potential applicants from within the state. This is often expressed in terms of equity for residents of the given state who may be potential students, as compared with that for residents of other states. Third, attention is focused on the possibility that the expansion of medical school facilities and faculty will help to attract additional interns and residents to the state (and the hope is then expressed that many will stay to practice in the state). This possibility is most often cited when consideration is being given to the opening of a new public medical school. In recent years, state support of new schools has also been justified on the grounds that the existence of a medical school raises the quality of care in the area and, further, that if the school's location is chosen "correctly," geographic maldistribution of health personnel can be partially overcome.

The conclusions reached in the studies of state support are dependent on a number of variables. Almost always of prime importance is the size of the state population and its expected growth. The weight given these factors stems from the fact that projected demands for medical services are heavily dependent upon population size and, furthermore, that it is necessary to have a population of adequate size and density in order to provide a medical center with the required number and variety of teaching

---

[6] Many of our comments are based on our study of the following state reports on medical education: Allen & Lawton, 1966; Bunnell & Malone, 1968; J. A. Campbell & Associates, 1968; Consultants to the Commission on Higher Education, 1967; *Delaware Medical School Feasibility Study,* 1964; Health Manpower Study Commission, 1966; Joint State Government Commission, 1967; Maine Legislative Research Committee, 1967; *Medical Education and Research Needs in Maryland,* 1962; Olson, 1968; *Report of the Committee of the Michigan Coordinating Council for Public Higher Education to Consider the Location and Sponsorship of the Expansion of Medical Education in the State of Michigan,* 1963; *The Report of the Governor's Task Force on Medical Education,* 1967; State of California Coordinating Council for Higher Education, 1963.

patients. Also of considerable importance are the migration patterns of physicians both into and out of the state. States which expect a substantial inflow of physicians trained in medical schools located in other states generally feel less of a need to expand their own training efforts. Conversely, states which anticipate a substantial out-migration of physicians trained in their state-supported medical schools will generally be less willing to support medical education programs. Another factor sometimes discussed is the availability of medical education at private schools in the state. Occasionally, openings at private schools appear to be considered perfect substitutes for openings at public schools, even though the behavior patterns of graduates from the differently controlled schools may show substantial variance (primarily because private schools generally select more of their students from states outside the one in which they are located).[7] Finally, the economic capability of the state to support medical education receives attention and consideration.

Level of Direct Support by Individual States

It is difficult to compare the efforts of the various states in support of medical education. Some states provide direct appropriations to the medical schools and to the teaching hospitals, some provide student aid, some provide support through regional compacts,[8] and, finally, some share in the provision of capital funds for con-

[7] An example of analysis which allows the presence of private school admissions to affect state support of medical education is provided by the 1962 study of medical education in Maryland. The computation of the required growth in admissions involved the determination of the proportion of national freshman openings which were located in Maryland, including those at The Johns Hopkins Medical School. It was then asserted that Maryland should aim to continue that degree of effort in the future. Private school admissions were included equally with the public medical school admissions in measuring state effort.

[8] Three regional groups have developed provisions for participating states to subsidize the cost of medical education for their citizens at medical schools in other states. Four states operating through the New England Board of Higher Education subsidize students from their states who attend the College of Medicine at the University of Vermont. Their payment in 1968 was $2,500 per year per enrolled medical student. Eleven states provide payments for medical education for their residents through the Southern Regional Education Board. They paid $2,500 per year per enrolled student in 1968. A large proportion of the funds are paid to Meharry Medical College. Finally, eight states provide funds through the Western Interstate Commission for Higher Education. They paid $3,000 per student per year in 1968.

struction and equipment. Because of data limitations, our analysis of state support will concentrate on the number of freshman openings at publicly supported medical schools and on state contributions to the operating expenditures of public and private medical schools (both directly and through the regional compacts). In the 1965 and 1966 academic years there was considerable variation in the individual states' expenditures for medical school operations relative to population and personal income (see Table 27). Utah spent about $299,000 per 100,000 population, while eight states spent less than $10 per 100,000 population. Utah also provided $1,242 per $100,000 of personal income, as compared with 13 states with less than $100 in expenditures per $100,000 of personal income.

The absolute number of freshman places in publicly controlled medical schools ranged from an average of 409 during the 1965 and 1966 school years for New York State to zero for 12 states (Table 28). The District of Columbia, not included in the table, also does not have any publicly controlled freshman places. These numbers will change substantially by 1975 as developing schools expand to their full size, as new schools which are already planned open their doors, and as established schools expand their class size. Dr. William Hubbard and Dr. William Anlyan, who conducted a recent survey of medical schools, have provided us with rough estimates of the number of public and private places planned for by schools in each state for 1975. We have related these to the projected 1975 population for each state in order to provide a rough approximation of the likely position of the various states in 1975 (Table 28). Furthermore, we have presented the critical relationship between state of graduation and location a decade later (Table 29).

Three states without public medical schools (Pennsylvania, Connecticut, and Massachusetts, as well as the District of Columbia) have private medical schools located within their boundaries.[9] The states without public or private medical schools are most

---

[9] Two of the "private" Pennsylvania schools have gravitated toward a quasi-public status. Pennsylvania residents attending the University of Pittsburgh and Temple University medical schools pay only $450 tuition, with the state paying the two schools tuition supplements of $1,260 and $1,034, respectively (in addition to the regular state appropriation). Connecticut and Massachusetts have publicly controlled medical schools under development.

TABLE 27
*Population,
personal income,
and state
support of
medical
education, by
states, average
of 1965 and
1966 academic
years*

State	Population (thousands)	Personal income (billions of dollars)
Alabama	3,500	7.0
Arizona	1,589	3.9
Arkansas	1,950	3.8
California	18,601	62.5
Colorado	1,951	5.5
Connecticut	2,858	10.2
Delaware	509	1.8
Florida	5,844	14.8
Georgia	4,420	10.0
Idaho	696	1.7
Illinois	10,712	36.6
Indiana	4,922	14.6
Iowa	2,761	7.9
Kansas	2,262	6.2
Kentucky	3,178	6.8
Louisiana	3,586	7.8
Maine	982	2.4
Maryland	3,571	11.2
Massachusetts	5,382	17.0
Michigan	8,395	26.6
Minnesota	3,565	10.0
Mississippi	2,329	4.0
Missouri	4,520	12.4
Montana	702	1.8
Nebraska	1,448	4.0
Nevada	432	1.4
New Hampshire	674	1.8
New Jersey	6,846	23.0
New Mexico	1,008	2.4
New York	18,156	61.6
North Carolina	4,954	10.8
North Dakota	647	1.5

	State expenditures for regular operating programs of medical schools	
Total (thousands)	*Per 100,000 population (thousands)*	*Per $100,000 personal income*
$ 2,673	$ 76.4	$ 382
171	10.8	44
1,830	93.8	482
14,888	80.0	238
1,371	70.3	249
116	4.1	11
0	0	0
3,410	58.4	230
2,350	53.2	235
86	12.4	51
4,550	42.5	124
4,299	87.3	294
5,670	205.4	718
1,452	64.2	234
4,973	156.5	731
4,093	114.1	525
41	4.2	17
1,847	51.7	165
170	3.2	10
9,162	109.1	344
3,947	110.7	395
1,578	67.8	394
2,851	63.0	230
59	8.4	33
1,166	80.5	292
23	5.3	16
17	2.5	9
1,599	23.4	70
25	2.5	10
15,062	83.0	245
1,768	35.7	164
497	76.8	331

TABLE 27
Population,
personal income,
and state
support of
medical
education, by
states, average
of 1965 and
1966 academic
years
(cont'd.)

State	Population (thousands)	Personal income (billions of dollars)
Ohio	10,310	30.4
Oklahoma	2,466	5.9
Oregon	1,955	5.6
Pennsylvania	11,594	33.2
Rhode Island	894	2.6
South Carolina	2,572	5.0
South Dakota	684	1.6
Tennessee	3,852	8.2
Texas	10,647	26.1
Utah	998	2.4
Vermont	407	1.0
Virginia	4,446	11.2
Washington	3,008	9.2
West Virginia	1,813	3.8
Wisconsin	4,156	11.8
Wyoming	325	0.8

SOURCES: Population and personal income—*Statistical Abstract of the United States, 1968*, pp. 12, 322; state expenditures—unpublished data from the AAMC and AMA annual questionnaires and unpublished data from the Southern Regional Education Board, the New England Board of Higher Education, and the Western Interstate Commission for Higher Education.

strongly characterized by their relatively small populations. Since an area with adequate population size and density is required to attract the diversity of cases required for the provision of clinical training, a number of smaller states support public (or private) two-year schools of medicine emphasizing the study of the basic medical sciences. The minimum population requirement for a four-year school is not known. Vermont, with a population of slightly over 400,000, has a four-year medical school; the state school in New Mexico granted its first M.D. degrees in 1968, and two other states with relatively small populations—Arizona and Connecticut—have public schools under development. The states of Idaho, Montana, Nevada, and Wyoming have been working to develop medical schools by pooling and coordinating their academic and

Total (thousands)	State expenditures for regular operating programs of medical schools	
	Per 100,000 population (thousands)	Per $100,000 personal income
7,864	76.3	259
1,345	54.5	228
1,920	98.2	343
8,531	73.6	257
24	2.7	9
2,167	84.3	433
402	58.8	251
2,710	70.4	330
7,928	74.5	304
2,980	298.6	1,242
1,118	274.7	1,118
2,712	61.0	242
2,818	93.7	306
2,126	117.3	559
3,240	78.0	275
42	12.9	52

Two items from the sources of funds reported by the medical schools in the AAMC-AMA survey were used in computing state expenditures: (1) state appropriations for defrayal of medical college expenditures (mainly public schools) and (2) state, city, and county grants-in-aid (private schools).

community hospital resources,[10] and the recent studies mentioned above of the feasibility of medical schools in Delaware and Maine suggested planning for a medical school in 10 to 15 years, in the case of the former, and the development of the student, university, and facility base, in the case of the latter.

While population size is of paramount importance in the decision to introduce medical education to a state, the variance in the ratios of freshman places to population clearly indicates that

[10] See Bunnell, 1969.

In 1969 the Nevada Legislature approved the establishment of a two-year medical sciences school, and arrangements have been made with the University of California and other out-of-state medical schools to accept transfer of its students at the start of their third year.

	Actual, average of 1965 and 1966 academic years			
State	*Freshman places*	*Freshman places at public schools*	*Freshman places per 100,000 population*	*Percent freshman places, public*
Alabama	80	80	2.3	100
Arizona	0	0	0	
Arkansas	106	106	5.4	100
California	497	280	2.7	56
Colorado	86	86	4.4	100
Connecticut	80	0	2.8	0
Delaware	0	0	0	
Florida	146	62	2.5	44
Georgia	178	102	4.0	58
Idaho	0	0	0	
Illinois	570	200	5.3	36
Indiana	216	216	4.4	100
Iowa	122	122	4.4	100
Kansas	120	120	5.3	100
Kentucky	174	78	5.5	45
Louisiana	276	141	7.7	51
Maine	0	0	0	
Maryland	220	130	6.2	58
Massachusetts	306	0	5.7	0
Michigan	351	351	4.2	100
Minnesota	161	161	4.5	100
Mississippi	83	83	3.6	100
Missouri	292	86	6.4	30
Montana	0	0	0	
Nebraska	164	86	11.3	52
Nevada	0	0	0	
New Hampshire	25	0	3.7	0
New Jersey	86	86	1.3	100
New Mexico	26	26	2.6	100
New York	1,106	409	6.1	38
North Carolina	210	72	4.2	36
North Dakota	24	24	3.7	100

Planned, 1975*	
Freshman places per 100,000 population	*Percent freshman places that will be public*
2.6	100
3.0	100
5.0	100
3.7	69
4.5	100
4.0	35
0	
2.2	38
3.6	56
0	
6.0	35
4.4	100
5.7	100
5.2	100
6.4	40
8.9	64
0	
5.7	62
8.2	21
5.4	100
6.2	83
3.7	100
7.4	28
0	
12.7	56
0	
6.6	0
2.2	100
4.0	100
6.6	34
4.7	38
6.9	100

		Actual, average of 1965 and 1966 academic years		
State	Freshman places	Freshman places at public schools	Freshman places per 100,000 population	Percent freshman places, public
Ohio	342	254	3.3	76
Oklahoma	106	106	4.3	100
Oregon	87	87	4.5	100
Pennsylvania	720	0	6.2	0
Rhode Island	0	0	0	
South Carolina	82	82	3.2	100
South Dakota	23	23	3.4	100
Tennessee	252†	198	6.5	78
Texas	347	262	3.3	76
Utah	66	66	6.6	100
Vermont	53	53	13.0	100
Virginia	184	184	4.1	100
Washington	78	78	2.6	100
West Virginia	61	61	3.4	100
Wisconsin	206	102	5.0	50
Wyoming	0	0	0	0

*The planned places as reported by the schools were rough estimates that are subject to considerable change between the March, 1968, survey and 1975. In the above calculations, planned places were treated as zero for the seven states that did not respond to the survey questionnaire.

neither the total number of public places nor the total number of places is directly proportional to population. Nebraska, Utah, and Vermont, for instance, had more than six freshman places in public medical schools per 100,000 population, while six of the states with public schools had less than two public school freshman places per 100,000 population. A number of factors may explain these differences: the number of private school places, the level of per capita personal income, the general attitude toward public expenditures in the state, and recent population growth. The last variable, however, may have both a positive and a negative effect. Projections of a continuing increase in population would call for considerable additions to the physician stock. However, it is also possible that legislators realize that, as will be shown later, newly trained physicians tend to locate where there is population growth,

Planned, 1975*	
Freshman places per 100,000 population	*Percent freshman places that will be public*
4.4	73
4.6	100
5.0	100
7.3	7
4.4	0
3.4	100
7.0	100
7.9	56
4.1	84
5.4	100
17.0	100
4.6	100
2.7	100
4.3	100
4.6	49
0	0

† Excludes Meharry Medical College, one of the two primarily Negro medical schools in the United States.

SOURCES: *Journal of the American Medical Association,* 1966, pp. 852–853, and 1967, pp. 730–731; *Statistical Abstract of the United States, 1968,* 1968, pp. 12, 13; Hubbard & Anlyan, 1968.

no matter where they have been trained. Public officials may also feel that today's population will not favor carrying the burden of preparation for future population growth, particularly when that growth is due to substantial in-migration from other states. If public support were based on such reasoning, one would expect that the greater the recent rate of growth in population, the fewer public places there would be for a given level of population. An additional reason why the number of public school places would not be proportional to population size relates to economies of size in the provision of medical education. These may lead smaller states which do support medical schools to have a larger number of places relative to their population.

The same factors discussed in the previous paragraph may also affect the amount of money the states provide for operation of

	State	Active U.S medical school graduates in state per 100,000 population in 1967	Total number who graduated from medical schools in the state between 1950 and 1959	Estimated percentage of 1950–1959 graduates from schools in state who were enrolled as residents of state
	District of Columbia	385	2,463	12
	Maryland	174	1,614	44
	Colorado	173	714	83
	Massachusetts	170	3,070	42
	California	168	3,185	79
	New York	145	7,930	70
	Vermont	144	398	58
	Connecticut	141	653	19
	Washington	138	613	88
	Minnesota	131	1,197	91
	Utah	130	424	84
	Oregon	129	654	77
	Pennsylvania	129	6,117	68
	Arizona	118		
	Florida	117	176	
	Nebraska	117	1,486	60
	Louisiana	114	2,214	63
	Tennessee	112	2,141	75
	Virginia	111	1,608	80
	Texas	110	2,867	93
	Rhode Island	109		
	Wisconsin	109	1,639	71
	Missouri	107	2,128	38
	Kansas	104	981	91
	Oklahoma	103	781	100
	Illinois	103	5,122	55
	Ohio	102	2,721	84
	New Hampshire	102		
	Georgia	102	1,418	76
	North Carolina	101	1,585	66

TABLE 29
Relationship between the states of graduation and location in 1967 for 1950–1959 United States medical school graduates, by states, ranked by total graduates practicing per 100,000 population

Ratio of change in population between 1954 and 1967 to graduates from schools in state between 1950 and 1959	Percent of graduates from U.S. medical schools between 1950 and 1959 who graduated from schools in state	Percent of graduates from U.S. medical schools between 1950 and 1959 located in state in 1967	Percent of physicians (1950–1959 graduates) located in state in 1967 who graduated from schools in state	Percent of 1950–1959 graduates from schools in state located in state in 1967
	3.8	1.0	39	11.0
620	2.5	2.5	30	29.6
680	1.1	1.6	28	39.6
170	4.8	3.2	50	33.0
2,010	5.0	13.7	27	73.1
320	12.3	9.0	59	42.8
100	0.6	0.2	38	12.6
1,040	1.0	1.7	11	19.1
950	1.0	2.0	25	50.9
390	1.9	2.0	47	51.0
650	0.7	0.6	46	40.6
570	1.0	1.2	36	44.2
130	9.6	5.5	71	41.0
		1.0	0	
	0.3	3.6	6	73.9
60	2.3	0.7	76	23.3
350	3.5	1.9	76	40.9
250	3.3*	1.9	67*	39.9
610	2.5	2.2	53	45.5
870	4.5	5.6	58	71.6
		0.3		
350	2.6	2.0	53	42.5
250	3.3	2.0	41	24.2
180	1.5	1.0	55	37.3
370	1.2	1.1	59	51.0
320	8.0	3.7	64	29.7
610	4.2	4.2	49	48.4
		0.2	0	
640	2.2	2.0	59	54.2
570	2.5	2.3	46	42.9

State	Active U.S medical school graduates in state per 100,000 population in 1967	Total number who graduated from medical schools in the state between 1950 and 1959	Estimated percentage of 1950-1959 graduates from schools in state who were enrolled as residents of state
Montana	100		
Delaware	99		
Nevada	99		
New Mexico	99		
New Jersey	98		
Michigan	96	2,122	90
Iowa	96	950	95
Kentucky	94	908	88
Indiana	93	1,268	96
Idaho	91		
South Carolina	89	642	100
Arkansas	88	726	100
Alabama	84	606	100
North Dakota	83		
West Virginia	82		
Maine	81		
South Dakota	79		
Mississippi	78	129	100

*Excludes Meharry Medical College. See Table 28, second footnote.
SOURCES: Theodore, Sutter, & Haug, 1968, tables 3, 7, 8; *Statistical Abstract*

medical schools. State support to public schools per M.D. candidate, according to the financial reports, range from a high of $13,900 in one state to a low of $3,400 in another. Of course, the influence of the various factors on dollar expenditures may be different from the influence on the number of medical school places since the states may use funds in various ways: to improve the quality of the medical school, to provide greater subsidies to students, or to support other medical school activities, rather than to increase the number of places.

In order to examine the relationships discussed above, we have

Ratio of change in population between 1954 and 1967 to graduates from schools in state between 1950 and 1959	Percent of graduates from U.S. medical schools between 1950 and 1959 who graduated from schools in state	Percent of graduates from U.S. medical schools between 1950 and 1959 located in state in 1967	Percent of physicians (1950-1959 graduates) located in state in 1967 who graduated from schools in state	Percent of 1950-1959 graduates from schools in state located in state in 1967
		0.3	0	
		0.2	0	
		0.2	0	
		0.5	0	
		2.8	0	
720	3.3	3.2	54	56.0
130	1.5	1.0	51	34.6
320	1.4	1.4	55	53.1
580	2.0	1.9	56	53.6
		0.3	0	
660	1.0	1.1	64	66.8
320	1.1	0.8	68	50.8
870	0.9	1.4	47	67.7
		0.2	0	
		0.5	0	
		0.3	0	
		0.2	0	
	0.2	1.0	14	65.1

of the United States, 1964, p. 11; *Statistical Abstract of the United States, 1968*, p. 12; *Journal of the American Medical Association*, 1950, pp. 120–121, and 1955, pp. 584–585.

used simple multiple regression analysis. Two dependent variables were analyzed. One of the dependent variables was the number of public freshman places, and the other was total state expenditures for support of current operations. Our sample included 48 states (Alaska, Hawaii, and the District of Columbia were excluded). The independent variables were (1) total population, (2) the number of freshman places in private schools, (3) per capita personal income, (4) the ratio of total state and local expenditures to personal income, and (5) the percentage increase in population during the previous decade. When the number of public freshman places was the dependent variable, the positive coefficient of population size and the negative coefficient of the number of private places were significant at the 1 percent level, while the negative coefficient of the rate of population growth was significant at the 10 percent level (Eq. D-1 in Appendix D). However, the elasticity at the mean of the number of public openings with respect to population size was 1.11, indicating that there were no direct effects of population size on the *ratio* of public places to population. Furthermore, the elasticity at the mean of the number of public places with respect to the number of private places was only -0.26, indicating that there was a reduction of 26 public places for every 100 private places. However, when state expenditures on medical school operations were used as the dependent variable, the number of private places was no longer a significant explanator, but the ratio of state and local expenditures to personal income was significant at the 5 percent level (Eq. D-2 in Appendix D). Seventy percent of the variance in public openings and 87 percent of the variance in state expenditures were explained by the equations.

In addition to their direct support of medical schools, states provide funds directly to teaching hospitals. It is difficult to calculate the amount of subsidies provided because financial reports are incomplete and there are differences in the procedures used to channel the funds to the hospital. However, Blumberg has used university financial reports and questionnaires sent to the relevant schools to estimate state subsidies of university-owned teaching hospitals for the fiscal year 1965–66. State appropriation figures with staff benefit and equipment adjustments were used when available; otherwise, hospital income was subtracted from expenditures to produce a residual estimate of state subsidy. The subsidies varied from $190,000 by the state of Utah to $8.5 million by California for the two medical schools at Los Angeles and San Francisco.[11] The states provided a total of $178.7 million for medical school construction in 1966–67 and 1967–68. Finally, a few states provide support directly to medical students. However, the only state with substantial support of students is New York, which provides 80 Regents scholarships annually for the

[11] See Blumberg, 1967. It should be noted that many publicly controlled schools were not included in the survey. For example, none of the New York public schools participated. However, the numbers do give some idea of the level of state subsidies to teaching hospitals.

study of medicine. These scholarships range between $350 and $1,000 per year, depending on the financial status of the student and his family.

Effects on the Location of Physicians

We have noted that the primary *raison d'être* for state subsidization of medical education appears to be the desire to provide for an adequate number of physicians practicing in the state. Decisions of states to act in order to attain that goal require the development of procedures to determine the desired future number and analyses of the probable effects of an increased number of M.D. graduates from schools in the state on its attainment.

Most analyses by economists have focused on the national stock of physicians. This is unfortunate because often, in making actual decisions regarding desired expansion, the state perspective is of greater importance than the more aggregative national view. State studies have relied exclusively on ratio analyses for indication of adequacy.[12] The present physician-population ratio is compared with a standard or "norm" such as the United States ratio or the average ratio for a group of states with populations having similar socioeconomic characteristics. If the ratio of the states under consideration is below the standard, the standard is set as the minimum goal. If the ratio is greater than the standard, maintenance of the ratio in the future is set as the minimum goal.

The ratio procedure can be criticized on a number of grounds. These relate to the fact that no evidence is provided that the given standard is optimum. Variability in the population's socioeconomic characteristics—age, income, education—can, and does, lead to differences in the effective demand for medical services. It also leads to variations in the "need" for medical care (as defined by physicians themselves). Similarly, the stock of physicians itself may not be a good proxy for the availability of physician services since differences in the number of hospital beds, in the number and type of other health personnel, and in the organization of medical practice can lead to variations in the productivity of physicians. An additional complicating factor is the fact that the geographic boundaries of the state are political boundaries and do not repre-

[12] For examples see Health Manpower Study Commission, 1966, p. 62; *The Report of the Governor's Task Force on Medical Education,* 1967, pp. 34–35; State of California Coordinating Council for Higher Education, 1963, pp. 13–15.

sent economic or market boundaries in the provision of medical care. Thus, the numerator or denominator, or both, in the physician-population ratio do not adequately measure that which they are intended to measure. A recent survey of Missouri doctors, for example, indicated that about 10 percent of the care they render is provided to out-of-state residents (Olson, 1968, p. 28). Physicians in states contiguous to Missouri serve Missouri residents, and thus the number of Missouri physicians understates the number of physicians (and services) available to Missouri citizens, while the size of the Missouri population understates the demands for the services of Missouri physicians. Finally, optimum standards cannot be set without explicit consideration of the total costs of attaining those standards. In some cases, it does appear that the budgetary costs may lead to adjustments and readjustments in the standards themselves, but the initial setting of standards seldom, if ever, seems to take into account the total real costs to society.

Whether a better methodology for state planning can be developed remains an open question, but it deserves substantial consideration. In any case, having set a future standard, consideration is frequently given to the locational behavior patterns of physicians, particularly newly trained physicians, so that the standards can be translated into educational requirements and so that efforts can be made to retain a greater percentage of the physicians so educated (J. A. Campbell & Associates, 1968, pp. 25–29; *The Report of the Governor's Task Force on Medical Education,* 1967, pp. 12–13).

Several studies by economists have related the location patterns of physicians to economic factors. Our survey is limited to studies using the state as the geographic unit of observation. Benham, Maurizi, and Reder (1968, pp. 332–347) used regression analysis to study the location of physicians in 1950 and 1960.[13] They found that size of population was the single most important factor in determining the number of self-employed physicians in a state. The coefficient of per capita income was significantly different from zero in both years. Computations of elasticities at the mean indicated that a 10 percent increase in per capita income would lead to slightly less than a 5 percent increase in the number of physicians. The number of places in medical school classes was not significant in either year, while the coefficient of barriers to entry, measured by the percentage of applicants for licensure who failed,

[13] The study also included an analysis of location in 1930 and 1940.

was significant in both years. When the variance in the per capita number of physicians between states was analyzed, per capita income, per capita training facilities, and barriers to entry were all significant explanators. However, the computations of elasticities found that the ratio of physicians to population was substantially more sensitive to differences in per capita income than to differences in per capita medical school places. Elasticities with respect to per capita income were 0.54 and 0.69 in 1950 and 1960, respectively, while elasticities with respect to per capita spaces were 0.04 and 0.05 in 1950 and 1960, respectively. Benham et al. (1968, p. 345) concluded that total effective demand for medical services within the states has depended mainly on size of population and secondarily upon per capita income and that physicians have located in accordance with the effective demand, subject to "a locational preference pattern that causes medics to sacrifice pecuniary income for the amenities of an urban environment."

Analysis of physician location behavior was also undertaken by Sloan (1968, pp. 285–396).[14] Sloan studied physician location patterns among states with the use of a model for a health system which included equations explaining physician supply, physician income, nurse supply, the number of medical students, the number of nursing students, hospital capital stock, and hospital insurance coverage. He estimated a large number of variants of his structural equations, but we shall concentrate on the variant of the physician-supply equation, which included all independent variables considered. The number of active, nonstudent physicians per 100,000 population in 1960 was the dependent variable. Significant independent variables were physician income, a measure of cyclical sensitivity of economic activity within the state, the number of undergraduate and graduate medical students in medical schools in the state, and the lagged dependent variable. Among the nonsignificant independent variables were the number of medical students from the state and failure rate of graduates from United States medical schools on the state licensing examinations (Sloan, 1968, p. 358). Sloan also estimated a recent graduate equation in which the dependent variable was the number of nonfederal, nonstudent physicians who received the M.D. degree between 1945 and 1954 and who were practicing in a given state in 1959, divided by the total number of active,

[14] Both Benham et al. (1968) and Sloan included the District of Columbia in their analyses.

nonstudent physicians in the state in 1960. While population growth and the failure rate on state licensing examinations were significant explanators of the variance in the dependent variable, the elasticities with respect to each of those two variables were less than 0.10. However, the percentage of physicians working over 49 weeks in 1960, which was used as a measure of excess demand, was significant, and the elasticity with respect to it was 1.39. The number of medical students from the state was not significant (Sloan, 1968, p. 377). Two relevant conclusions that Sloan reached on the basis of his extensive analyses were that a state's efforts to attract physicians by increasing the number of residents attending medical school through increases in public medical school places are in vain (1968, pp. 378–380) and that restrictive admission policies which favor citizens of that state are based on the same erroneous assumptions (1968, p. 381).

In the study most frequently referred to in the medical education literature on locational behavior, Weiskotten et al. (1960, pp. 1071–1121) used cross-tabulations of data compiled from surveys sent out nine years after graduation to the classes of 1945 and 1950. Between 45 and 46 percent of the graduates of both classes in private practice were practicing in the states in which the medical college they attended was located. This was true for 52 percent (1945) and 55 percent (1950) of the graduates of public medical schools, but for only 42 percent (1945) and 38 percent (1950) of the graduates of private medical schools. The study also found that 61 percent of the 1945 graduates and 58 percent of the 1950 graduates were practicing in their state of residence prior to medical school. However, the finding most often cited is that a larger portion of individuals with residency training were practicing in the state of their residency training than were practicing in the state of prior residence, state of medical college, or state of internship. Of the 1950 class, 63 percent were practicing in the state in which they took their residency training, compared with 42 percent who were practicing in the state of their medical college.[15] This relationship has frequently been cited as an indication that residency programs are a more effective mechanism by which to attract physicians than an expansion of the number of places in

[15] There was considerable overlap among the physicians' location during these different periods. About 29 percent of the 1950 graduates were practicing in the state where they had gone to school and had taken their internship and their residency training.

medical schools is. This conclusion, however, does not follow directly from the evidence. Because of licensing factors and the need to develop contacts and a reputation, it would be logical for physicians to take their residency training in the state in which they plan to practice, and the Weiskotten analysis does not enable us to take account of the directions of the causal relationships or of the timing of the location decision.

Our own empirical analysis concentrates on data prepared by the American Medical Association for its study of the location of medical school alumni (Theodore, Sutter, & Haug, 1968).[16] Analysis of these data disclosed that the number of graduates from United States medical schools practicing in the various states in 1967 (excluding the District of Columbia) ranged from 174 per 100,000 population in Maryland to 78 per 100,000 population in Mississippi (Table 29, pp. 148–151). These differences evolved over a long period of time, during which the population distribution and the characteristics of the individual states were changing. Each graduating class faced a new set of circumstances as the members of the class decided where to locate their practices. Furthermore, the number of graduates from schools in each state changed over time. Our analysis therefore concentrates on the location behavior of the graduates of the 1950 through the 1959 classes. Most of these physicians entered practice (after internship and residency) between 1955 and 1965. Even though a greater proportion of physicians who graduated in this period became specialists than of those who graduated in previous decades, very few were still in residency training in 1967.

The net success of a state in attracting recent graduates is dependent on the number of graduates from schools in the state and the ability of the state to "hold" those graduates, as well as the ability of the state to attract "immigrants" who graduated from schools in other states. The behavior of the 1950–1959 graduates will be studied within this framework.

California and New York attracted the greatest percentage of the 1950–1959 graduates—13.7 percent and 9.0 percent, respectively (column 6 of Table 29). Conversely, 15 states attracted less than 1 percent of the total graduates. However, schools in California were responsible for the training of only 5.0 percent of all graduates. The largest percentage of the total graduates, 12.3 percent,

16 This study showed the relationship between school of graduation, year of graduation (in five-year intervals), and state of practice in 1967.

were from medical schools located in New York, while medical schools in Pennsylvania and Illinois produced 9.6 and 8.0 percent, respectively. The latter two states had only 5.5 percent and 3.7 percent, respectively, of all graduates practicing within their boundaries. Thus, in order to obtain such a large proportion of the new physicians, California had to be relatively successful in keeping its own graduates, in attracting physicians educated in other states, or in both. Conversely, New York, Pennsylvania, and Illinois, with percentages of graduates practicing in the respective states lower than the percentages of physicians they graduated, had to be relatively unsuccessful. This is borne out by the data. In 1967, 73 percent of the 1950–1959 graduates from California medical schools were practicing in California (column 8 of Table 29). Immigration was also high, as is clear from the fact that only 27 percent of the 1950–1959 graduates practicing in California in 1967 were graduates of California schools (column 7). In contrast, New York, Pennsylvania, and Illinois were able to retain only 43 percent, 41 percent, and 30 percent of their 1950–1959 graduates, respectively. Furthermore, despite the fact that less than half their graduates remained to practice in those states, 59 percent, 71 percent, and 64 percent of the 1950–1959 graduates practicing in each of these states, respectively, were from a "local" school. Various factors help explain these differences in the relative success of the states to attract new M.D.'s:

1   The states attracting the most physicians were those with the greatest increase in population in the period 1954–1967: California (6.4 million), New York (2.5 million), and Texas (2.5 million). When the number of additional persons each new physician would be called upon to serve is computed (that is, the ratio of population change to new physicians), first impressions regarding the relative success of states in attracting new physicians are altered. There was an increase in population of 730 for each 1950–1959 graduate practicing in California, while in New York the increase was 440, and in Iowa it was 200.

2   The schools in the states which were most successful in holding their 1950–1959 graduates — California (73 percent), Texas (72 percent), Alabama (68 percent), and South Carolina (67 percent) — had a large percentage (79 percent or greater) of freshmen who were residents of the state (column 3 of Table 29). Yet not all states whose schools had a large proportion of freshmen who were in-

state residents were very successful in holding their graduates. Only 35 percent of the Iowa graduates and 37 percent of the Kansas graduates were practicing in Iowa and Kansas, respectively, although more than 90 percent of the graduates were estimated to be in-state residents. In addition to the large proportion of resident freshmen, California, Texas, and Alabama had large increases in population relative to the number of graduates from their schools (an increase of 2,010 persons per graduate in California, and of 870 in Texas and in Alabama). (Column 4, Table 29.)

3   In contrast, states which did poorly in holding their graduates— Vermont (13 percent), Connecticut (19 percent), Nebraska (23 percent), and Missouri (24 percent)—either had small percentages of freshmen in schools in the state who were in-state residents— Connecticut (19 percent) and Missouri (38 percent)—or had a small increase in population for each graduate—Vermont (100) and Nebraska (60).

4   The states which attracted the most "immigrant" physicians were California (6,424), New York (2,338), Texas (1,487), and Ohio (1,354). All these were states with significant population increases. Furthermore, the states in which a high percentage of the total number of 1950–1959 graduates practicing in the state were from out-of-state schools—Connecticut (89 percent), Washington (75 percent), and California (73 percent)—had large increases in population relative to the number of graduates from their own schools.

From the above discussion, it is clear that several factors interacted to produce variation in the number of new physicians locating in each state. It is also obvious that, to a large extent, the success of a state in attracting physicians is independent of the number of physicians trained in its schools. Attempts to estimate the effects of the individual factors, however, require the use of statistical techniques such as multiple regression analysis. Such analysis as we have undertaken assesses average incremental change. It should be clear that it can examine the influence of expansion of the number of medical school places but not, for example, the consequences of moving from no medical schools to one (or more) schools.

The regression model used to estimate *the relationship between the number of graduates from schools in a state and the ability of the state to attract physicians* used the total number of graduates from United States medical schools during the period 1950–1959 who were practicing in each state in 1967 as the dependent variable. Our sample consisted of 32 states with a significant (greater than 300) number of graduates during the period under consideration (excluding the District of Columbia). Four independent variables were used in the analysis: (1) the change in population between 1954 and 1967, (2) the change in income per capita between 1954 and 1967, (3) the number of graduates from schools in the state who were in-state residents,[17] and (4) the number of graduates from schools in the state who were not residents of the state. This model is based on the hypothesis that new physicians will tend to locate where the demand for physician service has increased the most and that relative changes in demand over a short period are in largest measure tied to changes in population and in per capita income, but that the location of the graduate's medical school may affect his decision regarding the state of practice. The estimated multiple regression equation explained 97 percent of the variance in the dependent variable. The coefficients of the change in population and the number of resident graduates were significant and had the expected positive sign (Eq. D-3 in Appendix D). However, the elasticity computed at the mean of the variables indicated that a 10 percent increase in the number of resident graduates would only lead to a 3.2 percent increase in the number of graduates locating in the state.[18]

The analysis of the *factors affecting the ability of a state to*

---

[17] This was estimated by averaging the percentage of freshmen in schools in each state in 1949 and 1954 who were residents of the state.

[18] The change-in-population variable is highly correlated with two other variables which may affect the relative distribution of new physicians among the states — the number of physicians at the start of the period who had left practice by the end of the period and the total population size. These relationships occur because states with large population growth over a period tend to have a relatively large number of physicians and a relatively large population at the start of the period. The former means that a relatively large number of physicians retire or die in those states during the period. The latter means that increases in per capita income over the period will provide for greater absolute increases in the demand for physician services where the absolute population size is relatively large. The simple correlation between the change in population and the number of physicians above age 55 in 1959 (used to measure potential retirements and deaths) was 0.692, and the simple correlation between the change in population and the absolute level of population was 0.857 for the sample of states under consideration. Various adjustments did not change the relevant findings of the model — change in population is of primary importance, and sensitivity of the number of new graduates practicing in the state to the number of graduates from the state is positive, but low.

"hold" its graduates used the *percentage* of those graduating from schools in the state between 1950 and 1959 who were practicing in the state in 1967 as the dependent variable. The independent variables were (1) the estimated percentage of graduates entering schools in the state who were nonresidents of the state, (2) the ratio of the change in population to the number of graduates from schools in the state, and (3) the change in per capita personal income. This equation explained 76 percent of the variance in the dependent variable. The coefficients of the first two independent variables were significant with the expected negative and positive signs, respectively, but the third variable, which added little to the explanatory power of the equation, had the incorrect sign (Eq. D-4 in Appendix D). The finding of a negative relation with respect to the estimated proportion of nonresident graduates may appear to be at variance with Sloan's conclusions (see pages 155 to 156). However, the size of the coefficient of that variable indicated that an increase of 10 percentage points in the proportion of resident graduates will lead to only a 3.9 percentage-point increase in the proportion of graduates from the state who practice in the state.

The significant positive coefficient of the ratio of change in population to graduates is of considerable import since the implied negative relationship between the ratio of graduates to change in population and the proportion of graduates who practice in a state provides evidence that those states devoting extra effort to the education of medical students (relative to the change in their population)[19] will not receive proportional returns in terms of increases in physician stock.

Finally, we estimated the *effects of five different variables on the number of graduates practicing in a state who graduated from schools in other states.* This equation explained 96 percent of the variance in the dependent variable. The coefficients of three variables were significant and had the expected sign (Eq. D-5 in Appendix D). Those variables (with the signs of their coefficients) were (1) the change in population (positive), (2) the number of resident graduates from schools in the state (negative), and (3) the number of residents from the state who were attending medical school in other states in 1954 (positive). The elasticity estimated at the means indicated that a 10 percent increase in the number of resident

---

[19] Since the change in the absolute size of population over short periods of time is highly correlated with the absolute size of population, it is possible to say the same thing about the ratio of total population to the number of graduates.

graduates led to a 3.8 percent decrease in the number of out-of-state graduates who were located in a state.

Thus, the empirical analyses indicate that the ability of states to attract new physicians is only marginally improved by increases in the number of physicians graduated from medical schools in the state.

Medical School Openings and Educational Opportunity for Residents

Most state reports on expansion of medical education have expressed an interest in the availability of opportunity for residents to attain a medical education.[20] It is assumed that increases in freshman openings within the state, particularly in public schools which show preferential treatment to state residents, will lead to corresponding increases in the number of entrants from the state. However, to the extent that the new openings are filled by out-of-state residents or by residents who would have gone to out-of-state schools, this effect is diluted. In this section we shall examine some factors which have affected the number of entrants to medical schools from their own states.

Judgments on the degree of educational opportunity that exists are usually based on indicators such as ratios in which the numerator is the number of entrants from the state or the number of freshman medical openings in the state and the denominator is the total population or college-age population in the state. The number of freshman openings in the state can affect the number of entrants from the state in several ways: (1) by lowering the direct costs to residents if the openings are in publicly controlled schools; (2) by reducing the direct costs of living expenses, depending on the location of the school and whether the openings are in publicly or privately controlled schools; and (3) by according preferential treatment to state residents in publicly controlled schools, which tends to increase the probability of acceptance of applicants from the state (and thus the probability of application, as well). While such preferential treatment has declined over the years (as evidenced by the increase in out-of-state freshmen accepted by public schools), it is still of considerable relevance (Table 30).

Our empirical analysis used data averaged for the school years 1965–66 and 1966–67. The total number of entrants (the number

---

[20] See, for example, Consultants to the Commission on Higher Education, 1967, pp. 11–15; Maine Legislative Research Committee, 1967, pp. 48–50; Olson, 1968, pp. 43–44.

TABLE 30	State	1949	1967	State	1949	1967
Percentage of freshmen at United States public medical schools who were residents of the state where school is located, 1949 and 1967*	Alabama	100	93	New Jersey		86
	Arizona		88	New Mexico		69
	Arkansas	100	99	New York	80	92
	California	97	86	North Carolina	91	76
	Colorado	87	80	North Dakota		78
	Florida		91	Ohio	89	84
	Georgia	100	100	Oklahoma	100	85
	Illinois	100	98	Oregon	75	76
	Indiana	95	93	South Carolina	100	90
	Iowa	96	87	South Dakota		57
	Kansas	95	83	Tennessee	100	73
	Kentucky		83	Texas	98	96
	Louisiana	100	99	Utah	92	76
	Maryland	59	83	Vermont	62	18
	Michigan	93	79	Virginia	81	62
	Minnesota	94	95	Washington	89	87
	Mississippi	100	97	West Virginia	100	71
	Missouri	100	84	Wisconsin	100	80
	Nebraska	91	86			

*The states not shown had no public medical schools.

SOURCES: *Journal of the American Medical Association,* 1950, p. 122; 1968, pp. 2096–2097.

of residents of a state who enter medical school in that and other states) per 1 million population ranged from 74 for New York to 16 for Maine (column 1 of Table 31). This ratio E/P can be separated and viewed as the product of three other ratios (shown in the last three columns of Table 31): the ratio of residents from the state who were college undergraduates in four-year institutions in any state in 1963 to state population (U/P) (Rice & Mason, 1965), the ratio of all medical school applicants from the state to undergraduate students in all colleges in the state (A/U), and the ratio of entrants from the state (into all medical schools) to all applicants from the state (E/A); that is, $E/P = (U/P) (A/U) (E/A)$. We shall use this framework to note the highlights of Table 31:

1   The high ratios of states with the largest number of entrants per 1 million population—New York (74), Utah (72), and North Dakota (72)—are

State	Entrants per 1 million population (E/P)	Total openings in schools in state	Total resident applicants	Total resident entrants
New York	74	1,106	2,730	1,340
Utah	72	66	163	73
North Dakota	72	48	63	47
Nebraska	68	164	199	100
Arkansas	60	106	214	117
New Jersey	60	105	861	409
Iowa	52	122	263	146
Kansas	52	120	209	119
Maryland	51	222	339	182
Minnesota	51	161	333	184
Pennsylvania	51	720	1,274	594
Tennessee	50	252*	317	192
South Dakota	49	46	64	35
Kentucky	48	174	275	155
Louisiana	48	276	332	173
Oklahoma	48	106	278	119
Indiana	47	216	440	231
Mississippi	46	83	195	105
Oregon	46	87	155	88
Illinois	45	570	1,057	481
Vermont	45	53	38	18
Colorado	43	86	178	86
Connecticut	43	80	279	121
Michigan	43	351	756	356
Georgia	42	178	390	179
West Virginia	41	61	127	74
Massachusetts	40	306	484	220
Wyoming	40		27	14
Wisconsin	39	206	335	166
Delaware	38		35	20
Ohio	38	342	863	398
Virginia	38	184	338	168
Florida	36	146	455	215

State resident undergraduates in all colleges per 1,000 population (U/P)	Ratio of applicants per 1,000 undergraduates (A/U)	Ratio of entrants to applicants (E/A)
1.4	10.8	0.49
2.2	7.6	0.45
2.2	4.5	0.75
1.6	8.4	0.50
1.3	8.4	0.55
1.4	8.9	0.48
1.6	5.8	0.56
1.9	4.9	0.57
1.2	7.7	0.54
1.8	5.2	0.55
1.2	8.8	0.47
1.2	6.9	0.61
1.9	5.0	0.55
1.1	7.9	0.56
1.3	7.1	0.52
1.8	6.3	0.43
1.2	7.2	0.53
1.4	5.9	0.54
1.8	4.6	0.57
1.5	6.8	0.46
1.3	7.5	0.47
1.6	5.7	0.48
1.6	6.1	0.43
1.4	6.7	0.47
1.0	9.0	0.46
1.2	5.7	0.58
1.5	5.9	0.45
2.0	4.2	0.52
1.5	5.4	0.50
1.3	5.5	0.57
1.3	6.7	0.46
1.2	6.6	0.50
1.2	6.3	0.47

TABLE 31
Entrants and applicants to United States medical schools, ranked by entrants per 1 million population, 1965–66 and 1966–67 (cont'd.)

State	Entrants per 1 million population (E/P)	Total openings in schools in state	Total resident applicants	Total resident entrants
Montana	36		51	26
South Carolina	36	82	208	93
Idaho	36		57	25
Washington	34	78	212	101
Missouri	34	292	281	151
Arizona	33		112	54
Texas	32	347	693	343
California	31	497	1,421	579
Alabama	30	80	220	104
New Mexico	29	26	61	30
New Hampshire	27	49	43	18
North Carolina	26	210	284	130
Nevada	22		23	10
Rhode Island	22		57	20
Maine	16		47	17

*Excludes Meharry Medical College. See Table 28, second footnote.
SOURCES: *Journal of the American Medical Association,* 1966, pp. 921, 928–929,

explained by different factors. New York had a high ratio because a large proportion of its resident undergraduates were applicants (10.8 applicants per 1,000 undergraduates) and despite the fact that only 1.4 New York residents per 1,000 population were undergraduates (in colleges in all states) in 1963. Utah's high ratio was related chiefly to its large number of undergraduates (2.2) per 1,000 population, and North Dakota's was related to the relative success of its applicants (75 percent entered medical school).

2   In contrast, the lowest ratios of entrants per 1 million population—Nevada and Rhode Island (22) and Maine (16)—were related to relatively small ratios of undergraduates to population (1.0, 1.2, and 1.1 per 1,000, respectively), and to small ratios of entrants to applicants (0.43, 0.35, and 0.36, respectively).

3   The two states with the largest number of applicants per 1,000 undergraduates—New York (10.8) and Georgia (9.0)—had one medical school opening per 229 resident undergraduates and 243 resident undergraduates, respectively. However, the state with the next greatest number of applicants per 1,000 undergraduates—New Jersey (8.9)—had only one medical school opening per 925 undergraduates.

State resident undergraduates in all colleges per 1,000 population (U/P)	Ratio of applicants per 1,000 undergraduates (A/U)	Ratio of entrants to applicants (E/A)
2.0	3.6	0.51
1.0	7.9	0.45
1.9	4.4	0.44
1.8	3.9	0.48
1.3	4.7	0.54
1.5	4.6	0.48
1.4	4.6	0.49
1.5	5.1	0.41
1.1	5.7	0.47
1.4	4.3	0.49
1.2	5.4	0.42
1.2	5.0	0.46
1.0	5.2	0.43
1.2	5.2	0.35
1.1	4.2	0.36

and 1967, pp. 812, 820–821; *Journal of Medical Education,* 1967a, pp. 34–35, and 1968a, pp. 12–13. Undergraduate residency data from Rice & Mason, 1965, pp. 46–47; population data from *Statistical Abstract of the United States, 1967,* p. 12.

4 The states with the largest number of entrants per applicant — North Dakota (0.75) and Tennessee (0.61) — had a large number of openings per resident applicant (0.76 and 0.79, respectively; columns 2 and 3 of Table 31). However, Vermont, which also had more than one opening for each of its resident applicants, had an entrant-applicant ratio of only 0.47.

Multiple regression analysis was also used to estimate the average *effects of the individual factors on the number of entrants from different states.* Four independent variables were used in the regression analysis: (1) the number of freshman openings in schools under public control, (2) the number of freshman openings in schools under private control, (3) per capita personal income, and (4) the number of undergraduate students in all four-year higher education institutions in 1963. The last two variables were included because of their likely effects on the demand for medical education by residents, while the differentiation between the first two variables was introduced because of the preferential treatment usually accorded resident applicants by the public school and because of the effect the different tuition levels might have on the number of in-state applicants.

The coefficients of both "freshman-place" variables were significant at the 1 percent level, while the coefficient of the numbers of undergraduates was significant at the 2.5 percent level (Eq. D-6 in Appendix D). The elasticities computed at the means indicated that a 10 percent increase in public medical school openings provided a 4.7 percent increase in entrants from the state, while a 10 percent increase in private openings would lead to a 3.1 percent increase in the number of entrants.

Thus, the empirical analyses indicate that, on the margin, the number of entrants from a state is sensitive to the number of openings at public medical schools in that state. There is a leakage, on the average, of about 53 percent. (Undoubtedly this is affected by the degree of restriction placed on the residence of entrants.) Nevertheless, it is clear that those states which judge it to be the public's responsibility to increase the number of residents who enter medical school can bring this increase about by providing an increased number of openings.

Effects on the Location of Interns and Residents Interns and residents constitute 17 percent of the nonfederally employed physicians in the United States. They provide a considerable proportion of health care services. In addition, they aid in the teaching of M.D. candidates. Given the low cost of their services—and the practice pattern of private physicians (principally office or clinics)—there is great competition among hospitals to attract interns and residents, particularly those who have matriculated from United States medical schools. In a broader context, this competition exists between states. In addition to the desire to receive the current services produced by interns and residents, health planners also hope that physicians who do their graduate medical education in the state will practice in the same area upon completion of that education.

Available data indicate that hospitals with medical school affiliation are considerably more successful in attracting interns and residents who have graduated from United States medical schools than nonaffiliated hospitals. In 1966–67, 68 percent of the internships in nonaffiliated hospitals were filled, and 48 percent of the interns were foreign graduates. Affiliated hospitals, on the other hand, filled 83 percent of their internships, and only 13 percent of the interns were foreign graduates. The success in filling internships varied considerably by states. For example, California filled 92 percent of its internships, and only 3 percent of the interns were foreign graduates. West Virginia filled 41 percent of its internships, and 24 percent of all interns were foreign graduates. And Connecticut filled 77 percent of its internships, with 51 percent of the interns being foreign graduates. A similar situation exists in the case of residencies. Nonaffiliated hospitals filled 77 percent of their residencies, and foreign graduates constituted 42 percent of the residents. For affiliated hospitals, 85 percent of the positions were filled, and 23 percent of the residents were foreign graduates.

Certainly, factors besides medical school affiliation can affect the success of hospitals (and the states) in attracting physicians. Larger hospitals, whether affiliated or nonaffiliated, have greater success than smaller ones in attracting graduates. The potential for future practice in the state (and possible future relationships with the hospital) can make some hospitals and states more attractive than others. Furthermore, there is considerable variation among states in the stipends paid to interns and residents (Tables 32 and 33).[21] The weighted average stipend for interns in Louisiana, for example, was $2,544 in 1966, while it was $4,532 in Nebraska. Other things being equal, the level of stipends may be an important factor in the location decisions of residents and interns.

The effects of medical school affiliation on the ability of states to attract interns and residents from United States medical schools can be divided into two parts. First, affiliation can affect the number of approved internships and residencies offered. There is significant variation among states in the number of approved internships and residencies (both in absolute terms and in relation to other variables). The number of internships offered per 1 million population varied from 110 in New York to 21 in New Mexico, and the number of residencies offered varied from 382 in New York to 42 in South Carolina. Second, the number of approved internships and residencies offered by hospitals affiliated with medical schools may affect the ability of the states to fill the internships and residencies offered. The ratio of interns who had graduated from United States medical schools to total internships offered varied from 0.89 in California to 0.13 in New Jersey, and

---

[21] Stipends were computed from data for 1966 (see American Medical Association, 1967). The computations exclude all nonmonetary income provided to doctors.

TABLE 32
*Relative success
in filling
internships in
United States
hospitals, by
states, 1966*

State*	Number of internships in state filled by U.S. medical school graduates per 1 million population	Number of internships offered by hospitals in state per 1 million population	Ratio of interns in state who graduated from U.S. medical schools to total number of internships offered by hospitals in state
Colorado	74.0	95.4	0.78
Utah	66.5	97.3	0.68
Maryland	58.3	106.2	0.55
California	57.4	64.5	0.89
New York	53.9	110.4	0.49
Washington	50.2	65.9	0.76
Tennessee	49.6	69.5	0.71
Massachusetts	49.1	78.6	0.62
Louisiana	48.0	69.3	0.69
Pennsylvania	46.3	87.0	0.53
Missouri	45.2	64.5	0.70
Georgia	39.2	62.5	0.63
Minnesota	39.0	67.0	0.58
Virginia	37.3	58.0	0.64
Michigan	37.3	75.3	0.50
Connecticut	36.2	96.9	0.37
Illinois	35.7	78.0	0.46
Texas	34.5	44.7	0.77
Nebraska	33.3	78.0	0.43
Oregon	32.3	51.0	0.63
Ohio	32.1	78.2	0.41
North Carolina	31.8	46.1	0.69
Rhode Island	30.2	90.6	0.33
Florida	26.6	55.4	0.48
Oklahoma	26.1	39.1	0.67
Kentucky	26.1	42.1	0.62
Wisconsin	25.0	55.1	0.45
Iowa	22.7	38.6	0.59
Arkansas	22.6	31.5	0.72

	Percent of accredited internships in the state that are in:	
Hospitals with major medical school affiliation	Hospitals without medical school affiliation	Weighted average of interns' stipends
19	44	$3,251
39	10	3,263
38	37	4,412
43	32	3,523
43	40	3,834
43	29	2,836
63	20	3,410
52	38	3,082
50	06	2,544
45	49	3,534
57	20	3,521
44	45	3,565
51	32	3,178
47	53	3,572
30	60	4,501
20	80	3,602
53	36	3,770
23	42	3,441
80	20	4,532
37	39	3,034
19	74	3,887
65	20	3,155
0	0	3,167
35	65	3,821
41	23	3,648
76	20	3,301
43	40	3,853
33	51	3,810
56	44	4,102

TABLE 32
Relative success in filling internships in United States hospitals, by states, 1966 (cont'd.)

State*	Number of internships in state filled by U.S. medical school graduates per 1 million population	Number of internships offered by hospitals in state per 1 million population	Ratio of interns in state who graduated from U.S. medical schools to total number of internships offered by hospitals in state
Indiana	21.4	33.3	0.64
Alabama	19.4	37.1	0.52
Arizona	18.3	47.6	0.39
South Carolina	18.0	40.7	0.44
West Virginia	18.0	57.8	0.31
Mississippi	17.1	23.2	0.74
Kansas	16.7	35.2	0.48
New Mexico	11.5	21.0	0.55
New Jersey	10.6	79.8	0.13

*Data for 38 states used in the regression analysis. These states, in our judgment, had a sufficient number of internships to give representative results.

the ratio of residents who were United States graduates to total residencies offered varied from 0.79 in three states to 0.20 in New Jersey. We have concentrated our analysis on the latter two ratios, that is, the ratio of United States graduates to internships offered and the ratio of United States graduates to residencies offered.

The consolidated list of approved internships and residencies divides hospitals into four categories denoted by *M, L, G,* or no affiliation. *M* signifies that the hospital is a major unit in the teaching program of the medical school, while *L* indicates that the hospital is used to a limited extent in the school's teaching program. *G* indicates that the hospital is used by the school only for graduate training programs. We combined all internships and residency programs in each state into three groups: (1) *Ms,* (2) *Ls* or *Gs,* and (3) no affiliation. Weighted average stipends were computed for each of the groups. In most states stipends increased as the degree of affiliation declined. Regression analysis was used to *test whether the percent of internships and residencies offered in a state and classified as nonaffiliated had an effect on the percentage of offered internships and offered residencies filled by*

Hospitals with major medical school affiliation	Hospitals without medical school affiliation	Weighted average of interns' stipends
	Percent of accredited internships in the state that are in:	
47	53	3,897
58	18	3,091
0	100	4,316
38	62	4,467
23	77	3,600
55	0	3,176
33	67	4,226
0	0	3,600
12	80	3,616

SOURCES: American Medical Association, 1967, p. 6; *Journal of the American Medical Association*, 1967, p. 812.

graduates of United States medical schools. Our sample included the 38 states that (in our judgment) had a sufficient number of internships and residencies to give representative results.

The dependent variable in the regression was the ratio of the number of interns or residents graduated from United States or Canadian medical schools on duty September 1, 1966, to the total number of internships or residencies offered on September 1, 1966.[22] The independent variables were (1) the percentage of internships or residencies classified as nonaffiliated, (2) the weighted average stipends for interns or for surgical residents, and (3) the ratio of the number of internships or residencies offered in a state to the number of 1950–1959 medical school graduates practicing in the state in 1967. The third variable was used to measure the influence of physicians' desired practice location on their place of internship or residency.

About 56 percent of the variance in the ratio of United States graduates to internships offered was explained by our equation.

[22] The data did not allow for separation of graduates from United States and Canadian schools. Canadian graduates are not considered "foreign" graduates.

TABLE 33
Relative success in filling residencies in United States hospitals, by states, 1966

State*	Number of residencies in state filled by U.S. medical school graduates per 1 million population	Total number of residencies offered by hospitals in state per 1 million population	Ratio of residents in state who graduated from U.S. medical schools to total number of residencies offered by hospitals in state
Minnesota	257.6	365.3	0.71
Massachusetts	188.5	321.1	0.59
New York	181.7	381.7	0.48
Maryland	178.4	313.6	0.57
Colorado	170.9	235.9	0.72
California	147.9	187.3	0.79
Louisiana	144.2	207.3	0.70
Missouri	133.3	260.1	0.51
Pennsylvania	124.3	233.8	0.53
Tennessee	121.2	172.9	0.70
Connecticut	119.4	239.5	0.50
Washington	118.3	150.6	0.79
Michigan	114.3	216.8	0.53
Oregon	112.9	153.5	0.74
Utah	111.2	179.6	0.62
North Carolina	109.9	138.4	0.79
Kansas	106.1	191.6	0.55
Ohio	102.6	220.5	0.47
Texas	100.6	144.6	0.70
Illinois	96.7	193.0	0.50
Georgia	93.3	149.5	0.62
Wisconsin	92.1	160.9	0.57
Virginia	84.1	145.3	0.58
Iowa	82.3	111.3	0.74
Oklahoma	79.1	115.7	0.68
Florida	72.1	132.7	0.54
Nebraska	67.9	101.1	0.67
Arkansas	66.6	92.3	0.72
Kentucky	59.3	119.5	0.50

Percent of residencies in hospitals with medical school affiliation	Percent of residencies in hospitals without medical school affiliation	Weighted average of stipends of residents
41	56	$3,724
73	18	3,590
51	29	4,289
51	27	5,020
42	21	3,921
48	28	4,290
50	4	3,910
69	12	3,887
60	29	3,546
70	23	4,118
36	64	4,142
57	21	3,601
42	46	4,727
62	22	3,242
63	0	3,600
81	11	3,916
47	37	4,107
38	58	4,289
31	39	3,860
72	20	4,159
62	22	3,855
74	15	4,326
64	33	3,458
80	19	4,271
69	15	3,640
56	34	4,277
97	3	4,325
83	13	3,770
67	16	4,134

	Number of residencies in state filled by U.S. medical school graduates per 1 million	Total number of residencies offered by hospitals in state per 1 million	Ratio of residents in state who graduated from U.S. medical schools to total number of residencies offered by hospitals
State*	population	population	in state
Alabama	56.5	94.2	0.60
Indiana	53.3	75.5	0.71
Rhode Island	50.3	159.9	0.31
New Mexico	49.7	104.2	0.48
Mississippi	42.5	58.7	0.72
Arizona	31.1	81.1	0.38
West Virginia	28.1	112.8	0.25
South Carolina	27.4	42.3	0.65
New Jersey	23.5	115.1	0.20

TABLE 33 Relative success in filling residencies in United States hospitals, by states, 1966 (cont'd.)

*Data for 38 states used in regression analysis. These states, in our judgment, had a sufficient number of residencies to give representative results.

Both the percentage of nonaffiliated internships and the ratio of internships to recent graduates practicing in the state were significant with the expected negative sign (Eq. D-7 in Appendix D). The coefficient of the nonaffiliation variable indicated that a percentage-point increase of 10 in that variable would lead to a percentage-point decline of 2.6 in the ratio of United States graduates to internships offered.

About 43 percent of the variance in the ratio of residents graduated from United States medical schools to residencies offered was explained by our equation. The coefficient of the nonaffiliation variable was significant at the 1 percent level. It indicated that a percentage-point increase of 10 in that variable would lead to a percentage-point decline of 3.6 in the ratio of United States graduates to residencies offered (see Eq. D-8 in Appendix D).

Thus, the analysis shows that the relative ability of hospitals in a state to fill their house-staff positions with graduates from United States medical schools is sensitive to the degree that these positions are offered in hospitals affiliated with medical schools. This appears to be more important than the variation in the level of stipends. However, it also appears that the attractiveness of a

Percent of residencies in hospitals with medical school affiliation	*Percent of residencies in hospitals without medical school affiliation*	*Weighted average of stipends of residents*
65	19	4,102
73	20	4,190
1	83	2,700
0	0	4,110
88	6	3,962
0	100	5,789
39	60	4,770
73	25	3,204
17	68	3,830

SOURCES: American Medical Association, 1967, p. 12; *Journal of the American Medical Association,* 1967, p. 812.

state as a place to practice significantly affects the ability of hospitals in that state to attract house staff graduated from United States medical schools.

Analysis of State Support In Chapter 3 we indicated that there had been a substantial increase in state and local government support of the operations of the medical schools. The size of the increase is evidenced by the fact that in 1947, state and local governments and university transfers, combined, provided $25 million, while in 1967, state and local governments alone provided $159 million. In 1947, 9,000 medical students (40 percent of all students) were attending the 29 public four-year schools. By 1967, there were 42 four-year public schools in full operation. They were responsible for 17,800 medical students, who made up 53 percent of the total national medical school student body. Furthermore, 13 of the 15 developing schools are publicly controlled. Thus, it is clear that the state-supported schools have been bearing the burden of most of the expansion in the number of medical students. As has been shown in this chapter, there is considerable variation in the willingness of states to provide support to medical schools (as measured by their provision of direct operating support). The evidence showed that, for 1965, this support varied with the size of population, the rate of growth in population, and the ratio of state and local expenditures to personal income. In addition, the number of public freshman places was inversely related to the number of private freshman places in the state.

It appears that the number of graduates from medical schools in a state does affect the number of physicians practicing in that state, but that the sensitivity of the latter to changes in the former is small. The primary factor affecting the location of new physicians is population change. Those states with substantial population increases attract new physicians, whether or not they are training them. States which have many graduates relative to their population find that a large proportion of the graduates move on to other states. The proportion of students in medical school who are residents of the state will increase the number who will practice in the state, but the size of this effect is not large.

The probable effects of location and expenditure patterns can be categorized in two ways. From an aggregate support viewpoint, states will tend to underrepresent the public demand for medical education. States which lose physicians educated with public support will feel that the costs of attracting additional physicians by increasing the number of places that are subsidized will be greater than the public-support cost required for an addition to the national stock of physicians. This differential rises as the percentage of publicly supported physicians trained in a state who practice in the state declines. At the same time, states which import physicians who are educated in other states make projections of these expected immigrants prior to estimating the number that they must educate in order to reach their planned physician-population ratio.[23] As a result, it is evident that although states use the physician-population ratio to set their standards, states which lose physicians and states with rapid population growth, which therefore gain physicians, would both lag in their support of medical education. The interaction of these behavior patterns will lead to public underinvestment by the states and to the need for a national role.

From an aggregate equity point of view, it may seem unfair that some states who have few graduates relative to their populations

[23] A specific example of this methodology is found in State of California Coordinating Council for Higher Education, 1963, pp. 14–15.

have been able to attract physicians educated in other states. During the period 1950–1959, California, for example, had only 2.5 graduates annually per 100,000 population. Three-fourths of the 1950–1959 graduates practicing there in 1967 had graduated from out-of-state schools. However, there are two offsetting factors to this judgment. A large part of the population growth in rapidly expanding states is brought about by migration from other states. Thus, 44 percent of the growth in California's population between 1955 and 1960 is attributed to net migration from other states (U.S. Bureau of the Census, 1963a). It is, perhaps, equitable for California to attract physicians from other states since, in the first instance, it is attracting the population from other states whom the physicians will serve. Nonetheless, however equitable, it is not likely that states that are losing population will knowingly see fit to educate (and lose) physicians to serve the out-migrating population.

The relationship between population movements and investment expenditures of states is complex, and there has been little study of the best institutional arrangements to take account of these migration patterns. Furthermore, many migrating physicians have been educated in private schools. As a consequence, little or no direct public expenditure for their education was involved. Some states attract a substantial proportion of all graduates from private schools, while others attract very few private school graduates (Table 34). Similarly, the residents of a few states account for a disproportionate percentage of the students attending private schools.

The effects of private schools on the efficiency and equity of state financing leads directly to the question of state support of private schools. The bulk of state support of operational expenditures is provided to public schools. However, several states do provide substantial support to private medical schools, and other states are giving consideration to the provision of such support (a discussion of various state programs of assistance is presented in Appendix E).

State subsidization of private medical schools is a very complex issue. In a number of states there may be legal questions in the provision of such subsidies. It is also clear that most states will undertake such financing primarily in order to increase the number of new graduates who eventually practice in the states. One possible result of this focus is that state aid to private schools may

TABLE 34 *Proportion of medical education in United States borne by private medical schools, by states, 1967*

State	Percent of all private medical school freshmen enrollees in 1967 who were residents of the state	Percent of 1950–1959 graduates from private medical schools who were located in state in 1967	Percent of U.S. population in state in 1967
Alabama	0.5	0.9	1.8
Arizona	0.5	0.8	0.8
Arkansas	0.1	0.2	1.0
California	7.0	15.2	9.7
Colorado	0.5	1.2	1.0
Connecticut	2.3	2.6	1.5
Delaware	0.3	0.3	0.3
District of Columbia	1.2	1.5	0.4
Florida	3.5	4.3	3.0
Georgia	1.3	1.7	2.3
Idaho	0.1	0.2	0.4
Illinois	6.9	3.9	5.5
Indiana	0.8	1.0	2.5
Iowa	0.6	0.6	1.4
Kansas	0.2	0.4	1.1
Kentucky	1.9	2.1	1.6
Louisiana	1.0	1.2	1.9
Maine	0.3	0.4	0.5
Maryland	2.3	2.8	1.9
Massachusetts	4.3	5.1	2.7
Michigan	1.2	1.9	4.3
Minnesota	0.8	1.2	1.8
Mississippi	0.6	0.8	1.2
Missouri	1.5	2.3	2.3
Montana	0.3	0.3	0.4
Nebraska	0.7	0.4	0.7
Nevada	0.1	0.2	0.2
New Hampshire	0.1	0.4	0.3
New Jersey	7.4	4.3	3.5
New Mexico	0.3	0.4	0.5
New York	20.7	11.6	9.3
North Carolina	1.4	2.6	2.5

State	Percent of all private medical school freshmen enrollees in 1967 who were residents of the state	Percent of 1950-1959 graduates from private medical schools who were located in state in 1967	Percent of U.S. population in state in 1967
North Dakota	0.1	0.2	0.3
Ohio	3.9	3.9	5.3
Oklahoma	0.4	0.4	1.3
Oregon	0.6	0.7	1.0
Pennsylvania	13.3	9.5	5.9
Rhode Island	0.6	0.5	0.5
South Carolina	0.6	0.5	1.3
South Dakota	0.2	0.2	0.3
Tennessee	1.0	1.2	2.0
Texas	2.0	3.8	5.5
Utah	0.4	0.4	0.5
Vermont	0.1	0.2	0.2
Virginia	1.4	1.3	2.3
Washington	0.8	1.6	1.6
West Virginia	0.3	0.4	0.9
Wisconsin	1.6	2.1	2.1
Wyoming	0.1	0.1	0.2

SOURCES: *Journal of the American Medical Association,* 1968, pp. 2094–2095; Theodore, Sutter, & Haug, 1968, table 7; *Statistical Abstract of the United States, 1968,* p. 12.

lead either to direct restriction on the state of residence of entrants or to the introduction of strong incentives that favor entrants from the particular state. This is a rational move by the state—although based on a narrow perspective—since often the migration patterns of graduates from private medical schools are such that the expense involved in a general subsidy by the state for every student would appear prohibitive when calculated as a subsidy per graduate eventually settling in the state. However, residence restrictions conflict with one of the major advantages of most private institutions—their nondiscrimination with regard to applicants on the basis of residence. Furthermore, if state support is not accompanied by reduction in tuition or substantial scholarship support, it is likely that children with wealthy parents will derive the benefits of the subsidization, since poor families cannot afford to pay the high tuition charges of private medical schools or meet the other costs (including opportunity costs) of attendance.

Nevertheless, conditions may be such that state support of private schools is preferable to the introduction of new public schools. It may be less costly, in terms of total costs, to expand existing schools than to introduce new ones. Furthermore, if a private medical school is in such dire straits that it may be forced to close or reduce its quality (as, indeed, may have been the case with some of the schools now receiving state support), the state may find that the marginal investment needed to keep the educational output at the same level is worthwhile. Faced with the alternatives of starting a new public school, taking over an existing private school and making it public, or giving incremental aid to private institutions, the state may find that from its point of view, the latter represents the most efficient solution.

Additional conditions call for state support for medical education. The benefits which are likely to accrue to the residents of a state, besides the attraction of future physicians, must be considered. As shown, medical school affiliation helps hospitals attract interns and residents. State support of medical education may also attract to the academic institution (that is, medical school and teaching hospital) highly skilled and specialized physicians who prefer an academic atmosphere. Both factors may raise the quality of medical care available to the population. This is particularly true if there is no medical school in the geographic area. Finally, as demonstrated, the number of residents from a state who enter medical school is positively correlated with the number of medical school openings. However, the number of residents who are able to attend medical school is small, and as a result it is not likely that citizens of a state would support medical education solely on the basis of this factor. More important may be the rationale provided for support for places for students from socioeconomic groups not now adequately represented in medical schools. Though their number, too, may be small, the benefits to society associated with substantial percentage increases in such enrollments may be quite large.

It is also true that our regression analysis indicates *average incremental* relationships. Our analysis does not indicate what might occur when a state without any school opens its first medical school. Furthermore, although "on the average" a 10 percent increase in the number of resident graduates leads to only a 3.2

percent increase in the number of graduates locating in the state, a particular state may feel that it will fare better. It may also believe that future relationships would differ from those of the past. In either of the last two cases, the state would, we believe, have to have some reason to believe that average relationships were not applicable to its special circumstances, such as offering a new type of program of medical education or a new pattern of medical care delivery.

Nonetheless, the relationships found and the arguments deduced suggest that the level of state support for medical education is, from the national perspective, inadequate. States have a tendency to underinvest in medical education. Given the national nature of medical education, which results from the migration of population and of physicians; given the goal of equal educational opportunity for students from all socioeconomic groups (and the fact that states with large numbers of low-income students have inadequate resources to meet the goal); and given the nature of federal as contrasted with state taxes and the fact that the tax burden is distributed in a more progressive fashion at the federal level (a matter discussed more fully in Chapter 6), the need for a federal role in medical education seems clear.

6. *Federal Aid to Medical Education*

Executive and congressional decisions with regard to federal aid to medical education have evolved within a framework dominated by studies indicating national shortages in the number of physicians being educated and weaknesses in the financial position of medical schools, by rapid changes in the nature of medicine and its scientific base and thrust, and by strong pressures by professional groups within organized medicine.

Consideration of the extent and form of the national role in supporting medical education requires an assessment of the various arguments for federal assistance and of the costs and benefits of alternative courses of action.

COSTS FOR RESOURCE EXPANSION We shall review the national studies regarding the shortage of physicians and the arguments and empirical evidence offered in support of federal assistance. This will require a discussion of the kinds of costs for resource expansion that must be considered in increasing the number of available spaces in medical schools and a brief discussion of other bases for federal support and of the progressivity and regressivity of state-local and federal tax structures. In the second part of the chapter we shall examine existing federal programs of direct and indirect federal assistance to medical education and their development.

Increasing Resources for Physician Education Underinvestment in medical education will be reflected in the annual graduation of a less-than-optimum number of physicians and/or in suboptimum quality of education and training. In order to make decisions concerning the national effort and federal role in medical education, the magnitude of the benefits expected from an increased number of graduating physicians or improved education and training programs should be compared with the real costs involved in making such changes. Unfortunately, the benefits which would accrue from improved training and education cannot easily be measured, and precise estimates of the costs are not available. Judgments with respect to the benefits from additions to the stock of physicians must rely on imprecise indicators of the value of, and need for, the increased services which additional physicians would provide.[1] These indicators include increases in the relative incomes of physicians, increases in the relative prices of physicians' services, long waits for physician services, increasing use of emergency rooms in hospitals for nonemergency services, reports of inability to obtain physician services at the going price for such services, vacancies in a large number of internships and residencies, and the admission of large numbers of graduates of foreign medical schools to practice in the United States. Though each of these bits and pieces of evidence has its own shortcomings, collectively they suggest both a maldistribution and inadequate supply of health manpower.

Our knowledge of the incremental costs involved in educating additional physicians (and particularly physicians with different levels of skills with which to assume different responsibilities) is equally unclear. Analysis is also complicated by the fact that expansion can be brought about either by expanding existing schools or by creating new schools (furthermore, the latter may be either two- or four-year institutions). Incremental costs are likely to be substantially different in the various institutions.[2] These costs are the value of the alternative production that society must forgo in order to educate the additional physicians. They include the value of incremental faculty time, the value of capital, and the net value of the potential production of the student in his next most productive occupation.

While the subsequent discussion of costs assumes that educating additional physicians requires the expansion of freshman admis-

[1] These estimates in turn require judgments as to where the physicians would practice and whom they would serve. Such matters would be affected by possible changes in the methods of financing medical care and in the delivery system and its organization (see Butter, 1967; Esposito, 1968; Fein, 1967; Sloan, 1968).

[2] If new schools are responsible for only the first two years, the older schools will have to increase the size of their third- and fourth-year classes. However, it is often suggested that clinical facilities are already available for this expansion.

sions, the reduction of attrition may be an alternative to some of the expansion. During the past six years, an average of 11.0 percent of medical students have graduated four years after entering medical school. However, the percentage declined from 12.7 percent for the class entering in 1961 to 8.0 percent for the class entering in 1965. A further reduction of 50 percent in the latter rate could lead to an annual increase in graduates of about 400 students, equivalent to four schools with class sizes of 112 students. This may be difficult to achieve since less than half the students who were not promoted with their classes in 1968–69 failed to be promoted because of academic reasons, and about 16 percent temporarily withdrew to pursue advanced study. To achieve a major reduction requires improvement in the quality of students entering schools with high attrition rates and increased counseling and tutoring resources. Information on the direct costs involved in changing the level of attrition, or on the effects of this type of expansion on the other operating costs of the medical school, is unavailable. Another alternative for the short-term expansion of graduates involves reducing the length of medical education (for example, from four years for the medical degree to three years), which can provide one-time expansion in the flow of new physicians. The advantages and disadvantages of such possible reductions are usually discussed in terms of the impact on the quality of the future physician. Cost data and estimates are lacking.

FACULTY COSTS In some medical schools the number of students studying for the M.D. could be increased perhaps by 10 percent without substantial increased demands upon faculty time and with only slight changes in costs. In fact, institutions have expanded their enrollments by such percentages and have found that virtually the only impact was on the capital budget for remodeling of space and purchase of equipment. Further, given tuition payments by students, expansion may have enabled schools to increase their nonsponsored funds. Many schools, over the years, have added significant numbers of graduate students in the basic sciences (with relatively little planning going into such expansion), even as they have argued that

The benefits of various expansion programs may also differ. As previously noted, a new medical school may help raise the general level of health care in the surrounding area. The degree to which this occurs would, however, depend upon the location of the school in question.

they were unable to finance any expansion of the number of students seeking the M.D. Nevertheless, significant increases in all probability cannot be absorbed. They are likely to lead to additional teaching requirements.[3]

Faculty time devoted to teaching more students could be taken from the time that faculty members currently spend on research efforts and on the provision of services. It could also be found by attracting qualified personnel from other research environments and from private practice of medicine who could devote some of their time to teaching.[4] The incremental faculty costs associated with additional students would therefore be equal to the value of research and services provided prior to expansion of enrollment minus the value produced after expansion. Since a significant number of medical school faculty members have little or no current teaching responsibilities, it may be possible to increase faculty teaching efforts at relatively little dollar cost, but the real cost would depend on the value of the research efforts forgone.[5] The temptation may be to overvalue research because of the relative ease with which it can be funded and because of the prestige attached to the research effort. However, there are times when the value of the research effort, because of both time preferences and estimates of the probability of success, is difficult to assess. The research results are likely to be available in the future, or the research effort may fail. Conversely, medical care services are available today and appear more "real" than the uncertain research effort. Even medical education is seen as certain of success; that is, physicians are educated, and the supply of services in the near

[3] We assume no significant change in the use of programmed instruction material or other changes in educational methods that would reduce the need for teachers.

[4] The services provided at the medical school and hospital by faculty are of a different kind from those which the faculty would provide as private practitioners. The degree of difference is dependent to some extent on the field of specialization of the physician. In general, however, the services provided by faculty are more specialized and involve "unusual" cases which are referred by other physicians and which often require considerable time.

[5] The productivity of the research effort is a major unknown. A 10 percent reduction in hours devoted to research is associated in an unknown way with output. Furthermore, it is not at all clear that those who do not teach should be doing so. There is more to teaching than standing before students for a given number of hours. It may be that those who do no teaching would make poor teachers. The dimensions of the problem are illustrated, however, by a 1968 survey of 344 full-time medical faculty members which found that 12 percent taught no courses (see Goldberg, 1969, pp. 61–62).

future is increased. The same time-preference considerations also apply to the choice between an increase in services *today* and an increase in the number of physicians for the *future.*

Thus, a difficult choice is involved if the medical school faculty is to be expanded by attracting additional physicians from the practice of medicine. These individuals provide services which are valued highly by society. It is difficult to strike a balance between the visible services provided today and the larger number of services that would be available in the future as a result of the additional physicians trained. Whether resources should be used for consumption or investment purposes is the issue. In considering these matters, decision makers would be aided immeasurably by having greater knowledge and understanding of the production function for medical education, the alternative ways that physicians can be educated, and the substitution possible among the various inputs.

The faculty is a critical element in producing new physicians, but the optimum faculty-student ratio is not clear. The number of full-time faculty members per medical student is quite different from, and much higher than, the number of faculty members per student in other parts of the university. In the period 1960–1968, the faculty member–medical student ratio dropped from 1 to 2.7 to 1 to 1.6. How much of this drop (that is, the increase in the number of faculty members per student) resulted from the need to transmit more knowledge, from the belief that there is a more than proportionate increase in learning associated with this increase, from the increased emphasis on the training of graduate students (non-M.D. candidates), or from the increased funding of research is unknown. The validity of projections into the future is therefore quite debatable. If the ratio (about 1 to 1.6, with 70 percent of the full-time faculty members holding M.D. degrees) were to remain stable, the tentative plans for an increase of about 8,000 medical students by 1975 would require an increase of about 5,000 faculty members, with about 3,500 holding M.D. degrees.[6] This can

---

[6] The Hubbard-Anlyan data (Chap. 5, Table 28) indicate that about 11,500 M.D. candidates will enter medical schools in 1975, as compared with 9,700 in 1968–69. Using estimated transition probabilities, we projected a total of 42,600 medical students in the same year. The Hubbard-Anlyan data indicated about the same increases each year through 1972 as those published in the 1968 education issue of the *Journal of the American Medical Association* (1968, p. 2013) (1972 was the last year included in the latter).

Both of the above surveys were made prior to the announcement of the Physician Augmentation Program under the Health Manpower Act of 1968.

be compared with an increase of over 8,000 full-time faculty members between 1960 and 1966 (including an increase of 6,650 with M.D. degrees). The 1960–1966 faculty increase was associated with an increase of only 3,135 students; thus most of the growth in faculty went into a significant increase in the number of faculty members per student. If this trend were to end, the faculty increase needed by 1975 would be manageable (at least as compared with the problems created in the period 1960–1966). However, there was an increase of 3,000 faculty members between 1966 and 1967, which indicates that the trend continues. It may be altered, however, by the severe stringency in the early 1970s in the federal budget for health research and by the impact of inflation on these limited dollars available.

It should be clear that—to the extent that the increase in faculty is not associated with, or necessary for, the education of M.D. students—this increase can in fact be substantially influenced by the funding policies followed by the federal government. If research dollars are available and educational dollars are lacking, medical schools will expand their research faculties. If they are able to obtain one full-time teacher by funding (with federal assistance) five research persons, each of whom spends 20 percent of his time teaching, they will do so. They may plead with legislatures and cajole alumni to give them funds to do the things that they would like to do. Yet, in the absence of such support, they will accept earmarked dollars since the things to be done with them are also considered of value. So it is that the direction of the schools, the growth of faculty, and the costs associated with that growth can and will be influenced by the level and kind of financial aid available to the schools themselves.

CAPITAL
COSTS
A substantial expansion in the student body will require more than additional faculty. Additional capital goods, equipment, buildings, and land will also be required.[7] The value of the alternative uses

---

This program is to provide support for the addition of 4,000 first-year places in schools of medicine and osteopathic medicine over the next four years, commencing with the addition of 1,000 in the fall term of 1970. There is some question whether the funds being made available will be able to induce expansion beyond the numbers already planned.

[7] Some innovative attempts are being made to reduce the use of capital goods in expansion. For example, George Washington University has developed a plan for expansion through double scheduling whereby each class would be admitted in two divisions, thus permitting substantial increases in class size

of buildings, equipment, and land is probably fairly well represented in the monetary costs that the schools are required to pay for them.[8] Regardless of the type of structure and location, building costs are considerable.[9] Often, therefore, medical educators find that their inability to fund construction, particularly of basic science facilities, is the principle obstacle to expansion. The need for clinical facilities, conversely, sometimes represents a less severe obstacle since (1) financial resources other than those earmarked for medical education may be used for their construction, (2) existing affiliated hospitals may be able to expand their educational and training programs, and (3) unaffiliated hospitals are often interested in developing an affiliation with existing or new medical schools. Because of specific differences in existing plants, in clinical needs, in planned functions, and in construction prices, capital construction costs can be estimated only on the basis of well-defined plans. They also depend upon such matters as the presence of clinical facilities, the depth of the research commitment, the degree of involvement in residency and house-staff training, and the size of the graduate training program in the basic sciences.

STUDENT COSTS

An additional cost involved in expansion of medical education is the opportunity cost connected with the student himself. Opportunity costs arise because students allocate their time to formal education rather than to current production or because they study medicine rather than pursuing other graduate programs. The value of students' production in other possible occupations must be

---

without the building of new teaching facilities and without a significant increase in clinical facilities (Peery, 1969). Other innovative expansion plans intend to use facilities available at regular university sites for part of the M.D. training, (Grove, n.d., Penrod & Irwin, 1966). It is not clear whether the use of the facilities for M.D. training would replace other uses of the facilities.

[8] Yet even in the case of capital resources there are problems of valuation. Land use in particular, presents such problems since the cost generally does not adequately reflect the value to society of open space or parks. Similarly, the social value of a neighborhood or community is not reflected in the monetary value of the housing.

[9] Total capital costs ranged from $11.9 million for a developing school utilizing some existing facilities to $77.7 million for another developing school (Smythe, 1967, p. 999). Smythe reported capital costs per square foot for developing medical schools which varied from $30.65 to $66.03 (1967, p. 999). A March, 1968, comparison of building cost indexes in 22 cities showed a range from 623 in Birmingham, Ala., to 852 in New York City ("Engineering News-Record Building Cost Indexes," 1968, p. 21).

considered when deciding whether to take national actions to increase the number of capable students studying medicine.[10] However, while opportunity costs will affect the student body, the selection process, and the socioeconomic characteristics of those who apply to an institution—and while these are matters of social concern—they do not represent out-of-pocket expenses to the school itself. Deans and legislators may wring their hands over the implications of these costs, but wringing of hands is relatively easy. It is the writing of checks that is hard. Opportunity costs do not enter medical school budgets. It is the capital and the operating expenses, therefore, that concern school officials on a continuing basis.[11]

IMPROVING EQUALITY OF OPPORTUNITY AND THE DISTRIBUTION OF PHYSICIANS

The national interest in providing equality of opportunity for persons of all income classes to attend medical school and in improving the distribution of physicians also affects the desired form, as well as the amount, of assistance provided by the federal government to medical education.

Chapter 4 showed that in 1967 almost two-thirds of all students seeking the M.D. degree came from families with incomes over $10,000, although only one-third of all families had incomes over that amount. Even though publicly controlled schools did not have as disproportionate a number of upper-income students as private schools (in publicly controlled schools 60 percent of the students came from families with incomes over $10,000 while this was true of 67 percent of the students in private schools), the bias in favor of students from wealthier families did exist. The disproportionate representation of low-income students is a result of a number of factors affecting the distribution of persons who apply for admission to medical school. But—to the extent that the distribution problem results from the student's inability to finance his education—state subsidies in the form of lower tuition may be

---

[10] Changes in curricula which reduce the time required after secondary school to become a practicing physician will reduce student opportunity costs and thus social costs.

[11] Just as the capital requirements vary, so also do the average annual operating costs. A recent attempt, based upon faculty-time allocation, to develop a methodology to estimate the costs of various programs at seven medical centers indicated a range from $2,800 to $4,300 per student for programs leading to the M.D. degree and from $5,300 to $9,100 for internship and residency programs (Association of American Medical Colleges, 1969, pp. 28, 30). See Appendix B for a discussion of this procedure.

helpful but also insufficient. Indeed, lower tuition may be of far more benefit to middle-income students than to low-income students.

Since much of the private cost of medical education takes the form of forgone earnings, students from poor families have difficulty supporting themselves and meeting any existing family obligations, even when tuition is low. Thus, the effective reduction in the cost of medical education via a reduction in tuition may be sufficient to enable many middle-income students to attend medical school, even while it is insufficient to enable low-income students to apply. This, of course, does not argue against state aid and scholarships. Rather, it suggests that *substantial* aid (over and above low tuition) is needed if low-income students are to attend medical school, that is, if the goal of equality of opportunity is to be achieved. Further, however, it indicates the need for a federal role since the poorer states (given their economic resources and the fact that it is those states which have a higher proportion of low-income applicants and students) would find it extremely difficult to provide sufficient aid.

Another reason often advanced for national action is the need to overcome the extreme differences in the physician-population ratio between the states. Although we have indicated the weaknesses in the physician-population ratio as a measure of the comparative adequacy in the supply of physician services available in relation to the need for such services, the extreme differences that exist in the various states are evidence of maldistribution and are ample reason for concern. A variety of possible actions might be taken that would affect the geographic distribution of physicians. It is not clear that the most direct or effective action would involve a role for the federal government in medical education. Nonetheless, though medical education may not represent the most direct way to attack the distribution problem, the federal government should be concerned that its aid to medical schools not compound the distribution problem and that as far as possible, and consistent with other goals, it help reduce its magnitude.

As shown earlier, the location of medical school facilities has a small, but significant, effect upon the ability of states to attract physicians, both because of the possibility that graduates will locate in the same state in which they attended medical school and because an area with high-quality facilities and internship and residency programs is attractive to physicians. Thus, given a decision to subsidize the expansion of medical education through national action, incentives might be given to locate the expansion in selected states so that some improvement in physician-population ratios might be induced.[12] If national aid is channeled to students, incentives through bonus grants, forgiveness clauses on loans, or alternatives to military service can be used in an attempt to alter location preferences.

The alternatives are numerous. The federal government (and others) could provide subsidies and bonuses to physicians who practice in the states with the greatest shortages. It could assist in providing improvements in medical facilities and could help organize better practice situations in an effort to make practice in certain states more attractive and rewarding (in a professional sense). It could attempt to increase the effective demand for physician services through support of medical care purchases. It could more heavily subsidize intern and residency programs in some states. The effectiveness and efficiency of these and other alternatives would depend upon many factors, including the behavior patterns and responses of the individuals affected.[13]

A detailed exploration of the wide range of issues involved in the geographic distribution of physicians and the various alternatives that could be utilized to affect the characteristics of the medical care delivery system is beyond the scope of this study. It is clear, however, that the variation in the distribution of physicians has not been modified to any great extent through national or special state programs.[14] Medical schools can perhaps reduce this variation by helping design models of care and communication systems which

---

[12] This policy is roundabout, and one must recognize that it may be only of limited effectiveness. This consideration is particularly important because the goal of expansion must meet other objectives as well: the largest amount of expansion per dollar expended, high-quality medical education, and so forth.

[13] Thus far the evidence on the causal relationships that produce the geographic distribution pattern is not fully clear, and we are not able to judge the contribution that each of the many factors makes to physician location decisions. In the absence of such knowledge the impact that a given change in one of the variables will have on the distribution of physicians cannot be assessed. The one thing that is clear, of course, is that the number of physicians per capita tends to be highest in those states with the highest per capita income. For empirical analyses of physician location patterns, see Benham, Maurizi, & Reder, 1968, pp. 332–347; Sloan, 1968, pp. 355–405.

[14] The coefficient of variation (ratio of standard deviation to the mean) of total physicians per 100,000 population was 0.25 in 1949 and 0.27 in 1967. The coefficient of variation of private-practice physicians per 100,000 population did decline from 0.23 to 0.20 in the same period.

will show physicians how to function far away from a sophisticated medical base and which will make such a practice more rewarding. Medical education and educators should make what contributions they can, but policies to assist medical education need not be justified on the basis of possible desirable impacts on geographic distribution. The other grounds for federal assistance are sufficient.

EQUITY BETWEEN BENEFITS AND PAYMENTS The role played by the federal government in support of medical education will affect the benefits and burdens which accrue to particular individuals and to different income classes. Increased general subsidization of the four years at medical school or increased stipends during the internship and residency will increase the private internal rate of return to the future physician unless it is associated with an expansion of the number of physicians large enough to reduce future relative incomes of the medical profession. Federal government support of the intern and resident would redistribute the burden now placed on private patients and third-party payees who today help finance educational costs at the small proportion of hospitals with extensive graduate training programs. Furthermore, an enlarged federal role, as contrasted with increased state roles, in support of medical education would alter the distribution of the tax burden.

Federal tax dollars are collected from the various income groups in different proportions from those in which state tax dollars are collected. The relatively progressive nature of the federal tax structure, as compared with state and local tax structures, means that an increase in federal rather than state support would place a relatively larger burden on higher-income groups. In general, students with parents in these income groups receive the greater part of the direct benefits from public subsidization of medical education. A shift of the tax burden to these income groups can therefore hardly be faulted on grounds of inequity. Using an analysis developed by Ott (n.d.) of the burden of various types of taxes on different income groups, we estimate that in 1965, families with incomes above $10,000 paid 46 percent of state income taxes and state sales taxes[15] but that 60 percent of students from families with those incomes attended public (primarily state-supported) medical schools in 1967. Families with incomes under $6,000 paid 27 percent of state income and sales taxes. This compares with the 10 percent of the students attending public medical schools in 1967

[15] If the burden of state corporate profit taxes and inheritance and gift taxes are included, families with incomes above $10,000 paid 51 percent of state taxes.

who came from families with incomes under $5,000. On the other hand, these estimates indicate that 69 percent of federal taxes were paid by families with incomes over $10,000 in 1965 while 12 percent of those taxes were paid by families with incomes below $6,000 (Ott, n.d., table 3). The fact that students are drawn from upper-income groups and that, in any case, when they become physicians they will be high-income earners strengthens the argument that any assistance offered should come from tax revenues raised in the most progressive fashion (that is, by the federal government).

EXISTING FEDERAL PROGRAMS The federal programs which have been developed to aid medical education can be separated into those which give direct aid to medical *education* and those which support research and services and indirectly benefit the medical education role of the medical schools and teaching hospitals. It will be useful to review the findings and recommendations of some of the studies calling for federal assistance and to take a brief look at the historic development of legislation prior to our discussion of the existing federal programs.

Federal Government Studies Two decades ago the 1950 study of the Surgeon General's Committee on Medical School Grants and Finances concluded:

No matter what problems confront research in medical schools, they fade in the presence of the acute and dangerous general financial stringency faced by the schools. The research function is more adequately supported than the teaching function. But this disparity itself creates serious problems. . . . But, as we reviewed the research picture, it became increasingly clear that general financial assistance, regardless of the source of aid, is the overriding need of medical schools (U.S. Federal Security Agency, Public Health Service, 1951a, p. 45).

The report of the President's Commission on the Health Needs of the Nation in 1952 made six estimates of physician requirements for 1960, which, combined with projections of the physician stock, led to predicted shortages of zero to 59,000 (Fein, 1967, pp. 8–11). It also concluded: "Hence, at the very time that medical schools are being pressed to train more physicians, they find it harder than ever to obtain the necessary funds" (The President's Commission on the Health Needs of the Nation, 1952, p. 14).

Some specific characteristics of the medical schools which alarmed the Commission were:

Deterioration of the physical plant, with insufficient funds for needed modernization. . . .

Inability to expand enrollment to meet the growing need because such expansion without adequate financial means would lead to lower standards of professional education.

Increasingly high tuition charges and rising cost of living for students which, with inadequate scholarship funds, mean that undertaking the study of medicine is increasingly more difficult for young people with limited financial resources. . . .

Reliance on research funds to support teaching personnel, so that the primary educational objective is threatened (pp. 14–15).

The Commission concluded:

The People as a Nation as well as individuals, benefit from the graduates of both private and State schools. No medical school today performs a purely local function; its graduates practice in many States, and an increasing number are called into Federal service. Medical schools can be located only in certain areas where proper training resources exist and not according to State political areas. The schools must now pay about three-fourths of the total cost of education. Hence, the Federal government should be prepared to assist both private and State schools whenever necessary (p. 15).

The third national study of relevance was published by the Surgeon General's Consultant Group on Medical Education (the Bane report) in 1959. This study concluded that there was a need for 11,000 medical school graduates per year by 1975.[16] Its recommendation with respect to the need for better support of medical students, general operations and research, and construction of medical schools included a number of suggestions of direct relevance to the federal role:

The Federal Government should establish educational grants-in-aid for medical students on the basis of merit and need, similar in value and proportionate in number to grants now made to graduate students in other fields of specialization. These educational grants should be available to students so that they could attend a medical school any place in the United States.

[16] At the time about 7,000 physicians were being graduated annually (see Fein, 1967, pp. 11–12, for a critique of this calculation).

Greater attention must be given to the problems of existing schools whose educational plants or programs are now inadequately financed.

The continuation of training grants, the payment of full indirect costs for research, and the development of Federal institutional research grants which would make possible greater stability and flexibility of research, would seem to be the best contributions of the Federal Government at this time.

The Federal Government over a period of the next 10 years should appropriate funds on a matching basis to meet construction needs for medical education, which include: expanding and improving existing schools, construction of new schools of basic medical sciences, construction of new 4-year medical schools, and construction of the necessary teaching hospitals.

Programs for the construction of teaching, research, and clinical facilities should operate within a common administrative framework in order to ensure proper balance in the planning and construction of facilities, uniformity of administrative methodology and practice, and program coordination *(Physicians for a Growing America,* 1959, pp. 59, 61, 62, 63–64).

Several other general suggestions were applicable to federal policy:

The cost of care of indigents should not be charged to the medical school budget. Medical schools should be reimbursed for or relieved of the expense of professional services rendered by the faculty.

The growing magnitude of sponsored research requires full reimbursement for indirect costs, to protect the basic operations of schools of medicine (p. 62).

More recently, the report of the Panel on Education and Supply of the National Advisory Commission on Health Manpower made the following suggestions with respect to the federal role:

1 That a federally administered program be developed which would allow health manpower students to distribute the cost of their education over the period of their income-producing life *(Report of the National Advisory Commission on Health Manpower,* 1967, p. 36). [17]

2 That, as a matter of basic policy, all Federal funds made available to health manpower schools for restricted or specific purposes should include the entire cost (direct as well as indirect) of the programs that they are intended to support.

---

[17] This recommendation resembles that of the Panel on Educational Innovation for an Educational Opportunity Bank plan (see *Educational Opportunity Bank,* 1967). We shall discuss this type of plan in Chap. 7.

3 That general institutional support grants, containing no restrictions as to use, be made to health professional schools (medical, dental, nursing, and pharmacy) up to a level commensurate with the need for maintaining existing programs as well as for planning and implementing new programs (p. 38).

Proposals for Federal Direct Aid

As early as 1949, major legislation was proposed in Congress to provide federal funds in support of medical education. These bills introduced the general types of programs which were to be considered during the next two decades. They included incentive plans for stimulating increased enrollments in medical schools through support of operational expenditures, construction grants for the establishment of new schools and for the expansion of existing facilities, and federal subsidies for scholarship assistance. (In our discussion, we have relied heavily on the analysis presented in Rayack, 1967.) One of these bills was unanimously approved by the Senate Committee on Labor and Public Welfare in August and unanimously passed by a voice vote of the Senate on September 23, 1949. This bill, S. 1453, would have provided for:

1 Payments to medical schools of $500 for each student enrolled up to a school's average past enrollment and $1,000 for each student enrolled in excess of average past enrollment. The latter payment would be limited to a 30 percent increase, and no payment to any school could exceed 30 percent of the school's budget, with the exception of new schools.

2 Five million dollars annually for grants for the construction of new schools for the health professions and for the improvement and expansion of existing schools.

3 Scholarships to be provided if the medical schools were unable to fill their enrollments with students who did not need such aid.

However, the companion bill in the House died in the House Rules Committee as the session of Congress ended.

Similar bills were introduced during the next 12 years, but did not proceed very far. Some, such as S. 1323 in 1955, concentrated only on construction grants. Others, such as S. 434, also provided for operational expenses. Finally, late in 1963, Congress passed the Health Professions Educational Assistance Act, which made construction grants available for educational facilities and loans for students. Amendments to this act in 1965 authorized a four-year program of operational aid in the form of basic and special improvement grants and also provided for a student scholarship program. Most recently, the Health Manpower Act of 1968 amended legislation dealing with direct federal aid. The current programs will be reviewed in detail in the next section.

While congressional decisions are affected by many factors, there is little doubt that professional associations can and do influence legislation dealing with their professions both through lobbying activities and in their role as technical advisers. A review of the attitudes of the American Medical Association (AMA)[18] and the Association of American Medical Colleges (AAMC) toward federal support of medical education is of particular relevance because of their possible implications for the future. Until 1968, the two associations held widely differing points of view concerning federal aid to medical education. Then they took the following common positions in their joint statement on health manpower:

Federal support for the educational component of medical center activity should be further encouraged. The full sums of money authorized under existing legislation should be appropriated. . . . Passage of the Health Manpower Act of 1968, which provides for funding for construction, operation and educational innovation in medical centers, is being strongly advocated by both Associations (*Journal of Medical Education,* 1968b, p. 1010).

The position statements of the AMA and the AAMC as presented in statements before congressional committees, in their professional journals, and in their reports provide an overview of the general tenor of their views (although there were frequent inconsistencies in statements made at different times). The AMA professed a general skepticism toward federal assistance, arguing that the academic freedom of the medical schools might be jeopardized.[19] It particularly opposed, on two grounds, the expansion incentive feature incorporated into much federal aid. First, it contended that the incentives for expansion would lead to a deterioration of medical standards (Rayack, 1967), and second, it questioned the evidence that a doctor shortage existed (pp. 82–86, 91–93). In

---

[18] The AMA was the leading lobbyist in spending in 1949 ($1.5 million), 1950 ($1.3 million), and 1961 ($163,000) and has been among the top lobby spenders (expenditures greater than $49,500) in 12 of the 17 years between 1946 and 1963 (see *Legislators and the Lobbyists,* n.d., pp. 31–37).

[19] See Rayack, 1967, pp. 88–89, 96; and the June, 1949, and December, 1950, positions of the AMA, recorded in American Medical Association, 1959, pp. 209–210.

June 1951 it stated the policy which was to be the basis for its approach to federal aid to medical schools:

The policy of the American Medical Association shall be the endorsement of the principle of a one-time federal grant-in-aid on a matching basis, based on the Hill-Burton Act formula and administrative machinery, for construction, equipment, and renovation of the physical plants of medical schools. No part of the funds shall be used in any manner for operational expenses or salaries (American Medical Association, 1959).

Nonetheless, the AMA specifically opposed the enactment of the Health Professions Educational Assistance Act of 1963 (which, as indicated, provided for grants for construction and loans for students).

In contrast, the AAMC has generally exhibited a more favorable attitude toward federal aid, although its positive attitude toward expansion of such aid has not always been as strong as it apparently is at present. In 1949 the AAMC stated that there was a definite need for federal aid, provided that the educational and administrative policies could continue to rest in the hands of the medical colleges and that incentives for new students should not be so attractive as to cause expansion beyond facilities at too rapid a rate (Rayack, 1967, pp. 82–83). In 1955, however, in discussing a bill then before Congress with an incentive section providing for a higher share of construction costs to be borne by the federal government if the school promised to increase enrollment by 5 percent, the AAMC held that the "incentive . . . will be a wholesome stimulus to the medical schools to expand as rapidly as possible without sacrificing the quality of their work" (Rayack, 1967, p. 92). And in 1962, AAMC representatives testified before Congress that, "we must in the short span of the next eight or nine years create facilities for an additional 4,000 students, or put another way, we must in a decade or less increase by 50 percent facilities that required nearly 200 years of private effort to establish" (Rayack, 1967, p. 96). They also strongly supported federal scholarship money for medical students. Even though the AAMC position has generally been supportive of federal aid for medical schools, much of the federal legislation that has affected medical schools has been developed and designed without the active participation of the AAMC or medical schools. They were generally reluctant to engage in such endeavors.

Current Federal Programs of Direct Aid At the present time direct federal aid is provided through five programs: institutional grants, special project grants, construction aid, loans to students, and scholarships to students.[20]

Institutional grants

Totaling $21 million for fiscal year 1969, institutional grants are distributed in the following manner. Each school receives $25,000, and of the remaining funds, 75 percent is distributed on the basis of (1) the relative number of full-time students in the given year and (2) the relative increase in enrollment of such students in the given year over the average enrollment of such students for the five school years preceding the year for which the application is made. The amount per full-time student is such that a school receives twice as much for each student in the increase as for other full-time students. The remaining 25 percent of the funds is distributed on the basis of the relative number of graduates in the given year. In order to be eligible for the basic improvement grants, each school must give reasonable assurance that it will expand its first-year enrollment by 2.5 percent above the average first-year enrollment' for the two school years having the highest such enrollment during the five school years from July, 1963, to June, 1968, or by five students, whichever is greater. The largest sum received by a single medical school under this program in 1969 was $471,000.

Special project grants

Totaling $19.8 million in FY1969, special project grants are given to assist schools in meeting the cost of new fiscal year projects or modifications of existing programs, to improve curricula, to support research related to education in the health professions, to develop training for new levels of health professions personnel, or to assist schools which are in serious financial straits to meet their costs of operation. In 1969, the largest grant was for $744,000 (and included a supplemental award).[21]

[20] "Institutional grants" replaced "basic improvement grants," and "special project grants" replaced "special improvement grants" under P.L. 90-490 (Health Manpower Act of 1968).

[21] In fiscal year 1968, prior to changes introduced by the 1968 act which removed per-project grant limitations ($300,000 in 1968) and permitted greater flexibility in giving grants for innovative programs, the largest grant in this program was almost $297,000, and most of the grants seemed to have been given to schools in apparent financial difficulty.

Construction aid

Medical schools used $152 million of federal funds for the construction of buildings in 1967–68. The federal share in construction projects had been limited to a maximum of 50 percent except in the case of a new school or a school planning a major expansion of training capacity, when the limit was 66 2/3 percent. However, under the Health Manpower Act of 1968, it may be as high as 66 2/3 percent in cases where a school is experiencing financial difficulties because of heavy expenses for projects such as major revisions in curriculum, replacing obsolete facilities, or moving to a new location.

Student loans

About $15.4 million in student loans was made available through federal programs in 1967–68. Almost all the funds were provided under the Health Professions Educational Assistance Act (HPEA). About 14,700 loans were reported, giving an average value of about $1,000 per loan. Under the Act of 1968 loans bear interest on the unpaid balance (computed only for the period for which the loan is repayable) at the rate of 3 percent per year. Repayment of a loan must be completed within a 10-year period which begins one year after a student ceases to pursue a full-time course of study. However, service as a member of the armed forces, the Peace Corps, or Vista or up to five years of advanced professional training is also a basis for postponement. The appropriated funds for this program are allocated to each school in proportion to its total enrollment, but no school can receive more than it requested. Each participating school is required to deposit in its loan fund an amount not less than one-ninth of the amount allocated to the fund by the federal government.

Scholarships

In addition to loans, scholarships of about $3 million were made available to 3,751 medical students under HPEA in 1967–68, averaging about $800 per scholarship. The funds for this program are currently allocated to each school by multiplying $2,000 times 1/10 of the number of full-time students in the school. Our analysis

---

It is interesting to note that schools of medicine, dentistry, pharmacy, osteopathy, optometry, veterinary medicine, and podiatry are treated in the same way under the two grants programs even though their costs differ considerably.

of the data for freshmen collected in the 1967 NIH-AAMC survey discussed in Chapter 4 indicated that 38 percent of the 517 respondents with family incomes under $5,000 and 25 percent of the 447 respondents with family incomes between $5,000 and $10,000 received HPEA grants. About three-quarters of all HPEA grants were given to students within those income brackets.

Indirect Federal Aid: Research

In 1950, federal funds in support of medical and health-related research totaled $73 million. By 1967, these funds had increased to $1.46 billion. The National Institutes of Health (including the National Institute of Mental Health) was provided $904 million in obligations, as compared with $8 million in 1947 and $125 million in 1957.[22] It has been estimated that in fiscal year 1968, 59 percent of NIH obligations for research were allocated to educational institutions. Most of the federally sponsored funds received by the medical schools are provided through NIH.

Other major providers of federal research funds are the Department of Defense, the Veterans Administration, the Department of Agriculture, the National Aeronautics and Space Administration, the Atomic Energy Commission, the National Science Foundation, the Health Services and Mental Health Administration, the Consumer Protection and Environmental Health Services, and the Social and Rehabilitation Service. While each of these agencies supports a small amount of research relative to the NIH, the sum of their support is considerable.

According to the AMA-AAMC liaison committee financial reports, medical schools actually received $390 million in federal contracts and grants for research in 1967–68 and $154 million in federal contracts and grants for teaching and training. They received another $74 million for overhead on federal contracts and grants. The National Institutes of Health provide research funds under numerous programs of grants and contracts. However, there are three major types of programs:

Research project grants are awarded to an institution in the name of a principal investigator for a specific project representing the

---

[22] For the most part, we shall be referring to *obligations* when dollar amounts are stated. This is money committed but not necessarily spent in a particular year. In effect, when NIH makes a grant, it extends a line of credit to the grantee, and much of the money committed in grants in a particular year need not be and generally is not spent during that year.

investigator's interest and based on his competence and the merit and relevance of the proposal.

The research program-project grant is awarded to an institution in the name of one or more principal investigators for a broadly based and usually long-term research program directed toward a range of problems with a central research focus.

General research support grants are also given to the schools. These are awarded on the basis of a formula grant which provides funds in proportion to the institution's involvement in sponsored federal and nonfederal research up to a specified maximum. In fiscal year 1968, general research support grants made up about 8 percent of the total NIH research grants.

NIH training support is given through training grants to eligible institutions or through fellowships to individuals sponsored by the institution of their choice. *Institutional training grants* may include funds for equipment or personnel, stipends for trainees, and other costs of expanding or improving an existing program or establishing a new program. Finally, NIH makes *grants for the construction of health research facilities* on a matching basis, not to exceed 50 percent of total necessary construction costs except for projects that the Secretary of HEW determines have special regional or national significance. The latter can be supported up to 66 2/3 percent by the federal government.

As indicated earlier, federal aid for research assists the medical schools in a number of ways in producing medical education. Research and education are closely linked and are joint products. Furthermore, research reduces the cost (to the school) of faculty. A faculty member may receive full-time support for research, but he is permitted to allocate some time to teaching. Federal funds in support of construction and equipment for research also aid the education function because of the intertwining nature of the two. Finally, funds used to improve the research capabilities of faculty members may maintain or improve their teaching ability. However, even with these apparent benefits, the effects of research grant programs on medical education can be questioned on four counts.

First, it has been asserted that the grant programs have led to an excessive allocation of medical school resources to the research function and that a by-product of this misallocation has been an adverse effect on the attitude of M.D. candidates toward the provision of services. Second, there has been continuing controversy over the extent to which the medical schools have had to bear some costs of sponsored research projects. Third, the distribution of research and training funds has been concentrated in such a way that extreme differences apparently exist in the resources available for educational purposes. Fourth, the apparent dependence on research funds to provide resources for educational purposes subjects the funding of the educational programs to federal budgetary decisions aimed at the research effort.

Unlike profit-making industrial contractors, universities have always been expected to share in the costs of federally sponsored research projects.[23] Until 1965, there existed arbitrary administrative limitations (which often differed by agency) on the amount of indirect costs, stated as a percentage of direct costs, which would be reimbursed by the individual federal agencies. The appropriations acts for fiscal 1966 substituted more general provisions which require that the total costs of projects be shared between school and agency and which allow the individual agencies to negotiate the amount. Since the schools must take their share from general operating funds, they have argued that research grants have damaged their other programs and even have made them poorer. Furthermore, schools argue that the overhead reimbursements are inadequate in that they do not permit interest to be stated as a reimbursable cost and do not permit "realistic" depreciation allowances.

It is difficult to measure the burden placed on the schools by their sponsored research projects. Undoubtedly it has differed considerably among schools. As Pettit pointed out in discussing the percentage limitation, "The distinction between them [indirect and direct costs] is artificial, being determined, within the appropriate Bureau of the Budget guidelines, by institutional management procedures" (Pettit, 1969, p. 1301). A National Science Foundation survey of 74 medical schools for 1957–58 provided estimates of indirect costs as a percentage of federally sponsored research operating expenditures which ranged from less than 18 percent for

[23] The rationale for this comes from the belief that research is one of the primary functions of universities, so that the government is simply "subsidizing" an activity that the institution would be engaged in anyway (see Keezer, 1959, p. 97; Pettit, 1969, p. 1301).

eight schools to between 45 and 50 percent for two schools (Comroe, 1962, p. 141). The weighted average for all schools was 25.1 percent. The medical schools paid $6.4 million, or 46 percent of the indirect costs, on $54.9 million of direct research costs in 1957–58 (National Science Foundation, 1960, p. 5). If this rate (25 percent) had continued through 1966–67, the total indirect costs related to federally sponsored research would have been $86 million. This would have been $31 million more than the overhead funds received by the medical schools for *all* federal contracts and grants as reported on their annual financial reports to the AAMC-AMA. The impact of this burden on the long-run growth of nonsponsored medical school funds is significant. If we assume the $86 million would have been spent to cover costs induced by sponsored programs, we must subtract that from the published figures for nonpersonal funds in order to promise a more precise estimate of nonsponsored funds. Then, if in addition we assume a 6 percent inflation rate, it appears that the real resources available for nonsponsored programs approximately doubled between 1947 and 1967.[24]

It is understandable that the federal government should set high standards of merit for the research projects which it funds. However, because of scientists' natural tendency to want to congregate together, and perhaps because of economies which come from concentration, there has been an extremely uneven distribution of research funds. In 1966–67 the 10 medical schools with the greatest amount of federal research support received 32 percent of the moneys, while the 13 schools with the least support received 3.6 percent. The moneys for federal teaching and training grants had a similiar distribution (Table 35). To the extent that these resources complement and benefit education programs, the quality of these programs is unconsciously differentiated. Furthermore, since research grants constitute the largest program of federal assistance to medical schools, those schools not receiving significant research grant support were in financial difficulty.

Finally, the amounts of money appropriated for research are based on analyses of the priority attributed to that research, in

---

[24] It must be kept in mind that the medical schools opted for the use of research grants even if accompanied by absorption of nonsponsored funds rather than not seeking the grants and using nonsponsored funds in another way.

TABLE 35
*Distribution of
federal research
and training
grants to 83
medical schools,
by deciles,
1966–67*

		Percent of total	
Decile*		*Research grants*	*Teaching and training grants*
First		32.2	28.2
Second		20.1	19.2
Third		14.5	14.4
Fourth		10.0	11.2
Fifth		8.1	10.1
Sixth		6.2	7.6
Seventh		5.2	5.5
Eighth		3.6	3.7
	TOTAL	100.0	100.0

* All deciles have 10 schools except the eighth, which has 13 schools. The schools were ranked according to the amount of funds received in each category.

SOURCE: Unpublished data from the AAMC and AMA annual questionnaires. Columns may not add to 100 because of rounding.

large measure without taking account of the effects on the education programs. The general budgetary stringency produced by the war in Vietnam, inflationary trends in the economy, and the impact of rapidly rising budget costs to finance health services has led to a situation that forced NIH to withhold money which had virtually been promised to researchers under long-term agreements — known as *noncompeting grants* — in order for NIH to limit reductions in its new and competing continuation grants.[25] NIH negotiated reductions on a grant-by-grant basis. The reductions averaged about 14 percent for the first half of fiscal year 1969. Even so, NIH expected to make 400 fewer competing grants (Boffey, 1968, pp. 340–342).[26] Schools which were planning on continued growth in NIH grants to partially support expansion in their resources have had to revise their plans. But even more damaging is the fact that the areas where the cuts will fall are unpredictable. Thus general planning is made difficult, and the overall programs of departments

[25] The death of Representative John E. Fogarty and the retirement of Senator Lister Hill left a vacuum in congressional leadership for health research. This may also have affected the NIH budget. A comprehensive health program memorandum prepared in the Department of Health, Education, and Welfare in August, 1969, reportedly projected stability of biomedical research support at approximately the current level through 1975 (see *Medical World News,* 1969, p. 12).

[26] The number of project research grants declined from 12,324 in 1965 to 10,985 in 1969 (see Walsh, 1969, p. 1333).

strongly dependent on projects which are cut can be severely hurt.

There is little question that the budget cuts (or even stability in a period of inflation) mean many fewer resources for health research. There is also little question (but much less awareness) that these cuts (which come at a time when schools are being called upon to undertake new tasks) will also have a substantial impact on the educational mission of the medical school.

Indirect Support: Financing of Health Services The clinical education of M.D. candidates and the training of interns and residents are inexorably tied to the provision of health care. These services are provided by the attending physician as well as by the students. Historically, a large number of the patients treated in education-oriented institutions have been unable to pay for the services provided. Therefore, most medical education institutions were not able to rely upon payment for the services provided by their faculty and students for their financial resources. The federal government began to participate in financing medical care for the indigent in 1950 under the public assistance programs and expanded its support of medical assistance for the aged under the Social Security amendments of 1960. By 1965, medical vendor payments under the public assistance programs had reached $1.5 billion, with $632 million being provided by the federal government. That year, Congress enacted Medicare and Medicaid legislation.[27] This paved the way for major increases in federal funds for the support of the purchase of medical care services. In fiscal year 1969, total payments under these programs amounted to $10.3 billion, of which $8.5 billion was provided by the federal government. While no data are available to indicate how much of the Medicare and Medicaid moneys have provided increased financing for medical education institutions, particularly since much of it is channeled through the teaching hospitals, the recent rapid increases in medical school expenses paid by teaching hospitals and clinics and by medical service funds (from about $26

[27] Medicare, Title XVIII of the Social Security Act, provides for the aged, without regard to income, a hospital insurance plan financed by social security taxes and offers an optional supplementary insurance plan covering physician services, with a monthly premium paid by the individual and matched by the federal government. Both programs involve deductibles and coinsurance. Medicaid, Title XIX of the Social Security Act, helps to finance medical care for certain categories of the poor and medically indigent with funds supplied on a variable matching basis by the state and federal governments.

million and \$22 million, respectively, in 1964 and 1965 to \$37 million in 1967 and \$48 million in 1968) provide some idea of the early impact of the two programs.

The major area of controversy in the relationship between the federal programs which help finance the purchase of medical care and the medical education institutions had concerned the procedure for reimbursement for services provided by attending physicians and trainees.[28] Provision is made in the Medicare legislation for reimbursement of an appropriate part of the net cost of approved educational activities. An "appropriate part" means the net cost of the activity apportioned in accordance with the percentage of the overall hospital cost allocated to Medicare beneficiaries (Somers & Somers, 1967, p. 163). This has been interpreted to include the salaries of interns and residents as well as other medical education expenses including staff salaries, overhead, and other costs. The law precludes separate charging for residents' and interns' services. However, Medicare will recognize a charge made by the attending physician for the medical services that he personally provides to a Medicare patient. According to Arthur Hess of the Social Security Administration, this means that

The teaching physician would have to provide personal and distinguishable guidance and direction to interns or residents in any given case in order for the program to recognize a fee charged by him to a patient whose care rested mainly in the hands of the house staff. In the case of major surgical procedures and other complex and dangerous procedures or situations, care would have to include supervision in person by the attending physician to warrant collection of a fee (*Bulletin of the American College of Surgeons,* 1969, p. 94).

The problem that arises is that the senior resident, who has considerable independence, may provide services for which he cannot charge a fee, while the attending physician receives reimbursement for the same procedure.

The issues that arise also become complex because of the problem of payment for services of supervisory physicians in teaching hospitals. Physicians who supervise the training of interns and res-

---

[28] A side effect which has been feared is that there may be a shortage of patients for training purposes, particularly for surgical residents, since many poorer patients can now demand and afford a "private" physician. Thus far, no general problems of this type seem to be appearing, although some county hospitals have experienced difficulty (see Paxton, 1967a, pp. 36–42; 1967b, pp. 42ff).

idents are often designated as the attending physician for patients who do not have a private physician. The staff of the Senate Finance Committee estimates that Medicare payments to supervisory physicians may involve $100 million or more annually.[29]

Traditionally, such physicians have not been paid on a fee-for-service basis for the supervisory services rendered, nor has the patient or third-party payer been billed for such services. Under Medicare, however, such payments have been made—and have provided financial support for medical education.

Under the Medicaid program, the individual states are permitted to make their own decisions regarding payments provided to trainees and attending physicians. Most of the states follow the Medicare guidelines.

The question arises, however, whether it is appropriate to have medical services paid for twice: once as the costs of hospital care under Part A of Medicare (where costs include the costs of interns and residents) and, as it were, again on a fee-for-service basis under Part B. It is also reasonable to ask whether Part B of Medicare is the appropriate vehicle through which to provide support for medical education. The fact that medical education receives insufficient assistance has led to a situation in which funds other than educational funds are used to support educational purposes. This, we believe, causes confusion and has deleterious effects.

Some medical schools are expressing concern that they may once again be embarking on a dangerous route: a route where their educational mission is supported out of funds generated by another activity (this time service rather than research). Though this type of support may prove most helpful, the danger is that once again national priorities may change and the school's service-derived funds may be cut.

SUMMARY The federal government is the major provider of funds to medical schools and also furnishes substantial support to teaching hospital operations. Direct support of medical education is relatively small. Substantial indirect support is provided through the financing of research projects. Indirect support provided through the purchase of patient care services is growing. There has been little coordination of these various federal funding programs, and little effort

[29] *Medicare and Medicaid: Problems, Issues, and Alternatives,* 1970, p. 71. The vexing issues involving supervisory physicians are discussed on pp. 71–79.

has gone into analysis of their total effects on the programs in individual schools or on medical education in general. NIH is now responsible for both the research programs and the direct aid to medical schools, so that administrative coordination for that set of programs may be easier to achieve.

7. Summary, Conclusions, and Policy Alternatives

The following is a summary of major arguments and analyses:

1 The financing system in which medical schools participate does much more than simply provide funds to the medical schools. It affects the economic decisions of the faculty, both individually and collectively, and helps to determine the allocation of the medical schools' resources (including faculty) to their multiple outputs: education, service, and research. Furthermore, it affects the behavior and characteristics of graduating physicians.

2 The distribution of funds among schools should be based on the total value of the multiple outputs produced by each school. Programs should allocate additional resources to those schools in which the total value of additional education, service, and research outputs will be greatest.

3 In order to make optimum decisions regarding the allocation of funds (resources) to medical schools and the allocation of faculty efforts to the multiple outputs of the schools, we need knowledge of the production function for health and of the production functions for the various outputs. There have been a few suggestive studies on these questions, and some schools have undertaken studies for their internal use. Nonetheless, there is little information about functional relationships.

4 There is no single model of a medical school. Schools exhibit considerable variation in size, wealth, apparent quality of their students, and the allocation of their efforts among the different outputs. In general, the characteristics of schools are interrelated. On the average, those schools with the largest expenditures per full-time student attract M.D. candidates who have higher scores on the

science section of the MCAT. These schools allocate relatively more effort to the training of interns, residents, and graduate students in the basic sciences than schools with lower expenditures.

5   Because of differences in orientation and environment, schools differ in the type of physicians they train. Thirteen percent of the 1950–1959 graduates of the 10 privately controlled schools with the largest expenditures per full-time student were full-time medical school faculty members in 1967, as compared with 4 percent of the graduates of the 11 publicly controlled schools with the least expenditures per full-time student. Similarly, 10 percent of the graduates of the former group of schools considered themselves to be general practitioners, as compared with 30 percent of the graduates of the latter group.

6   Various institutional arrangements influence the behavior of medical schools, affect their financial status, and complicate the interpretation and comparison of their financial data. One such arrangement deals with the medical school–teaching hospital relationship. Some teaching hospitals are owned by medical schools, but most are not. The distribution of responsibility between the hospital and school for faculty salaries and intern and resident stipends varies, almost individually by school and hospital. A different set of arrangements deals with the compensation of the clinical faculty. These vary within schools as well as between them and determine the proportion of the income of a clinical faculty member which is to come from salary and the proportion which is to come from fees collected for service.

7   The financing problems most often discussed by medical educators fall into three categories. First, there are difficulties assumed to be faced by almost all institutions. These are associated with the structure of financial support and relate chiefly to the dichotomy between "hard" and "soft" money and to the restrictions imposed on the uses to which sponsored funds can be put. Second, there are problems related to the increasing demands placed upon the medical schools as perceived and felt by medical school administrators. Finally, there are the special difficulties faced by the less affluent schools (including the possibility that they may close or lose their accreditation).

8   Expenditures of United States medical schools increased at an annual rate of 14.6 percent between 1947 and 1967. When adjusted

for inflation, the rate of increase in expenditures (in constant dollars) was 8.25 percent a year. The rapid growth in real resources is illustrated by the expansion of the number of full-time faculty members from 3,577 in 1951 to 22,163 in 1967.

9 Most of the increase in expenditures was financed by research grants and other sponsored funds. Sponsored research funds (including overhead) accounted for more than one-half of the total increase in medical school receipts between 1947 and 1967. Federally sponsored research accounted for almost 90 percent of that growth. Nonsponsored funds, adjusted for inflation, increased at a rate of only 4.25 percent a year over the period 1947–1967.

10 The sources of financing differ among schools, and the funds from these sources are unevenly distributed among schools. In 1965–66, federal and other research and training grants, for instance, provided 57 percent of the support for the lowest-expenditures-per-student private schools and 79 percent of the support for the highest-expenditure-per-student private schools. The latter group received 27 percent of all federal funds, while the former group received only 6 percent.

11 The change in the level and the structure of financing has been responsible for several changes in the medical school environment. One effect has been a relative increase in emphasis on outputs (including educational outputs) other than M.D. education. A second effect—difficult to measure, but one on which there is substantial agreement—is that the increased availability of (and dependence on) grants awarded to individual faculty members has put additional limitations on the ability of deans to control the distribution of medical school faculty effort and resources among programs. Furthermore, the fact that the increased funding has been provided to such a great extent for research purposes, and not for other purposes, has placed a number of schools that have not been able (or have not chosen) to attract research-oriented faculty in a relatively disadvantageous financial position, even threatening their survival.

12 The costs of medical education to the student include both the direct costs of tuition, fees, books, and materials and the opportunity costs of forgone income. The latter costs are by far the higher of the two. Since the stipends of interns and residents—even in spite of a rapid increase—remain considerably below alternative earnings, the prospective practicing physician continues to pay for his training throughout his residency.

13   The average physician earns considerably more over his working lifetime than the average individual in other graduate fields and a great deal more than the average B.A. recipient. This is true even if adjustments are made to help take account of differences in the intellectual ability of physicians and others. The attraction of this high income must be considered in conjunction with the costs of training, the long hours of work, and the lack of fringe benefits for the private practitioner.

14   There is little knowledge about the kind of information that prospective medical school applicants use in projecting their economic future in the medical profession. Nor do we know what weights are assigned to the streams of costs and incomes which the applicant foresees or what index he uses to combine alternative streams. The "internal rate of return," an index frequently used by economists and one which relates monetary income to monetary costs, indicates that, in general, physicians appear to be "fairly well off." However, since the shape of the time streams of income and costs can itself play an important role in the behavior of the prospective applicant, and since the physician faces a long period of education (in which costs exceed income), it is difficult to judge the adequacy of the rate of return in medicine as compared with that in other occupations. The evidence that there are twice as many medical school applicants as there are openings and the suggestion that perhaps one-third of those not accepted are qualified to attend seem to indicate that returns are sufficiently attractive (in terms of their impact on aggregate supply). Monetary costs and benefits also have a considerable impact on the characteristics of the student and, perhaps, on his behavior after completing his training and entering practice.

15   Medical students tend to come from the higher socioeconomic groups. Forty-one percent of freshmen students in 1967 came from families with incomes of $15,000 or over, while only 19.3 percent of all families in which the head was between 45 and 54 had incomes of $15,000 or over. This disproportion is even greater for the privately controlled schools with the greatest expenditures per full-time student, where 53.2 percent of the freshmen students in 1967 came from families with incomes of $15,000 or more.

16 In 1967, almost 25 percent of medical students at public medical schools and almost 35 percent of those at private medical schools received financial assistance in the form of nonrefundable grants. The average grants received by the two groups were for $700 and $975, respectively. In total, medical schools administered $8.7 million in such grants—an average of $250 per enrolled student. These student grants were unevenly distributed among schools: the 10 privately controlled schools with the greatest expenditures per full-time student administered 2 1/2 times as many total dollars as the 12 private schools with the least expenditures per full-time student (and $592 per M.D. candidate, as compared with $180 per M.D. candidate).

17 The rationale for public support of medical education is provided primarily by the need to overcome the tendency to less-than-optimum production of medical education and of physicians. Suboptimum production of physicians by the private sector would be induced by the failure to account properly for externalities in health and by differences in public and private rates of time preference. Furthermore, though society does not yet do so, it should provide equality of educational opportunity for all its citizens. Public support is necessary to achieve that goal and to make the opportunity to become a physician more equable for individuals from different socioeconomic backgrounds.

18 State governments provide considerable support for operating expenditures of public medical schools in addition to the capital funds they make available (and a few states now give some direct financial assistance to private schools). The absolute amount of this support varies considerably among the states, as does the extent of support in relation to population and personal income. Several factors account for the state variation in the number of public openings in medical schools and in the public provision of operating funds. Regression analysis indicates that population size and the number of private spaces in the states are of primary importance in explaining the former and that population size, the propensity for public expenditures (measured by the ratio of total state and local expenditures to personal income), and the rate of growth of population are paramount in explaining the latter.

19 State support of medical education has usually been based on three major objectives. Foremost are considerations dealing with the

adequacy of the number of practicing physicians who would be available to provide services within the state at some future date. The other objectives are *(a)* to provide an adequate number of places in order to extend equable opportunity for medical education to potential applicants from within the state and *(b)* to attract additional interns and residents to the state.

20 Numerous factors help account for the variation in the number of new physicians locating in each state. The most important single factor appears to be population growth. In our cross-sectional regression analysis, the number of graduates who were residents of a state was a significant explanator of the variance in the number of new physicians attracted to that state. Yet a 10 percent increase in the number of resident graduates led to only a 3.2 percent increase in the number of graduates locating in the state.

21 Differences between states in the number of places for entering medical students in public medical schools do not lead to proportional differences in the number of entrants from the states. Since most state schools give preferences in admission to in-state applicants, it is highly probable that additional spaces would be filled by residents of the state. However, a number of these resident students might have attended private schools had expansion in public places not occurred. Using cross-sectional data, we estimated that a 10 percent increase in spaces in public medical schools provided a 4.7 percent increase in the number of medical school entrants from the state.

22 The greatest direct benefits provided to the citizens of the state by public medical schools may be derived from training programs for interns and residents (house staff). Because hospitals affiliated with medical schools are more successful in attracting interns and residents, the valuable services of house staff are more available within states where medical school graduate clinical programs are large. Furthermore, the availability of superior M.D. graduates as interns and residents may help to attract practicing physicians who value their aid in providing efficient, high-quality care.

23 The effects of the migration patterns of physicians and of the existence of private medical schools on the expenditure patterns of the states would—under rational behavior—lead the states to underinvest in medical education. Our study of state reports provides some indication that this is true of their actual behavior.

24 Not all states are likely to be able to meet the national objective of equality of educational opportunity since the states with many students from low-income families are also the states with few economic resources.

25 If optimality calls for public expenditures for medical education, and if states underinvest (as we find they do), federal assistance is required. The principle federal role in the funding of medical education is largely an indirect one related to support of research and training programs at the medical schools. Historically, the role of the federal government in direct support of medical education has been small. However, since 1963, this role has increased. At the present time it includes programs of direct institutional aid, support of construction, and provision of funds for loans and grants to students.

26 Estimates of the quantitative benefits which would accrue from improved education programs and judgments with respect to the benefits to be derived from additions to our stock of physicians must rely on a variety of imprecise indicators of the value of, and need for, the increased services which physicians would provide. Knowledge of the incremental costs involved in training additional physicians is also lacking.

27 Federal research and training grants have provided considerable aid to the medical schools. Some portion of this aid has been beneficial in producing medical education. However, the impact of the research and research training grant programs on medical education can be questioned on four counts. First, it has been stated that these programs have led to an excessive allocation of medical school resources to the research function. Second, a continuing burden (whose extent is unknown) is placed on medical schools by the indirect costs of these sponsored projects. Third, the distribution of research and training funds has been concentrated in such a way that extreme differences apparently exist between schools in the availability of these resources. Finally, the apparent dependence on research funds to provide resources for educational purposes subjects the fortunes of the educational programs to federal budgetary decisions aimed at the research effort.

THE POLICY ALTERNATIVES   The material presented in the first six chapters and briefly summarized in the preceding pages helps serve as the basis for our discussion of policy alternatives regarding the financing of medical education. Our concern is with the development and elucidation of general principles around which proposals for action can be developed, considered, and debated. It is not our intention to offer detailed legislative recommendations or administrative procedures to alter the financial base for American medical education, nor do we provide detailed cost estimates or dollar figures for the suggested policies we propose. Such cost estimates would be required for legislative action, but we believe that the discussion of general approaches will be more meaningful if we do not offer precise dollar suggestions. It would be regrettable if instead of stimulating a discussion of principles, suggested dollar figures sent those concerned with medical education to their desk calculators to ascertain whether they would fare better or worse under the proposed changes than they do now. We want to avoid this narrow, but understandable, focus. Furthermore, changes in the structure of medical education (and perhaps in its length—including internship and residency) would alter the cost of training and any suggested assistance figures we might offer. Thus the cost estimates would run the danger of being outdated even as they were being considered.

There is little question that this is a critical time for medical schools and for the system of medical education. Increasing demands are being placed upon the schools (and the teaching hospitals, which bear a large part of the cost of education beyond the receipt of the M.D.). There is pressure for expansion in the number of M.D. candidates to be educated and for changes in the socioeconomic mix of students admitted to degree candidacy. There is pressure for the development of education and training programs for new types of health personnel. Schools (and teaching hospitals) are asked to develop new patterns of patient care with emphasis on expansion of services outside the hospital walls and on community involvement. Responsibility for planning and regionalization of the delivery of medical services is often being delegated to the medical school. Medical education is being asked to assume a leadership role in changing the system of medical care delivery and organization. Pressure is being exerted on the schools to change their apparent priorities from research to service and education—though funding mechanisms do not enable such changes to be made easily and though there is little agreement on whether this shift should be accompanied by a cutback on research. Demands are made on the schools for increased "relevancy"—though agreement on what constitutes relevancy is lacking. These pressures, these demands for expansion of activity, are being articulated at the very time when the dollar level of federal support for medical schools—largely through research support—is jeopardized (particularly when account is taken of inflation). Never, perhaps, has there been as much need—and as much opportunity—for a rational examination of the total activities of medical schools, an examination that would seek to replace the existing crisis-oriented, patchwork-quilt approach of past years.

To a significant extent, of course, the increasing pressures being placed upon medical schools are directly derived from an overall questioning of the existing health care system. There is doubt that this system—if it can be characterized as a system—is serving the nation effectively and efficiently. The rapid expansion in demand for health services by a more affluent and better-educated population, combined with rapid changes in medical science and technology, has led many observers to question the ability of the system to continue in its present form. The increased emphasis on the difference in the quantity and quality of health care services available to the rich and to the poor, in the suburb and in the ghetto and rural area, has also added to the disquietude. That medical education is not the only part of the system being asked to re-examine itself is clear. That, as a major part of the system, it cannot adopt a limited perspective and consider itself to be uninvolved and exempt from examination is, however, also evident.

Such examination must—and, we believe, will—be undertaken. We also believe, however, that the structure of finance for the education mission of medical schools must be examined *and altered* if the schools (and if the medical care system) are to be enabled to better handle the problems of the coming decades. This, we feel, is more than a matter of the level of funding and degree of support. It involves, as much of the material presented earlier has attempted to make clear, the structure and method of financing, the sources of support, and the purposes for which the support is made available.

While the subsequent discussion will focus on each potential financing source separately, an optimum financing structure will require that the various sources be intermeshed into a systematic whole. As a result of these interrelationships, there is considerable overlap in the following discussion. Our proposals will be limited to *medical education.* It is clear, however, that they would have "side effects" on other medical school activities and thus on the medical care system as well.

It is important, before examining possible sources of support, that we make one premise clear: We believe that there should be a basic public subsidy to reflect the public demand for medical education. The rationale for such a subsidy is not unlike the rationale for public provision of, or subsidy for, other areas of education. While it is true that education brings private benefits to the recipient, it brings public social benefits as well. These public benefits must be taken into account. One objective of a public subsidy, therefore, is to increase the amount of resources allocated to medical education in order to take account of public benefits from medical *education* (in a more direct fashion than is done by support of research).

A second objective of a public subsidy is to alter the socioeconomic characteristics of students who attend medical school in order to help achieve the goal of equality of educational opportunity (and to provide for physicians who may be better equipped, because of their background, to deal with the problems of certain groups, for example, blacks, Mexican-Americans, and people from low-income families).

We believe that the public subsidy should be provided by the federal government because (1) migration patterns of physicians suggest that (collectively) states would not provide sufficient funds to medical education, (2) *national* equality of educational opportunity cannot be achieved by actions taken by individual states because some states may lack commitment and because many (poor) states lack resources, and (3) federal taxes are more progressive than state taxes. Thus, when we speak of a public subsidy we speak of federal financial assistance.

These objectives—expanding medical education and increasing educational opportunity—can be met by providing the public subsidy directly to students or by providing it directly to schools. The same method, however, would not work with equal efficiency in attaining both objectives. If the goal of expanding resources were to be met by giving the subsidy to students, we would be relying on medical schools to raise tuition and, thus, to capture the subsidy. We see little merit in using the student as a fiscal intermediary or "pass-through" mechanism and favor providing the subsidy designed to expand resources directly to schools on a per-student basis. This is a more direct and assured approach.[1]

Conversely, however, the subsidy that is addressed to the problem of the effects of the income distribution on the socioeconomic characteristics of students who attend medical school is best provided directly to the student. This would be a more efficient way to affect his decisions and the probability of his attending medical school.

Thus, we believe that federal aid for medical education should provide both for student and for institutional aid. We shall examine each of these, turning first to the student aid program.

Student Aid Four major parameters must be considered: (1) the characteristics of the student, (2) the total number of applicants, (3) the behavior of the graduate upon entering practice, and (4) the total amount of funds made available to the medical education system through the student.

There are those who suggest that the medical student, that is, the future practicing physician, represents an important potential source of income to the medical school. In 1967 students provided $48 million of support (4 percent of the total income of medical schools). Those who believe that this support could be appreciably increased base their argument on the fact that the rate of return to the student on his investment in medical education is high. They feel that it could be lowered (as a consequence of increasing the costs of education) without affecting the number or quality of students admitted to medical schools.

We suggest, however, that a policy of increasing tuition payments for medical education cannot be advocated without considering the possible impact of such increases on each of the parameters mentioned. Higher tuition may affect the mix of students in terms of their socioeconomic characteristics (and in an unfavorable way); it may induce undesirable increases in fees as physicians attempt to recoup their educational investment; and it may affect the number and quality of applicants (a consideration that may be important if the number of medical school places is itself increased substantially). The issues are more complex than the simple effect

---

[1] For a discussion of the two alternative approaches to the provision of the subsidy, see *Toward a Long-Range Plan for Federal Financial Support for Higher Education,* 1969.

on medical school income and on "rates of return" to medical education.

Our policy suggestions concerning the M.D. candidate are based upon two premises. The first premise is that the effect of family income on the capability of an individual to finance his medical education should be eliminated.[2] The considerable costs (including opportunity costs) and time required to become a practicing physician suggest that the demand for medical education is related to the ability to finance such education. The data we presented bear this out. This is neither equitable nor desirable for America or for American medicine. Our second premise is that all M.D. candidates should be able to finance their education through loans, if they so desire. There are students whose family income is too high to readily justify a full subsidy (given the existing distribution of income and incidence of taxation) and yet too low to permit them to enter and attend medical school in the absence of loan funds. While some students might assume debts in excess of what others may believe to be prudent or reasonable, we do not believe that the individual's time preferences (as between present and future consumption, for example) should be entirely ignored by the failure to make adequate provision of loan funds.

To achieve the goal of altering the effects of the income distribution we suggest direct assistance for the candidate for the doctorate of medicine. Such assistance would provide an effective way to take account of our first and second premises. The next two policy suggestions deal with such direct assistance.

The most equitable way to overcome the effects of income on the individual demand for medical education is to have student aid programs that are continuous in nature and vary inversely with income. One program that could satisfy the requirement would provide support covering a percentage of the student's tuition, other education expenses, and basic subsistence (that is, living expenses). The percentage would be determined by the relationship between the average parental income of the student for a period of time prior to admission to medical school (for example,

---

[2] The elimination of an income effect on ability to *attend* medical school is difficult to achieve since much education precedes medical school and since the impact of income is more than a matter of availability of funds with which to pursue further education. Individual preferences regarding a medical career may differ by parental income class. Our suggestions relate to the ability to finance the education, if one desires and has the abilities to attend medical school.

during the three years prior to admission) and the average median income for the same time period for families headed by a male between the ages of 45 and 54. A suggested schedule relating the percentage of tuition and basic subsistence support to parental income is presented below. This schedule is offered as an illustrative example, as a matter for further discussion and debate.

In addition to this type of nonrefundable grant assistance, offered directly to students, there is a need for long-term loan funds. We suggest that direct public loans be used in order to guarantee that there will be sufficient funds to satisfy the demand. The interest rate should be equal to the long-term federal government borrowing rate (perhaps with a small increment because of the greater risk involved in the individual loans), and repayment should be deferred during the training period. The total of public grants plus loans made available to all students should equal tuition plus subsistence. Students who receive less in nonrefundable grants (because of higher parental income) would have more available to them in the form of loans. For the purpose of arriving at the amount that can be borrowed, subsistence might be defined as an amount higher than the subsistence figure used in computing the subsidy grant. This would enable those students who—because of family obligations—have need to finance their opportunity costs to do so.

A possible alternative to the program of support outlined above would involve combining a grant program (at a more modest level than the one outlined) with a contingency repayment loan plan

Relationship of parental income to median income, U.S. families (head 45 to 54 years of age)	*Percentage of tuition and basic subsistence support*
Up to 1/4	100
1/4 to 1/2	90
1/2 to 3/4	80
3/4 to median	70
Median to 5/4	60
5/4 to 6/4	50
6/4 to 7/4	40
7/4 to twice	30
Twice to 9/4	20
9/4 to 10/4	10

(often known as an *Educational Opportunity Bank* program). Under the latter type of plan—which would bear most of the burden of direct student aid—the federal government would make loans available to students, who would repay these funds through an increase in the federal tax rates applied to their incomes after completion of training. The amount of increase in income tax rates would be related to the amount borrowed. In the aggregate the repayment would equal the funds borrowed plus an appropriate interest payment. The individual would, however, not be obligated to repay a fixed dollar amount. Rather, his repayment would be related to future income (which would be higher as a result of the increased education).[3]

There are a number of benefits to be derived from the Educational Opportunity Bank approach. First, there would be "insurance" for higher-risk students (many of whom might be from lower-income families) who might be reluctant to obligate themselves to repay sizable amounts of regular debt. A student might be willing, however, to assume debts via the Educational Opportunity Bank since his repayment would be related to his future income rather than to a fixed dollar obligation. Thus, if future income is low, the amount repaid is reduced. Second, in time the system would be self-financing (through the repayment flow). Third, the unusual time stream of a physician's costs and income—perhaps the most severe problem confronting him—would be directly faced and, in large measure, overcome without raising the rate of return to medical education. Fourth, the program would be equitable in a prospective sense in that those who gain equally (in a money sense) from their medical education at a given school would pay equal amounts for that education.

Such plans have been discussed for all higher education, and there are some who feel that there are considerable advantages in introducing this approach initially in medical education. First, the problem of the "negative dowry" for women would be reduced. The problem of the negative dowry relates to the fact that if women borrow and are obligated to pay back funds on the basis of future income, the tax rates for repayment have to be extremely high (given labor-force participation rates and future earnings), or the obligation (the negative dowry) has to be assumed by the husband. But the proportion of women in medicine is far lower than the propor-

[3] See *Educational Opportunity Bank,* 1967; Shell et al., 1968, pp. 2–45.

tion in higher education in general, and earnings (in relation to amounts borrowed) are likely to be higher. The second advantage in introducing the Educational Opportunity Bank in medical education is that there is a significant reduction in the chances of adverse selection (a bias towards high-risk individuals with relatively poor income prospects). Most M.D. candidates have good income prospects, and the cost and income life-cycle pattern of the M.D. candidate would provide a strong rationale for most students to take advantage of the program.

While there are apparent advantages to beginning this approach to student financial assistance with medical students, there are disadvantages as well. One major concern is that this type of financing, combined with an apparent need to rely on (less than fully effective) moral suasion to control physicians' fees, might lead future physicians to pass their "additional" burden on to the public. While the same problem exists with any loan funds, we believe the problem would be more severe if all — or a high proportion of — physicians utilized essentially similar loan funds (as would be the case with the Educational Opportunity Bank) and paid back through the extra tax.

A very different problem would have to be faced were the program to spread from the medical school to all higher education. Perhaps the Educational Opportunity Bank concept may be desirable for all higher education. Beginning the plan with the medical school, in the hope that it would then spread, may present difficulties. If the program is to provide for supplementary tax payments, it should "pool" all students rather than use "experience rating." Though supplementary tax rates may differ by level of education, they should not differ for each occupation. This principle, however, may call for an increase in the supplementary rate that future physicians would have to pay as the number of other students (with potentially lower future incomes) is increased. The problem in having multiple tax rates which would change, dependent on when the individual entered the program and how large the pool of entrants was at that time, is obvious.

We feel that the Educational Opportunity Bank concept bears further exploration and consideration. It would perhaps be possible for individual institutions to adopt the concept on an experimental basis for their students. There would be risks in so doing because institutions cannot use the Internal Revenue mechanism for collection purposes. Nonetheless, experiments can be designed to examine the potential effects of such a program. We urge that this be done. The Educational Opportunity Bank concept has not yet become part of the public debate. We believe it should. Pending debate, we favor our first alternative: a combined grant and loan program. Such a program does not "lock" medical school financing into a particular mold. We can adopt and implement it and still remain free to shift at some later time to the Educational Opportunity Bank approach combined with a (modest) grant program, which we believe would remain necessary for students from very low-income families.

Our suggested program of federal grants and loans addresses problems that stem from the existing income distribution. It is designed not only to help the students now attending medical schools but also to alter that mix of students. It can achieve maximum effectiveness—particularly for potential students from low-income groups—only if it is well publicized and if prospective students are fully aware that financial assistance will be available if they are admitted to medical school. The reader will remember that the data indicate that decisions concerning possible entrance into medical school are often made early in a student's career. Those are the decisions which must be affected.

The most equitable of policies at the level of the medical school can have only partial and limited success if earlier barriers to equal opportunity are not removed. We do not offer proposals affecting elementary, secondary, and undergraduate education, but we do recognize the importance of measures that affect those areas. A national public policy consistent with the traditional aims of this country would dictate that opportunities in higher education in general be opened in greater dimension to persons in lower-income groups. We do not suggest that medicine offer higher inducements than other fields—except as such may be consistent with nationally determined priorities.

Earlier in the discussion we indicated the importance of, and the costs associated with, the years of training and education that follow the receipt of the M.D. degree. Internship and residency are part and parcel of the education of the physician. Our next proposal addresses the problems of the intern and resident (persons who are receiving training, but who—at the same time—also render service). We believe that a policy for internship and residency education should be defined by four basic conditions. The first is that all medical *services* produced by the intern and resident should be paid for. This payment for services rendered should be made by sources external to the hospital (by patients, third parties, or physicians), at an appropriate rate that takes into account the abilities, education, and experience of the graduate physician. The second condition is that the graduate physician should be paid a stipend to compensate him for the service he renders that would be commensurate with his abilities, education, experience, and effort.

One mechanism for paying for services and distributing the moneys so derived might be to place the amounts obtained in a general house-staff fund. Money for services provided by the graduate physician when he assumes major responsibility for a patient (that is, if there is no payment to a practicing physician) should be paid directly to the fund. Practicing physicians, whose patients receive services rendered by the house staff, should pay a sum into the fund based on the number of patient days of services rendered (or, in lieu of this, provide formal instruction to the house staff). Interns and residents might then be paid, in part, out of this fund. When a medical school is affiliated with a number of hospitals and is involved in internship and residency training in various institutions, it may be desirable to pool the funds in one general fund, rather than in funds associated with each hospital. That such a mechanism creates some difficulties is clear. We believe they can be overcome.

In addition to the two conditions related to services that interns and residents render, there are two conditions that relate to the education they receive. First, we believe that there should be a basic federal subsidy for graduate medical training. Our second condition is that the intern or resident bear the burden of training costs not covered by the public subsidy. The income distribution problem having been taken account of via the salaries paid, the public subsidy is justified on the basis of externalities and the social, as contrasted with private, return for the education. Since, however, there are private returns, the suggested assistance should be less than a full subsidy. Costs of training would therefore be shared by the public and the physician in training.

Such an arrangement would pay for services in a direct manner rather than by some roundabout budgeting process that mislabels payments, it would provide for a substantial increase in incomes of house staff (justified on the basis of the service they render), and it would provide for an educational subsidy by the public (not mislabeled as a service payment or research grant) and for an educational payment by the physician. We indicated earlier that one of the problems in the financing of medical education in the past has been the "mislabeling" of funds received. We would hope to avoid this problem in the future and therefore suggest that—at least conceptually—the differences between service and education be taken account of.[4]

**Institutional
Aid**

The federal government support provided to institutions, we believe, should be considered in the light of three parameters: the total number of medical students, their geographic distribution, and the overall equity and efficiency of the financing mechanism.[5]

The federal government's major effect on the total number of medical students and their geographic distribution should be extended through the introduction of a program of 100 percent support (on a selective basis) of the capital construction required for expansion. Support (both total and partial and, again, on a selective basis) should also be available for improvement of plant and equipment. All support should be provided on a discretionary and limited basis.

Our suggestion that 100 percent support is required stems from a belief that formulas that require states or institutions to match federal funds would make expansion difficult in those very areas now in need of new or expanded institutions since those areas often are poor in financial and other resources. We see little justification for requiring that matching funds be provided. Our belief in selectivity and discretion is based upon the need to exercise control (particularly when 100 percent funding is available and no

[4] The program outlined would increase the incomes of the house staff by a substantial amount. It would also provide increased *educational* income for the educational institution. While we do separate the finances involved in service and those involved in training, it is not required that separate transactions take place. If, for example, the service fund received $18,000 per house-staff member, and if it were estimated that the education of graduate physicians costs $8,000 per student, then, if the public subsidy were $2,000, the stipends would average $12,000.

The public subsidy could, if it were desired, be used to define needed areas of specialty training and thus to help allocate the number of residencies for the various specialties. It could also be used to help move an increasing number of training opportunities into relationship with the medical schools. Finally, since public money would be provided for training, the federal government would have the duty (and right) to set training standards.

[5] This discussion cannot be viewed separately from the one on student assistance and financing immediately preceding.

matching funds are required and in the presence of budget constraints) and the need to affect the geographic distribution of medical school places.[6]

There is the danger that the expectation of the enactment of the suggested (or a similar) program might lead to a delay in implementation of already existing expansion plans. Institutions may delay construction and expansion in the hope of receiving more federal support in the future than is currently available. This danger can be overcome by making the discretionary guidelines clear as early as possible and by making the discretionary support available retroactive to the date when legislative debate commenced (or even somewhat earlier).

We further recommend that (over and above construction grants) the federal government make payments to assist in covering operating expenses for the *educational* activity of the schools. Basic payments should be made for each M.D. candidate enrolled. This basic payment would represent a governmental sharing in the cost of medical *education*. We do not offer a specific recommendation as to the appropriate dollar amount for the basic educational payment. Nonetheless, it is necessary to make it clear that legislators will be misleading themselves if they feel that small dollar-per-student grants (such as $500) will have a substantial impact on medical school financing and medical school activities. If the grant approach is warranted — and we believe it is — it is warranted because, at proper levels, it can bring substantial public benefits. Such levels may require grants on the order of $2,000 to $2,500 per enrolled student or even larger. Such sums, leading to a significant increase in the amount of nonearmarked funds, would provide deans with the resources that would give them additional decision-making powers. We have discussed this matter earlier and believe it to be of considerable importance.

If basic grants were sufficiently large, the income structure of schools would be greatly altered — medical schools would have considerable additional financial resources. We believe that, with these resources, schools would see fit to expand. The pressures for expansion already exist, and the availability of resources should enable those who determine the policies of medical schools to act in the national interest. It will be necessary to maintain these

---

[6] It should be clear that we do not favor geographic discrimination in admission policies, and surely not in institutions funded largely by the federal government.

pressures so that schools do not simply expand faculty or the number of students in the basic sciences. We believe, however, that the schools will respond to the nation's needs.

We conceive a system of basic grants which provides schools with adequate resources and which is based on assistance for M.D. candidates rather than a system with inadequate resources per student but with significant special assistance for expansion. The financial foundation of medical school education needs strengthening. To expand without strengthening the base on which the enterprise rests would not be an optimum policy.

Furthermore, "bonus grants" (for expansion), as they are sometimes conceived, may be unrelated to the real costs incurred in expansion and become a way to help some (but not all) medical schools. Under such a system, the medical school would once again be engaged in a process which is misleading (in terms of budget allocations). Additionally, such payment may lead to a misallocation of expansion as between new schools and increased enrollment in existing schools. The real costs may be lower in the latter, but the dollar costs to the federal government authorities (if significant bonus payments are made) would not reflect these differentials in real costs.

Under a system of federal grants to institutions, schools would receive grants on a per-student basis for all students including expansion students. While we question whether special bonuses over and above these basic grants (which do reward expansion) are necessary or justified in order to stimulate expansion, it is obvious that the lower the basic support figure (and the consequent support of medical school education), the less likely schools are to expand in the absence of special expansion payments. Thus, the level of basic support is inversely related to the degree of possible expansion bonus support required.

If bonus expansion support were felt to be required in order to stimulate expansion, it could be provided in a number of ways. Any such mechanisms, however, should be geared to past expansion as well as future expansion so as not to penalize schools which have made an extra effort in the past and have already expanded (in response to the various formulas already legislated to reward expansion directly).

We have already indicated that the medical schools and affiliated hospitals should receive federal payments in support of educational programs for interns and residents. These educational payments, for house staff in training programs which are the responsibility of medical school faculty, need not be in the same amount as those provided for the M.D. candidate.

State Governments Though we have thus far focused on the public subsidy to be provided by the federal government, there is a role for state governments as well. The parameters to be considered in determining state policy are the total number of physicians a state wishes to have at some time in the future (but this must take account of physician migration patterns), the number of interns and residents the state wishes to attract, and the size of the subsidy it wishes to provide its own residents and students who attend its schools from out of state.

Because of differences in preferences and incomes, states can be expected to have different demands for physicians relative to population. It is unlikely that the federal government will provide the 100 percent capital support for the expansion necessary to fulfill all the states' goals. Some states, particularly those with relatively high demands (and high incomes), will have to provide their own capital funds for expansion of the training of M.D. candidates (but only if they believe that such expansion will sufficiently improve their chances of attracting more practicing physicians in the future). The states will also most probably (and appropriately) supplement the basic federal subsidy to the school for the M.D. candidates by providing funds which will allow tuition charges to be less than the estimated cost of the training minus the federal subsidy. Furthermore, because of the importance of internship and residency programs to the population of the state in the present and future, states may wish to provide funds in order to improve these programs or to increase the net income of the house staff so that more and better graduate physicians can be attracted. While we do not believe that states will provide sufficient basic support for medical education, and therefore suggest an expanded role for the federal government, we do expect that states will continue to support medical education for the reasons just cited. Such support, of course, is desirable. It must, however, come in the context of an adequate level of federal support so that richer states do not price poorer states out of the market.

The Size of Subsidies We have not specified the size of per-student payments or the total amount of subsidies to be provided by the public; instead, we have concentrated on the form of the programs. The actual levels and amounts of institutional aid will have to be determined by the value placed on the education of physicians by the executive and legislative branches of the federal government and the state governments. If, for example, the federal representatives felt that $100 million was too large an amount, relative to other expenditures, to spend on the education of the M.D. candidates, and if there were 40,000 such candidates, this would necessarily imply that the representatives did not place the public value at $2,500 per student. They would then have to consider alternative levels, for example, $80 million ($2,000 per student), $60 million ($1,500 per student), $40 million ($1,000 per student), or $20 million ($500 per student), continuing this pattern of consideration until they finally determined that they were unable to use the money for other purposes to better advantage. The same approach can be followed by state representatives. The decision concerning levels is one that should be made by the public representatives. Such decisions, however, do require that the issues be addressed in explicit fashion and that the possible effects of the decisions and the financial environment in which medical education functions be understood. Such decisions also require that the public at large be concerned with the issues involved and that this public be defined as broadly as possible (not limited, therefore, to those directly concerned with, and part of, the medical education system). It is our hope that our analysis, formulation, and discussion of issues will assist in developing a meaningful discussion of the public policy aspects of the financing of medical education.

Appendix A : The Data

At an early date in this study, we decided that the expenditure of time and resources needed to gather new data through an extensive survey was not warranted. The available data, even with their shortcomings and weaknesses, were adequate for the general overview and analysis that we planned to undertake. Nevertheless, the type of data which were available and their quality played an important part in determining the scope and shape of the analyses. The fact, for example, that data had been systematically collected for medical schools, but not for teaching hospitals, led to a much greater emphasis on the financing of the former. Similarly, weaknesses in the time series available on financing medical schools limited our use of those data to descriptive analyses for two fiscal years instead of the more sophisticated statistical analyses which we originally planned. A discussion of the major pieces of data will point out the limitations in our analysis and the direction for future data collection. The order in which the data are discussed corresponds to that in which they were presented in the preceding chapters.

Chapter 2: The Medical School: Some General Characteristics

Full-time Students The data on the total number of full-time students in 1965 and their distribution among M.D. candidates, other clinical students (interns, residents, clinical fellows, and postdoctoral students), and graduate students in the basic sciences (M.A. candidates, Ph.D. candidates, and postdoctoral fellows) were taken from the table on the teaching responsibilities of medical faculty in the 1965–66 Education Issue of the *Journal of the American Medical Association* (1966, appendix 1, table 3). One fairly large category of students was excluded from our computations. It comprised those in a column headed "other students" in the table and included dentistry students, nursing students, and other undergraduate and graduate students not enrolled in the medical school. Since these students make only partial demands on the faculty, each school is requested to estimate the full-time equivalency of the burden placed on their faculty. However, the ratio of the number of students listed under "other students" to the estimated full-time equivalence varied among the schools to such a great extent[1] that we excluded the group completely from the analysis. To the extent that certain groups of schools have a larger burden placed on their faculty by "other students," we underestimate, relatively, their teaching burden and overestimate their expenditures per full-time students.[2]

Medical School Alumni

The data on the graduates from each school who were in general practice or who were full-time faculty members in a medical school were taken from Theodore et al. (1968). The designation of their specialty and professional activity was based on the physicians' own responses to the annual verification of their activities by the AMA's Physician Records Service. It should be noted that this survey indicated that at the end of 1967, there were 11,402 physicians in the United States classified as medical school faculty, while the AAMC-AMA annual survey of the medical schools showed 13,277 full-time faculty with the M.D. degree for the 1966–67 school year. Some of the latter "faculty" may have felt that their principal professional activity should be classified as research, administrative work, or patient care rather than medical school faculty duties.

Faculty Salaries

Data on faculty salaries were taken from *Medical School Salary Study 1967–68,* published by the Association of American Medical Colleges in December, 1967. The study was based on salary information reported by 61 United States medical schools. Fifty-one of those schools reported salaries for strict full-time faculty, 27 schools reported the base salaries paid to geographic full-time faculty, and 17 schools reported the approximate total annual income of geographic full-time faculty.

[1] The ratio for all schools was about 7 to 1, but for one school it was 1,000 to 1, and for another the ratio was unity.

[2] For a discussion of other possible biases in these data, see Wing & Blumberg, 1969, pp. 36–37.

Chapter 3: Funding Problems and Evolution of the Financial Structure

Expenditures and Sources of Funds

The data on individual school expenditures and sources of income for 1959–60 and 1965–66 were provided by the AAMC and the AMA. The information was collected through the two associations' Liaison Committee on Medical Education annual medical school questionnaires. The questionnaires were framed and the responses edited by the late A. J. Carroll, assistant director of the AAMC Division of Operational Studies. As already noted, the only adjustments we made in the data were to omit entirely Agency for International Development grants and contracts for foreign teaching programs and to use only one-half the federal teacher and training funds. Our information indicated that about one-half of the latter funds provide student aid funds. Wing and Blumberg (1969, pp. 31–32) discuss some biases that perhaps occur as a result of the use of gross rather than net amounts for certain categories in the questionnaires: income from college services, income from medical services, income from teaching or research institutes, and income from teaching hospitals. Furthermore, it is our understanding that, while the questionnaires define each item in some detail, there may be differing interpretations of the proper allocation of funds. Finally, some items, such as funds from teaching hospitals or clinics, obviously require arbitrary allocation procedures that would not be consistent across schools.

Chapter 4: The Medical Student

Socioeconomic Characteristics of, and Student Aid for, Medical Students

The Office of Physician Resources of the National Institutes of Health in cooperation with the AAMC surveyed the sources of finance and the expenses of medical students at all United States medical schools in 1967. The attempt was made to have a census of the students; that is, no sampling procedures were used. As would be expected, the variance in returns between schools was substantial. We decided to concentrate most of our analyses on freshmen students, who have tended to provide the best response to this type of survey in the past. In this particular survey, about 73 percent of the freshmen responded. Rather than blow up the responses for each school in analyzing the requests for, and receipt of, student aid, we used the responses which were received. However, as noted, when it was necessary to compute weighted averages for characteristics of students within groups of schools, we dropped those schools which had less than a 50 percent response rate and blew up the number of the freshmen in other schools to the size of their freshman class as reported in the *Journal of the American Medical Association.*

Our study of the debt of seniors was based only on the responses of the 55 percent who replied to the survey.

Chapters 4 and 5: Expansion of Enrollment

Planned Increases in Medical School Enrollments
These analyses were based on data collected from responses to a letter sent to each school in March, 1968, by Dr. William N. Hubbard, Jr., and Dr. William G. Anlyan. The responses were collated by the Office of Program Planning and Evaluation of the National Institutes of Health. Replies were received from 80 out of 85 established four-year medical schools, 2 out of 4 two-year medical schools, and 14 developing schools. The questionnaire responses were divided into three categories: (1) planned increases; (2) longer-range, less definite plans; and (3) plans that could be implemented with special help. Planned increases that were spread over several years were apportioned among the years, and the second year was used if two years were given. According to the responses, there was a planned increase of 1,927 freshman places by 1975, of which 663 would be at developing schools (and 48 at two-year schools) (Hubbard & Anlyan, 1968). It was the planned increase which we used in our analysis.

Appendix B: Joint Production and Costs at the Medical Schools

One of the complicating factors in the determination of the optimum financing structure for the medical schools is the joint production of several levels and types of education, research, and medical services by the faculty and students at these institutions. Common facilities, equipment, and material are used in the varied aspects of production as well. This combined production makes it difficult to answer the four basic questions society is faced with in allocating resources to medical schools:

1   How much total resources should be allocated to the schools?

2   What should be the mix of outputs produced at the schools?

3   How should the resources be distributed to different schools?

4   How should the burden of financing the schools be distributed among the purchasers of their outputs?

Danière has pointed the way to the answers to questions 1, 3, and 4 within a joint production framework with the following three rules:

1   New resources should be shifted to higher education [medical schools] as long as the combined value of all additional services rendered is higher than the cost of resources involved (Danière, 1964, p. 49).[1]

2   Of all combinations of services that may be produced through given additional resources in higher education [medical schools], that with the highest value should be chosen (p. 49).

---

[1] We have inserted "medical schools" in brackets to indicate the application of Danière's general rules to our special case. This discussion owes much to Danière's insightful presentation, especially pp. 48–65, 72–79.

3 The correct price to students should equal total production cost net of charges to other beneficiaries. . . . [Other products produced should be] sold competitively in a market which includes other producers (pp. 22, 77).

We can develop a similar rule to respond to the third question:

4 Additional resources should be allocated to those medical schools where the incremental value of all additional services rendered is greatest.

The preceding rules are efficiency conditions which must always be applied within constraints of equity considerations.

Let us apply each of these rules to the medical school in order to obtain some insight into their operational significance. The first rule says that the *total value* of increased training, additional research, and additional services provided at the medical schools by the transfer of resources to them should be compared with the value of the resources' production in their alternative use. The second rule indicates that medical schools should compare the incremental value of shifting some of their effort to the production of one of their outputs with the loss from reduced production in other outputs (this, of course, assumes that some substitution is possible). For example, is the expected loss in the value of research from having a faculty member teach an additional two hours a week greater or less than the value of the gains in educational output? The third rule says that the medical care services produced by medical school faculties should be paid for at the same rates that nonaffiliated physicians receive and that research projects should be supported at the same level that they would be if the research was performed outside the medical school.[2] The remainder of the costs are to be financed by students and other supporters of medical education such as governments and foundations. Finally, the fourth rule requires that the *total value* of increased training, additional research, and additional services provided by adding resources to one school be compared with the total value of the outputs which would be produced if the resources had been allocated to other schools. Do research grants which allow an instructor to join the faculty of a high-expenditure school where he can perform better research overlook the fact that the total value of his re-

[2] The latter point presents serious difficulties since research is not sold in a competitive market. What is needed is some indication of the value of the research effort to the purchaser, who, in most cases, is a public agency.

search, education, and service outputs might be greater at a low-expenditure school?

These rules provide a useful conceptual framework for policy decisions. However, exact application of the rules is impossible. They all require estimates of the value of benefits. Since operational procedures for quantifying these values for all outputs are not available, reliance must be placed on informed judgments as to relative values. Nevertheless, exact values of the benefits need not always be known to make comparisons with costs. Judgments need be made only with respect to the relative sizes of the two quantities. For example, if a potential additional faculty member would earn $20,000 a year, it is necessary only to judge whether the incremental output he produces is worth more than that figure, not the exact value of his output. Since, according to the rules, the decision-making process is approached from the resources side, none of the usual costs of production—related to outputs—are required. This is fortunate since, as Ciriacy-Wantrup pointed out several decades ago (1941, p. 798), in joint production situations we are limited to trying to answer the question, "What is the theoretically least unsound of technically simple bases for the allocation of joint costs?" That is, no procedure of allocating joint costs could satisfy the conceptual desire to find the "true" average costs of production. Nevertheless, there have been three recent attempts, which we shall briefly review, to estimate the costs of the different programs at medical schools and teaching hospitals.

The AAMC Cost Studies

The AAMC has made two surveys of program cost allocation as estimated by individual schools. The schools involved in the surveys relied on the methodology devised by the late Augustus Carroll, author of *A Study of Medical College Costs* (1958). His methodology is dependent basically upon each faculty member's estimation of the distribution of his total salaried *effort* to each of the various programs to which he contributes. The difference between time and effort is emphasized.[3]

The first cost allocation study gave detailed data in tables for 12 individual schools and comparable average figures for 14 schools for the 1959–60 school year. It provided estimates of the distribution of total program costs among the different programs as well as estimates of unit costs of education programs. The average

[3] Association of American Medical Colleges, 1965. An additional study of interest prepared for the AAMC is Carroll, 1969.

figures indicated that undergraduate medical education was responsible for 16 percent of total program costs and about 50 percent of education program costs. The unit costs of undergraduate and intern and resident education programs were about the same, but the costs of graduate education programs in the basic sciences were somewhat higher (unpublished tables provided by the AAMC). The second study of program costs was published in 1969 (T. J. Campbell, 1969). It reviewed cost allocation estimates from seven medical centers. Since the medical centers were the unit of attention, the scope of the study was much broader. In particular, the inclusion of the teaching hospital directly in the study allowed for a more complete coverage of costs. We summarize the findings below:

1 The percentage of Total Program Costs allocated to . . . this program [undergraduate medical education] ranged from 3.9 per cent to 6.2 per cent with an average of 6.1 per cent. The program cost per undergraduate medical student ranged from $2,800 to $4,300 with the average cost per student of $3,700 (p. 28).

2 The percentage of Total Program Costs [for master's and Ph.D. degree candidates] ranged from 2.8 per cent to 6.1 per cent with an average of 4.2 per cent. The cost per graduate student education ranged from $3,700 to $11,700 with an average of $7,200 (p. 28).

3 The percentage of Total Program Costs of the medical center devoted to Intern and Resident Education ranged from 3.7 per cent to 7.1 per cent, with an average of 5.0 per cent. The program cost per intern and resident ranged from $5,300 to $9,100, with an average of $7,000 (p. 30).

4 Research costs [of the medical center] ranged from 17.3 per cent to 26.5 per cent, with an average of 22.3 per cent of total program costs (p. 33).

5 Patient Care Program Costs [of the medical center] ranged from 42.1 per cent to 55.7 per cent with an average being 49.0 per cent of the total program costs (p. 33).

University of California Study The Office of Health Planning for the University of California recently circulated a paper which used cross-sectional multiple regression analyses, with the individual schools as the units of observation, to make estimates of program costs for the academic year 1964–65 (Wing & Blumberg, 1969). Some of the estimates from this study correspond closely to those found in the second AAMC study. For example, when all schools were used in the sample, the estimated cost of medical undergraduates was $4,016, the cost of basic science students was $6,978, and the cost of interns, residents, and clinical fellows was $4,182.[4] All the estimated co- efficients for these three groups were significantly different from zero.

The regression procedure is commonly used to estimate cost functions. However, there are a number of institutional problems which affect the applicability of the procedure for medical schools. First, medical schools are nonprofit institutions; hence, there is no force which leads them to use similar production functions. In fact, the differences between the curricula for M.D. candidates in the various medical schools are so great that there appears to be no reason to believe that they use the same production function. Second, the differences in the proportion of strict full-time, geo- graphic full-time, and volunteer faculty among schools lead to dif- ferences in expenditures which do not truly reflect differences in real costs. In studies, investigators have attempted to compensate for these problems by grouping schools into homogeneous units, such as private schools with high research expenditures, but groupings alone will not overcome the problems created by the inherent characteristics of medical schools.

---

[4] Wing & Blumberg, 1969, p. 10. These were the results from a regression forced through the origin.

Appendix *C*: *Private* *Rates* *of* *Return* *to* *Medical* *Education*

A student considering the extension of his formal education can be expected to take account of the streams of monetary costs and benefits which will accrue from his decision. There are a variety of ways that these streams can be combined to provide a ranking of alternative actions. Little study has been made of the comparative ability of alternative procedures of determining cost and benefit streams to explain the behavior of students. However, the most frequently used procedure is to compute the internal rate of return.[1] This procedure requires the computation of the discount rate $\bar{r}$, which equates the present value of the revenue stream and the present value of the cost stream, as shown in Eqs. C-1 and C-2:

$$\sum_{(i\,=\,1)}^{n} \frac{R_i}{(1 + \bar{n}/r)^i} = \sum_{(i\,=\,1)}^{n} \frac{C_i}{(1 + \bar{n}/r)^i} \qquad (\text{C-1})$$

where n is the total number of years in the time horizon considered when making the decision, R_i is the expected revenue or earnings in the ith year, and C_i is the expected cost in the ith year.

$$\sum_{(i\,=\,1)}^{n} \frac{R_i - C_i}{(1 + \bar{n}/r)^i} = 0 \qquad (\text{C-2})$$

The costs would have to include both the explicit expenditures for education (tuition, books, materials) and the implicit costs introduced by forgone earnings.

There are a number of problems an investigator faces in computing rates of return. The major one is the choice of which streams of

---

[1] See the thorough discussion of this concept by Becker, 1964, pp. 37–66.

monetary benefits and costs he should use. The student, in making his choice, may find a number of sources of information which could be useful in predicting streams of income from alternative occupations or the attainment of different higher education degrees. He can depend on the current age-income relationships to project future earnings, or he can make his own projections of the age-income relationships under the assumption of some rate of real growth for the earnings in the occupational or educational categories. A priori, there is no reason for the investigator to favor one or the other method in explaining the behavior of students on the average. Furthermore, there are usually a number of cost streams which could be used to measure opportunity costs. Also, the investigator has to make a decision with respect to factors such as armed forces experience.

The most recent study of internal rates of return to physicians' education was included in a doctoral dissertation prepared by Sloan (1968). He used the incomes of physicians in different age groups (through age 65) in a particular year to construct a revenue stream and used the incomes of college graduates at different ages for the major part of the cost stream. (See Table C-1.)

We were most interested in computing internal rates of return in order to simulate the effects of differences in certain assumptions or changes in policy on the internal rate. Therefore, we used three different basic streams of revenues and costs. The former were based on median earnings of different age groups as compiled in the *Medical Economics* survey, while the latter were based on median earnings of white male bachelor's degree graduates with an upward adjustment of 10 percent to take account of the abilities of medical students. In two of the cases the streams were computed

TABLE C-1
Sloan's estimates of internal rates of return to physicians' education, selected years, 1941 to 1966, in percentages

Year	Internal rate of return
1941	13.2
1947	17.9
1959	14.7
1962	16.6
1963	15.9
1964	16.1
1965	17.5
1966	18.2

SOURCE: Sloan, 1968, p. 164.

by applying an overall growth rate, related to the annual growth rate in median incomes of all practicing physicians, and an age-specific growth rate in income. The formula for this computation is given in Eq. C-3,[2]

$$Y_i = Y_{i-1} (1 + G)(1 + A_i), \qquad i = 1, n \qquad \text{(C-3)}$$

where Y_i is earnings in year i, G is projected annual growth rate in median incomes of all practicing physicians, and A_i is the age-specific growth rate in income.

In the other situation, we used the current income in each age bracket as estimated in the survey conducted by *Medical Economics* and the U.S. Bureau of the Census in *Current Population Reports.*

The three assumptions used for the basic alternative streams were that (1) M.D. incomes grow at a rate of 8 percent annually (with a 3 percent rate of inflation), versus a growth in B.A. incomes of 7 percent per annum; (2) M.D. incomes grow at a rate of 6 percent annually (with a 2 percent rate of inflation), versus a growth in B.A. incomes of 5 percent per annum; and (3) M.D. incomes are assumed to be the same for all ages within an age grouping for 1966. The same was assumed for the B.A. recipient.

The basic streams of income used in our calculations assumed that the potential medical student foresees four years of training as an M.D. candidate, one year of internship, two years of service in the armed forces, and three years of residency prior to the start of private practice. They were derived in the following manner:

1   Using the 1963–64 Public Health Service–Association of American Medical Colleges survey of medical student financing, we estimated that the medical student would earn one-sixth of the median income of all males with the B.A. during his first two years of medical school and one-fifth of the median income of all males with the B.A. during the last two years (Altenderfer & West, 1965).

2   We assumed that the mean monetary salaries of interns and residents would grow at an annual rate of 9 percent per year from their levels of $4,322 and $4,295 in 1966–67, as reported in the *Journal of the American Medical Association* (1967, pp. 768, 773). We also used information from surveys published in *Hospital*

---

[2] It may be true that physicians of all ages do not benefit equally from the overall growth rate in physicians' net practice income, but we could not find adequate evidence to make any adjustment.

Physician to adjust for the first, second, or third year of residency. The mean incomes of interns had increased at a rate of 9 percent per year between 1961 and 1966, while the mean incomes of residents had increased only 5.5 percent annually, but we felt that the obvious current pressures to increase all house salaries should lead to an estimate of greater future growth in the resident's income.

3   For the estimates which assumed annual growth rates in income of 8 percent and 6 percent we used *Medical Economics* data for 1966 to estimate the median earnings for physicians in private practice at age 32. This estimate was used as the base for our calculations. Again using the *Medical Economics* data, we estimated a 5 percent annual growth in incomes associated with age for M.D.'s between the ages of 32 and 39, a zero rate of growth associated with age for M.D.'s between the ages of 39 and 46, a decline of 0.33 percent per year associated with age for M.D.'s between the ages of 46 and 56, and a decline of 1.85 percent per year associated with age for M.D.'s between the ages of 56 and 64.

4   For the stream of income which did not project an annual rate of growth we used the 1966 income for various age ranges as published in *Medical Economics*.

5   We assumed that while in the Army, the physician was paid at rank O-3 (for a captain with four years of service), which would have been about $10,925 (composed of basic pay, quarters, subsistence, and special pay for doctors) in 1968. This was adjusted under the assumption that there would be increases (in part to account for inflation) at 4.5 percent per annum.

The basic cost stream used in calculations when the bachelor's degree was taken as the alternative was computed in the following manner:

1   The direct costs associated with attendance at public schools were taken to be $600 tuition plus $200 miscellaneous expenditures plus $750 in the first year for a microscope (see *Medical School Admission Requirements, U.S.A. and Canada,* 1967–1968), less $112 in scholarship funds.

2   We used *Current Population Reports* data to estimate that the earnings for a bachelor's graduate in 1968 at age 22 were $9,308

and $9,015 for the annual growth rates of 7 percent and 5 percent, respectively. The age factors were a 2.5 percent growth between the ages of 22 and 39, a 0.5 percent growth between the ages of 39 and 49, and a 0.75 percent annual rate of decline between the ages of 49 and 64.

Prior to computation of the internal rates of return, the income streams were deflated and adjusted for federal income taxes, using average tax rates given in Pechman, 1966. (See Table C-2 for listings of the deflated, after-tax revenue and cost streams used in our computations.) During the computation of the internal rates we weighted the incomes at each age by the related mortality probability.

The basic results are presented in the first section of Table C-3. The rates of return varied from 0.151 for the zero growth assumption to 0.184 for the assumption of an 8 percent annual income growth. The variance shows the difficulties involved in making this type of computation meaningful.

We next introduced some changes into the income and cost streams to see the effects on the rate of return. The changes and the results are listed below:

1 We assumed that the opportunity costs were based on income of Ph.D.'s in the biological sciences.[3] The cost streams used in the calculations when the Ph.D. degree was taken as the alternative were computed in the following manner:

a The direct costs for the M.D. student were the same as those in the bachelor's cost stream (item 1). We also assumed, on the basis of information from several sources, that the Ph.D. student attending a public university received a $3,000 stipend, earned $2,000 in outside work, paid $600 in fees, and took five years to receive his degree.

b In order to make the Ph.D. alternative as favorable as possible, we assumed that Ph.D. incomes would increase at the same aggregate rate as M.D. incomes (at 8 percent per year), even though neither projections of past trends nor projections of future supply and demand conditions would lend confidence to that projection.

[3] Our data were from National Science Foundation, 1968, and machine tabulations.

TABLE C-2 **Deflated, after-tax revenue and cost streams used in authors' internal rate of return computations, by age and selected degree and annual income growth assumptions, in dollars**

| | Revenue assumptions | | | Cost assumptions | | | | |
| | Medical doctor with annual income growth of: | | | Bachelor's degree with annual income growth of: | | | Ph.D. with annual income growth of:* | |
Age	8%	6%	No growth	7%	5%	No growth	8%	No growth
22	1,506	1,473	1,457	9,572	9,407	9,348	5,619	5,788
23	1,603	1,554	1,457	9,355	9,098	8,598	4,749	5,038
24	2,049	1,968	1,748	9,607	9,550	8,598	4,610	5,038
25	2,182	2,039	1,911	10,170	9,732	9,333	4,920	5,538
26	5,186	5,446	6,012	10,178	9,596	8,645	4,744	5,500
27	10,220	10,836	12,203	10,837	10,125	8,645	10,666	7,691
28	9,922	10,623	12,203	11,540	10,684	8,645	11,547	7,691
29	6,146	6,645	7,786	12,288	11,273	8,645	12,501	7,691
30	6,504	7,101	8,486	13,084	11,895	8,645	13,067	9,048
31	6,883	7,588	9,250	13,452	12,551	8,645	14,147	9,048
32	28,981	28,788	20,558	14,323	13,243	8,645	14,628	9,048
33	31,907	31,413	20,558	14,567	13,491	8,645	15,837	9,048
34	35,129	30,641†	20,558	15,511	14,235	8,645	17,145	9,048
35	38,676	33,435	20,558	16,516	15,021	10,705	18,562	10,252
36	42,581	36,484	20,558	17,586	15,137	10,705	20,095	10,252
37	46,881	39,810	25,129	18,726	15,972	10,705	21,517	10,252
38	51,614	43,440	25,129	19,939	16,853	10,705	23,040	10,252
39	56,826	47,401	25,129	21,231	17,782	10,705	22,054	10,252
40	59,584	49,260	21,529	22,166	18,396	10,705	23,615	11,653
41	62,477	51,191	21,529	20,688	19,032	10,705	25,286	11,653
42	65,510	53,199	25,694	21,598	19,690	10,705	27,076	11,653
43	68,690	55,285	25,694	22,549	20,370	10,705	28,992	11,653
44	72,024	57,453	25,694	23,542	21,074	10,705	31,044	11,653
45	75,520	59,706	25,694	24,579	21,803	11,224	33,241	12,617
46	79,186	62,047	25,694	25,661	22,556	11,224	35,594	12,617
47	82,756	64,268	25,694	26,791	23,336	11,224	37,739	12,617
48	86,487	66,568	25,694	27,970	21,581	11,224	40,015	12,617
49	90,387	68,950	25,694	29,202	22,327	11,224	42,427	12,617
50	94,461	71,418	25,694	30,108	22,812	11,224	44,985	13,581
51	98,720	73,973	25,694	31,043	23,306	11,224	47,697	13,581
52	103,171	76,621	24,142	32,007	23,812	11,224	50,572	13,581
53	107,822	79,362	24,142	33,000	24,328	11,224	53,621	13,581
54	112,683	82,203	24,142	34,025	24,856	11,224	56,854	13,581
55	117,763	85,144	24,142	35,081	25,395	10,448	60,282	14,019
56	123,072	88,191	24,142	36,170	25,946	10,448	63,916	14,019
57	126,659	89,954	24,142	37,293	26,509	10,448	67,018	14,019
58	130,351	91,752	24,142	38,451	27,084	10,448	70,272	14,019
59	134,150	93,587	24,142	39,644	27,671	10,448	73,683	14,019
60	138,060	95,457	24,142	40,875	28,272	10,448	77,260	14,019
61	142,084	97,366	24,142	42,144	28,885	10,448	81,010	14,019
62	146,225	99,312	20,008	43,452	29,511	10,448	84,943	14,019
63	150,487	101,297	20,008	44,801	30,152	10,448	89,066	14,019
64	154,873	103,322	20,008	46,192	30,806	10,448	93,390	14,019

*Assumes income based on a Ph.D. degree in the biological sciences.

†Decline due to substantial change in tax rate.

SOURCE: Authors' computations.

We used the 1966 data from the National Register to estimate a starting income of $14,535 at age 27 in 1973. The age factors were 3.25 percent between 27 and 37 years, 2.12 percent between 37 and 47 years, 1.12 percent between 47 and 57 years, and zero growth between 57 and 64 years.

c For the stream of income which did not project an annual rate of growth we used the 1966 income shown for each age range in the National Register for each age in the range.

Even with the favorable assumptions, the rates of return to M.D. training increased considerably above the levels when B.A. recipients' income was used as the alternative cost. They were 23.9 percent and 22.6 percent for the two alternatives used (Table C-3).

2 We assumed that all bachelor's and Ph.D. degree recipients went into the armed forces upon receipt of the bachelor's degree. We used the pay for a recruit, grade E-1 with less than two years of service from the table entitled "1968 Basic Pay for Military Personnel," provided by the U.S. Department of Defense. We then averaged three years' income (including the prior two years) from the original (non-Army) stream during the first two years in the work force after separation from the armed services, and then reverted to the non-Army stream.

The rate of return to medical training increased about 20 percent when the B.A. degree was the alternative and about 30 percent when the Ph.D. degree was the alternative (see Table C-3).

3 We introduced additional scholarships of $2,500 for each of the four years of medical school. This increased the rate of return in the range of 10 to 20 percent for the B.A. alternatives (see Table C-4).

4 We increased interns' and residents' salaries by about 60 percent above our predicted values (to $10,000, $14,000, $15,000, and $16,000 for internships and each of the three years of residency, respectively). This increased the rate of return in the range of 5 to 15 percent for the B.A. alternative (see Table C-4).

5 We did both (3) and (4). This increased the rate of return in the range of 15 percent to 40 percent for the B.A. alternatives (see Table C-4).

6 We found the addition to the average tax rate which, when applied to the postresidency income of the physicians in cases 3, 4, and 5,

TABLE C-3
Internal rates of return under selected degree and annual income growth assumptions

		Cost assumptions					
		Bachelor's degree (no armed forces experience) with annual income growth of:			Bachelor's degree (armed forces experience) with annual income growth of:		
	Revenue assumptions	7%	5%	No growth	7%	5%	No growth
M.D. (8% growth, 3% inflation)		0.184			0.221		
M.D. (6% growth, 2% inflation)			0.178			0.217	
M.D. (1966)				0.151			0.196

*Assumes income based on a Ph.D. degree in the biological sciences.
SOURCE: Authors' computations.

TABLE C-4 *Internal rates of return with selected changes in revenue or cost streams, and rates which equalize to original*

	Internal rates of return— bachelor's degree (no armed forces experience) with annual income growth of:			Rates which equalize to original internal rates of return—bachelor's degree (no armed forces experience) with annual income growth of:		
Change	7%	5%	No growth	7%	5%	No growth
A. Increased scholarships by $2,500 annually						
M.D. (8% growth, 3% inflation)	0.201			9%		
M.D. (6% growth, 2% inflation)		0.199			9%	
M.D. (1966)			0.184			16%
B. Increase intern and resident stipends by 60%						
M.D. (8% growth, 3% inflation)	0.194			6%		
M.D. (6% growth, 2% inflation)		0.190			7%	
M.D. (1966)			0.173			12%
C. Both A and B						
M.D. (8% growth, 3% inflation)	0.213			16%		
M.D. (6% growth, 2% inflation)		0.215			16%	
M.D. (1966)			0.214			28%

SOURCE: Authors' computations.

Ph.D.* (no armed forces experience) with annual income growth of:		Ph.D.* (armed forces experience) with annual growth of:	
8%	No growth	8%	No growth
0.239		0.336	
	0.226		0.290

will give the same internal rates of return as in the original basic computation. For case 3, the required increase in the average rate of taxation ranged from 9 to 16 percent; for case 4, the required increase in the average rate of taxation ranged from 6 to 12 percent; and for case 5, the required increase in the average rate of taxation ranged from 16 to 28 percent.

It should be noted that these simulations were done in order to provide some indication of the possibilities of changing the time stream of physician incomes without changing the internal rate of return.

Appendix D: Regression Equations

The least-squares multiple regression technique was used to estimate each of the regression equations discussed in Chapter 5. This technique calculates the coefficients of the independent variables which lead to the minimum squared derivation of predicted values from actual values of the dependent variable.[1] The regressions below are listed in the order in which they were discussed. Beneath each coefficient the corresponding t value is shown in parentheses. These numbers provide information on the significance of the coefficients. Significance is measured by the probability of getting the estimated sample coefficient if the true population coefficient were zero. If a coefficient is significant at the 5 percent level (a t value of 1.96 or above for our sample sizes), it indicates that the probability of getting the estimated coefficient would be less than 5 percent if the population coefficient were zero. We also include the value of R^2, which indicates the proportion of the variance in the dependent variable explained by the variance of the independent variables.

DESCRIPTION OF REGRESSIONS

State expenditures for medical schools (average of 1965 and 1966 academic years)

Sample size $= 48$

$$PS = 40.2 + 0.027P - 0.325PR - 199.8PG + 0.035SL$$
$$\quad\quad\ (8.8)\quad\quad (4.2)\quad\quad\ (1.8)\quad\quad\ (0.1) \quad\quad \text{(D-1)}$$
$$\ - 0.004PI$$
$$\quad\ (0.2)$$

---

[1] The computer program used in the computation was the DAM-67 regression program of The Brookings Institution.

$$R^2 = 0.697$$

$$SM = -2.32 + 0.0009P - 0.003PR - 6.01PG$$
$$(12.9)(1.7)(2.3)$$
$$+\ 0.019SL - 0.21PI \tag{D-2}$$
$$(2.6)(0.45)$$

$$R^2 = 0.874$$

PS = Public freshman places (average of 1965 and 1966 academic years)

P = Population (average of 1965 and 1966)

PR = Private freshman places (average of 1965 and 1966 academic years)

PG = Percentage increase in population (1955 to 1964)

SL = Ratio of state and local expenditures in 1966 to average of personal income in 1965 and 1966

PI = Personal income per capita (average of 1965 and 1966)

SM = State expenditures for current operations of medical schools (average of 1965 and 1966 academic years)

Location of 1950–1959 graduates in 1967
Sample size = 32

$$G = -813.3 + 111.3PC + 0.66IC + 0.405GR$$
$$(18.3)(1.5)(5.0)$$
$$+\ 0.121GN \tag{D-3}$$
$$(0.9)$$

$$R^2 = 0.969$$

$$PG = 0.648 + 20.3PCG - 0.393PN - 0.0002IC$$
$$(5.7)(5.8)(1.7) \tag{D-4}$$

$$R^2 = 0.765$$

$$I = -725.6 + 91.5PC + 0.650IC - 0.248GR$$
$$(18.9)(1.8)(3.1)$$
$$+\ 0.036GN + 2.01RG \tag{D-5}$$
$$(0.4)(2.6)$$

$$R^2 = 0.958$$

G = Total number of 1950–1959 graduates from United States medical schools located in the state in 1967

$PC =$ Change in state population between 1954 and 1967

$IC =$ Change in income per capita between 1954 and 1967

$GR =$ Estimated number of graduates from schools in the state (1950–1959) who were residents of the state

$GN =$ Estimated number of graduates from schools in the state (1950–1959) who were not residents of the state

$PG =$ Proportion of graduates from schools in the state (1950–1959) who were practicing in the state in 1967

$PCG =$ Ratio of change in population (1954–1967) to the number of graduates from schools in the state (1950–1959)

$PN =$ Estimated percentage of graduates from schools in the state (1950–1959) who were nonresidents of the state

$I =$ Number of graduates practicing in the state in 1967 who graduated from schools in other states (1950–1959)

$RG =$ Number of residents from the state who were attending medical school in other states in 1954

Medical school entrants from the state (average of 1965 and 1966 academic years)

Sample size $= 48$

$$E = -79.0 + 0.867PS + 0.718PR + 0.025PI$$
$$\quad\quad\quad (5.1) \quad\quad\quad (7.5) \quad\quad (1.0)$$
$$+ 0.948ST$$
$$\quad (2.5)$$

$\quad\quad\quad\quad\quad\quad\quad\quad\quad\quad\quad\quad\quad\quad\quad\quad\quad$ (D-6)

$R^2 = 0.913$

$E =$ Number of entrants from the state (average of 1965 and 1966 academic years)

$PS =$ Freshman class openings in public schools (average of 1965 and 1966 academic years)

$PR =$ Freshman class openings in private schools (average of 1965 and 1966 academic years)

$PI =$ Personal income per capita (average of 1965 and 1966)

$ST =$ Number of resident undergraduate students in four-year higher education institutions in 1963

Interns and residents (1966)

Sample size $= 38$

$$\frac{USI}{IO} = 1.08 - 0.26NI - 0.00007SI - 0.70GI$$
$$\quad\quad\quad\quad (3.2) \quad\quad\quad (1.7) \quad\quad\quad (2.9)$$

$\quad\quad\quad\quad\quad\quad\quad\quad\quad\quad\quad\quad\quad\quad\quad\quad\quad$ (D-7)

$$R^2 = 0.562$$

$$\frac{USR}{RO} = 0.85 - 0.36NR - 0.00002RS - 0.12GR \qquad \text{(D-8)}$$
$$\phantom{\frac{USR}{RO} = 0.85 -\ } (4.2) \qquad\quad (0.6) \qquad\quad (1.53)$$

$$R^2 = 0.431$$

$\dfrac{USI}{IO}$ = Interns graduated from United States and Canadian medical schools divided by total number of internships offered in 1966.

NI = Percentage of internships in nonaffiliated hospitals

SI = Weighted average stipend for all interns

GI = Number of internships offered divided by number of graduates from United States medical schools in 1950–1959 classes who were practicing in the state in 1967

$\dfrac{USR}{RO}$ = Residents graduated from United States and Canadian medical schools divided by residencies offered in 1966

NR = Percentage of residencies in nonaffiliated hospitals

RS = Weighted average stipend for all residencies

GR = Number of residencies offered divided by the number of graduates from United States medical schools in 1950–1959 classes who were practicing in the state in 1967

Appendix E: State Support of Private Medical Schools

This appendix presents a description of some of the state arrangements for support of private medical schools. The details of programs change from year to year, but this summary will illustrate the general approaches and some of the issues raised in public support of private medical education.

Pennsylvania makes a payment to all medical schools in the state based on the number of students enrolled, whether or not they are residents of the state. This appropriation, which differs slightly among medical schools in Pennsylvania, increased from $2,073 per student in 1955–56 to $3,840 per student (including the tuition supplement to the medical schools of state-related Temple University and the University of Pittsburgh) in 1966–67 (Joint State Government Commission, 1967, p. 3). Similarly, Florida makes a payment to the University of Miami School of Medicine (but for Florida residents only); Kentucky makes an annual appropriation to the University of Louisville School of Medicine, which also receives municipal support; and Ohio has recently begun to support Case Western Reserve University School of Medicine. Finally, New York State has developed two types of support for expansion of enrollment in private medical schools:

One type of support is for the construction of new facilities or the renovation of existing facilities to permit the increased enrollment of medical students. The formula on which this funding is based is as follows, namely, if the enrollment with the increase results in a total student body of from 300–399, the State will provide up to 3 million dollars in matching funds; if the total enrollment is from 400–499, the State will provide 4 million dollars; for anything over a 500 enrollment, the State will provide 5 million dollars. The State insists, however, that all plans for renovation or new construction must be approved by the Health Professions Educational Assistance Agency.

259

The second type of assistance is in the form of operational grants. This formula calls for support in the amount of $6,000 for each additional student enrolled above the average base line for the past 5 years. However, in order to qualify for any State assistance, the school must take into any given class at least 5 additional students above the previous base line enrollment.[1]

The maximum expansion which will be supported is 25 students.

Other states have given consideration to supporting private medical schools. The 1963 report of the State of California Coordinating Council for Higher Education indicated that grants-in-aid of $3,000 to $4,000 per year per undergraduate medical student in private medical schools would provide roughly the equivalent of one new medical school in California at no capital cost to the state since apparently it had been indicated that capital funds for expansion could be raised from community resources. However, it was noted that the California constitution forbids use of public moneys for support of any school not under the exclusive control of the officers of the public schools. It was also indicated that the Legislative Council of the state of California believed that indirect support of private medical schools through scholarship programs providing state scholarships for medical students in amounts approaching the actual instructional costs of undergraduate medical students would probably be held invalid by the courts as an appropriation to a private institution. It was therefore suggested that some type of contract between the state and the private school to provide the state with patient care in teaching hospitals would present fewer constitutional difficulties. Los Angeles County Hospital, which paid Loma Linda University Medical School and the University of Southern California annual sums running into six figures based upon the faculty time spent in patient care and house-officer education, was offered as an example of an institution involved in such an arrangement (State of California Coordinating Council for Higher Education, 1963, pp. 20–21).

The study of physician manpower in Missouri discussed the possibility of subsidizing professional education for residents of the state who attended private medical schools in Missouri. It was pointed out that residents who have graduated from private medical schools in Missouri tend to remain in the state at twice the rate

[1] Personal communication from Arthur W. Wright, Acting Secretary, Board of Medical Examiners, State of New York, Albany, Apr. 22, 1969.

of residents from other states educated in private medical schools in Missouri and that the state subsidy would induce greater admissions of Missouri residents at the private institutions. An "order of magnitude" estimate of the cost of four years of undergraduate medical education to the state was $21,110 per graduate. Assuming that one-half of those graduates would practice in Missouri, it was estimated that the cost per physician ultimately added to the stock of the profession practicing in Missouri would be $42,220 (Olson, 1968, pp. 83–85).

The Task Force on Medical Education for Wisconsin discussed the request of the Milwaukee Center Steering Committee and the Marquette University School of Medicine for approximately $1.3 million in state funds to be appropriated to Milwaukee County in each year of the 1967 biennium to cover the deficit anticipated by the medical school. The proposal was that the county would enter into a contract with the medical school for purchase of educational services. At that time, the county was paying the Marquette School of Medicine $1 million annually toward the salaries of clinical teaching staff who provided services at Milwaukee County Hospital. The request for appropriation of state funds raised constitutional and public policy questions by members of the task force. In September, 1967, the Marquette University Medical School Corporation was reorganized, the medical school severed all ties with Marquette University, and the name was changed to the Marquette School of Medicine, Inc., with all members of the board named from the public at large. The attorney general, in response to a request for an opinion, responded that funds could be appropriated to Milwaukee County for the stated purpose.[2]

Finally, we note the recommendations of the study of education in health fields for the state of Illinois. The suggestions made by this study were for a single, nonrecurring program of expansion grants to be made to each of the private schools for planning and for capital construction attendant upon increasing their enrollment. It was suggested that no grant be given for any expansion of less than 20 Illinois resident students and that the amounts granted be $50,000 for each of the first additional 20 Illinois resident students and $20,000 for each Illinois resident beyond this level. In addition,

[2] *The Report of the Governor's Task Force on Medical Education,* 1967, pp. 23–34. In October, 1969, the Wisconsin State Legislature appropriated $3.2 million for operating support of Marquette School of Medicine during the next biennium.

state subsidization of the operations expenditures of these schools at the rate of $6,000 annually would be provided for each of the additional Illinois residents (with the requirement that at least 20 additional Illinois residents be enrolled in each entering class in order to receive a grant), and an annual stabilization grant of $1,000 per student would be awarded on the basis of the number of Illinois residents enrolled in 1967.[3]

[3] J. A. Campbell & Associates, 1968, pp. 23–24. In November, 1969, Illinois provided $6.1 million to the Chicago Medical School to help finance construction that will permit the school to double its 1968–69 enrollment of 294 medical students within six years.

References

Abel-Smith, Brian: *An International Study of Health Expenditure and its Relevance for Health Planning,* World Health Organization, Public Health Papers 32, Geneva, 1967.

Adelman, Irma: "An Econometric Analysis of Population Growth," *American Economic Review,* vol. 53, no. 3, June, 1963.

"Ailing Medical Schools Face Budget Cut Coup de Grace," *Evening Star,* Washington, D.C., June 13, 1968.

Allen, John S., and Alfred H. Lawton: *Planning for the University of South Florida Medical Center,* University of South Florida, Tampa, 1966.

Altenderfer, Marion E., and Margaret D. West: *How Medical Students Finance Their Education: Results of a Survey of Medical and Osteopathic Students, 1963–64,* U.S. Department of Health, Education, and Welfare, Public Health Publication 1336, 1965.

American Medical Association: *Digest of Official Actions of the AMA, 1846–1958,* Chicago, 1959.

American Medical Association: *Directory of Approved Internships and Residencies, 1967–68,* Chicago, 1967.

American Medical Association: *Directory of Approved Internships and Residencies, 1968–69,* Chicago, 1969.

Association of American Medical Colleges: *Medical College Costs and Manual of Procedures,* Evanston, Ill., 1965.

Association of American Medical Colleges: *Medical School Salary Study, 1967–68,* Evanston, Ill., December, 1967. (Mimeographed.)

Association of American Medical Colleges: *Program Cost Allocation in Seven Medical Centers: A Pilot Study,* Association of American Medical Colleges, Evanston, Ill., 1969.

Association of Professors of Gynecology and Obstetrics: *Analysis of Departments of Obstetrics and Gynecology,* Aug. 1, 1967. (Mimeographed.)

Astin, Alexander W., Robert J. Panos, and John A. Creager: *National Norms for Entering College Freshmen, Fall, 1966,* vol. 2, no. 1, American Council on Education, Washington, D.C., 1967.

Bator, Francis M.: "Government and the Sovereign Consumer," in Edmund S. Phelps (ed.), *Private Wants and Public Needs: Issues Surrounding the Size and Scope of Government Expenditure,* rev. ed., W. W. Norton & Company, Inc., New York, 1965.

Becker, Gary: *Human Capital,* Columbia University Press for National Bureau of Economic Research, New York, 1964.

Benham, Lee, Alex Maurizi, and Melvin W. Reder: "Migration, Location, and Remuneration of Medical Personnel: Physicians and Dentists," *Review of Economics and Statistics,* vol. 50, no. 3, August, 1968.

Berry, Ralph E., Jr.: *An Analysis of Costs in Short-term General Hospitals,* Harvard Institute of Economic Research Discussion Paper 30, 1968.

Blumberg, Mark S.: *State Support (Subsidy) for Selected, State Owned University Teaching Hospitals,* Apr. 10, 1967. (Mimeographed.)

Blumberg, Mark S., and Eve C. Clarke: *Major Locational Factors: U.S. Medical Schools,* University of California, Berkeley, May, 1967. (Mimeographed.)

Boffey, Philip M.: "Budget Paradox: Spending Holds Even, Yet Researchers Are Hurt," *Science,* vol. 162, no. 3,851, Oct. 18, 1968.

Borland, Melvin, and Donald E. Yett: *Trends in the Return on Investments in Higher Education, 1949–1959.* (Mimeographed.)

Bunnell, Kevin P.: *New Approaches to Health Manpower Production: "The Western Interstate Plan,"* paper prepared for the American Medical Association Congress on Medical Education, Feb. 10, 1969.

Bunnell, Kevin P., and Julia V. Malone (eds.): *Medical Education for Sparsely Settled States,* Western Interstate Commission for Higher Education, Boulder, Colo., April, 1968.

Butter, Irene: *Health Manpower Research: A Survey,* University of Michigan, Ann Arbor, June, 1967. (Mimeographed.)

Campbell, James A., and Associates: *Education in the Health Fields for State of Illinois,* prepared for State of Illinois Board of Higher Education, vol. 1, June, 1968.

Campbell, Thomas J.: *Program Cost Allocation in Seven Medical Centers: A Pilot Study,* Association of American Medical Colleges, Evanston, Ill., 1969.

Carroll, Augustus J.: *Program Cost Estimating in a Teaching Hospital: A Pilot Study,* Association of American Medical Colleges, Evanston, Ill., 1969.

Carroll, Augustus J.: *A Study of Medical College Costs,* Association of American Medical Colleges, Evanston, Ill., 1958.

Caughey, John L., Jr.: "Clinical Experience and Clinical Responsibility: The Attitudes of Students," *Journal of Medical Education,* vol. 39, no. 5, May, 1964.

Chiang, C. L.: *An Index of Health: Mathematical Models,* U.S. Department of Health, Education, and Welfare, National Center for Health Statistics, ser. 2, no. 5, 1965.

Ciriacy-Wantrup, S. V.: "Economics of Joint Costs in Agriculture," *Journal of Farm Economics,* vol. 23, November, 1941.

Clute, Kenneth F.: *The General Practitioner: A Study of Medical Education and Practice in Ontario and Nova Scotia,* University of Toronto Press, Toronto, 1963.

Cohn, Victor: "U.S. Science Is Feeling Budget Pinch," *Washington Post,* Aug. 4, 1968.

Commission on Professional and Hospital Activities: *PAS Reporter,* vol. 6, no. 7, Ann Arbor, Mich., June 10, 1968.

"Compensation of Interns and Residents," *Journal of the American Medical Association,* vol. 182, no. 4, Oct. 27, 1962.

Comroe, Julius H., Jr.: "The Effect of Research Emphasis on Facilities and Support of the Medical Schools," in Julius H. Comroe, Jr. (ed), *Research and Medical Education, Journal of Medical Education,* vol. 37, no. 12, part 2, December, 1962.

Consultants to the Commission on Higher Education: *Medical Education in South Carolina,* 1967. (Mimeographed.)

C. R. Dean Economics, Inc.: *An Inventory of Pediatric Departments,* New York, 1967.

Crocker, Anna R., and Louis C. Remund Smith: *How Medical Students Finance Their Education: Results of a Survey of Medical and Osteopathic Students, 1967-68,* U.S. Department of Health, Education, and Welfare, National Institutes of Health, to be published in 1970.

Danière, André: *Higher Education in the American Economy,* Random House, Inc., New York, 1964.

Darley, Ward: "The Financial Status of Medical Education," *Journal of Medical Education,* vol. 28, no. 2, February, 1953.

Datagrams, vol. 8, no. 9, Association of American Medical Colleges, March, 1967.

Davis, James A.: *Great Aspirations: The Graduate School Plans of America's College Seniors,* National Opinion Research Center, Aldine Publishing Company, Chicago, 1964.

Davis, James A.: *Undergraduate Career Decisions: Correlates of Occupational Choice,* National Opinion Research Center, Aldine Publishing Company, Chicago, 1965.

Deitrick, John E., and Robert C. Berson: *Medical Schools in the United States at Mid-century,* McGraw-Hill Book Company, New York, 1953.

Diehl, Harold S., Margaret D. West, and Robert W. Barclay: "Medical School Faculties in the National Emergency," *Journal of Medical Education,* vol. 27, no. 7, part 1, July, 1952.

Delaware Medical School Feasibility Study, report prepared for the Medical School Feasibility Survey Committee of the Delaware Academy of Medicine, July, 1964.

Economic Report of the President, President's Council of Economic Advisors, Washington, D.C., 1968.

Educational Opportunity Bank, report of the Panel on Educational Innovation, U.S. Government Printing Office, August, 1967.

"Engineering News-Record Building Cost Indexes," *The Architect's Exchange,* vol. 16, no. 2, 1968.

Esposito, Louis: "An Analysis of the Economic Factors Determining the Number of Applicants to Medical School," doctoral dissertation, Boston College, Boston, Mass., 1968.

"Factors Affecting Choice of Medicine as a Career by High School Students in Project Talent," American Medical Association, Chicago, July 26, 1967. (Unpublished draft.)

"Factors Affecting Graduate Medical Education in 1968," *Bulletin of the American College of Surgeons,* vol. 54, no. 2, March–April, 1969.

Fein, Rashi: *The Doctor Shortage: An Economic Diagnosis,* The Brookings Institution, Washington, D.C., 1967.

Freeman, Richard: "The Labor Market for College Manpower," (doctoral dissertation), Harvard University, 1967.

Funkenstein, Daniel H.: "A Study of College Seniors Who Abandoned Their Plans for a Medical Career," *Journal of Medical Education,* vol. 36, no. 8, August, 1961.

Funkenstein, Daniel H.: "Testing the Scientific Achievement and Ability of Applicants to Medical School: The Problem and a Proposal," *Journal of Medical Education,* vol. 41, no. 2, February, 1966.

Goldberg, Joel H.: "How the Academic Physician Spends His Time," *Hospital Physician,* vol. 5, no. 1, January, 1969.

Grove, William J.: *The University of Illinois Plan for Expanding Medical Education,* n.d. (Mimeographed.)

Haidak, Gerald: "We're Going to Need Ceilings on Stipends," *Hospital Physician*, vol. 4, no. 3, March, 1968.

Hardy, Clyde T., Jr.: "Group Practice by Medical School Faculty," *Journal of Medical Education*, vol. 43, no. 8, August, 1968.

Hardy, Clyde T., Jr.: *Medical Schools and Group Practice*, Winston-Salem, N.C., n.d. (Mimeographed.)

Health Manpower Study Commission: "Health Manpower for the Upper Midwest," study sponsored by the Louis W. and Maud Hill Foundation, St. Paul, Minn., June, 1966.

Heller, Walter W.: "Reflections on Public Expenditure Theory," in Edmund S. Phelps (ed.), *Private Wants and Public Needs: Issues Surrounding the Size and Scope of Government Expenditure*, rev. ed., W. W. Norton & Company, Inc., New York, 1965.

Hepner, James Orville: "Financial Support of Hospital Programs for Graduate Medical Education," doctoral dissertation, State U. of Iowa, 1964.

Hubbard, William N., Jr., and William G. Anlyan: "Analysis of Replies to AAMC Letter," unpublished tabulation collated by office of Program Planning and Evaluation of the National Institutes of Health, Nov. 25, 1968.

Hunter, Thomas H.: "Compensation of Clinical Faculty at the University of Virginia," *Journal of Medical Education*, vol. 31, no. 7, July, 1956.

Hutchins, Edwin B.: "The Student and His Environment," *Journal of Medical Education*, vol. 37, no. 12, December, 1962.

Hutchins, Edwin B.: "The AAMC Longitudinal Study: Implications for Medical Education," *Journal of Medical Education*, vol. 39, no. 3, March, 1964.

Ingbar, Mary Lee, and Lester D. Taylor: *Hospital Costs in Massachusetts: An Econometric Study*, Harvard U. Press, Cambridge, Mass., 1968.

Jarecky, Roy K., Davis G. Johnson, and Dale E. Mattson: "The Study of Applicants, 1967–68," *Journal of Medical Education*, vol. 43, no. 12, December, 1968.

Johnson, Davis G.: *Comparative Characteristics of All Freshmen, Selected Professional Aspirants, and Selected Physician Aspirants in the 1966 Entering Class of U.S. Undergraduate Colleges*, Association of American Medical Colleges, Evanston, Ill., Feb. 14, 1968. (Mimeographed.)

Johnson, Davis G., and Edwin B. Hutchins: *Doctor or Dropout?* Association of American Medical Colleges, Evanston, Ill., 1966.

Joint State Government Commission: *Medical Training Facilities and Medical Practice in Pennsylvania*, General Assembly of the Commonwealth of Pennsylvania, Harrisburg, Pa., 1967.

Journal of the American Medical Association, vol. 144, no. 2, Sept. 9, 1950; vol. 147, no. 2, Sept. 8, 1951; vol. 159, no. 6, Oct. 8, 1955; vol. 174, no. 11, Nov. 12, 1960; vol. 178, no. 6, Nov. 11, 1961; vol. 182, no. 7, Nov. 17, 1962; vol. 190, no. 7, Nov. 16, 1964; vol. 198, no. 8, Nov. 21, 1966; vol. 202, no. 8, Nov. 20, 1967; vol. 206, no. 9, Nov. 25, 1968; vol. 210, no. 8, Nov. 24, 1969.

Journal of Medical Education, vol. 36, no. 4, April, 1961; vol. 37, no. 11, November, 1962; vol. 42, no. 1, January, 1967a; vol. 42, no. 2, February, 1967b; vol. 42, no. 7, part 2, July, 1967c; vol. 43, no. 1, January, 1968a; vol. 43, no. 9, September, 1968b.

Kaitz, Edward M.: *Pricing Policy and Cost Behavior in the Hospital Industry,* Frederick A. Praeger, Inc., New York, 1968.

Keenan, Boyd R. (ed.): *Science and the University,* Columbia University Press, New York, 1966.

Keezer, Dexter M. (ed.): *Financing Higher Education: 1960-70,* McGraw-Hill Book Company, New York, 1959.

Kidd, Charles V.: "The Effect of Research Emphasis on Research Itself," in Julius H. Comroe, Jr. (ed.), "Research and Medical Education," *Journal of Medical Education,* vol. 37, no. 12, part 2, December, 1962.

Larmore, Mary L.: "An Inquiry into and Econometric Production Function for Health in the United States," doctoral dissertation, Northwestern University, 1967.

Legislators and the Lobbyists, Congressional Quarterly Service, Washington, D.C., n.d.

Lindsay, Cotton M.: "Supply Responses to Public Financing of Medical Care in the United States," doctoral dissertation, University of Virginia, 1968.

Lyden, Fremont J., H. Jack Geiger, and Osler L. Peterson: *The Training of Good Physicians: Critical Factors in Career Choices,* Harvard University Press, Cambridge, Mass., 1968.

Maine Legislative Research Committee: *The Feasibility of a Medical School,* Report to 103d Legislature, Publication 103-1, January, 1967.

Mattson, Dale E., Davis G. Johnson, and William E. Sedlacek: "The Study of Applicants, 1966–67," *Journal of Medical Education,* vol. 43, no. 1, January, 1968.

Medical Economics, December 11, 1967; April 29, 1968a; June 10, 1968b; December 9, 1968c.

Medical Education and Research Needs in Maryland, report of the Subcommittee on Medical Education and Research, Maryland State Planning Commission Committee on Medical Care, State Planning Department, Baltimore, Md., 1962.

Medical School Admission Requirements, U.S.A. and Canada, Association of American Medical Colleges Bulletin, 1967–68.

Medical World News, Sept. 5, 1969.

Medicare and Medicaid: Problems, Issues, and Alternatives, report of the staff to the Senate Committee on Finance, 91st Cong., 1st Sess., 1970.

Millett, John D.: *Financing Higher Education in the United States,* staff report of the Commission on Financing Higher Education of the Association of American Universities, Columbia University Press, New York, 1952.

National Science Foundation: *Reviews of Data on Research and Development,* no. 17, January, 1960.

National Science Foundation: *American Science Manpower, 1964,* 1966.

National Science Foundation: *American Science Manpower, 1966,* 1968.

National Society of Professional Engineers: *Professional Engineers' Income and Salary Survey, 1967,* Washington, 1968.

"1968 Survey of Dental Practice II: Income." "Income of Dentists by Location, Age and other Factors," *Journal of the American Dental Association,* vol. 78, February, 1969.

Nourse, E. Shepley: "Topography, Problems and Essential Elements of School-Hospital Affiliations," in George A. Wolf, Jr., Ray E. Brown, and Robert Bucher (eds.), "Report of the Second Administrative Institute: Medical School–Teaching Hospital Relations," *Journal of Medical Education,* vol. 40, no. 11, part 2, November, 1965.

Olson, Stanley W.: *A Survey of Physician Manpower in Missouri for the Missouri Commission on Higher Education,* May, 1968.

Ott, David J.: *Background and Basic Assumptions of Tax-transfer Chart Data,* Council of Economic Advisers, n.d. (Mimeographed.)

Page, Irvine H.: "Social Planning and Our Medical Schools," *Science,* vol. 159, no. 3812, Jan. 19, 1968.

Panos, Robert J., Alexander W. Astin, and John A. Creager: *National Norms for Entering College Freshmen: Fall, 1967,* American Council on Education, Washington, D.C., 1967.

Pauly, Mark V.: "Efficiency in Public Provision of Medical Care," doctoral dissertation, University of Virginia, 1967.

Paxton, Harry T.: "How Medicare Is Affecting Training," *Hospital Physician,* vol. 3, no. 8, August, 1967.

Paxton, Harry T.: "Where Medicare/Medicaid Hit Training Hardest," *Hospital Physician,* vol. 3, no. 8, August, 1967b.

Pechman, Joseph A.: *Federal Tax Policy,* The Brookings Institution, Washington, D.C., 1966.

Peery, Thomas M.: *The George Washington Plan,* paper read before the 65th Annual Congress on Medical Education, Chicago, Feb. 10, 1969. (Mimeographed.)

Penrod, Kenneth E., and Glenn W. Irwin: "A Proposed Statewide Medical School for Indiana," *Journal of Medical Education,* vol. 41, no. 11, part 1, November, 1966.

Pettit, Lawrence K.: "Congress, Confusion, and Indirect Costs," *Science,* vol. 163, Mar. 21, 1969.

Physicians for a Growing America, report of the Surgeon General's Consultant Group on Medical Education, U.S. Department of Health, Education, and Welfare, Public Health Service Publication 709, 1959.

Powers, Lee, Ward Darley, and K. C. Oppermann: "National Goals for the Construction of Medical School Facilities," *Journal of Medical Education,* vol. 35, no. 2, February, 1960.

The President's Commission on the Health Needs of the Nation: *Findings and Recommendations,* vol. 1, Washington, D.C., 1952.

The President's Commission on the Health Needs of the Nation: *America's Health Status, Needs and Resources: A Statistical Appendix,* vol. 3, Washington, D.C., 1953.

Projector, Dorothy S., and Gertrude Weiss: *Survey of Financial Characteristics of Consumers,* Federal Reserve System, Washington, D.C., August, 1966.

Rayack, Elton: *Professional Power and American Medicine: The Economics of the American Medical Association,* The World Publishing Company, Cleveland, 1967.

Reed, Louis S.: *Studies of the Incomes of Physicians and Dentists,* U.S. Department of Health, Education, and Welfare, Social Security Administration, 1968.

Report of the Committee of the Michigan Coordinating Council for Public Higher Education to Consider the Location and Sponsorship of the Expansion of Medical Education in the State of Michigan, November, 1963.

The Report of the Governor's Task Force on Medical Education, Madison Wis., December, 1967.

Report of the National Advisory Commission on Health Manpower, vol. 2, Washington, D.C., 1967.

Rice, Mabel C., and Paul L. Mason: *Residence and Migration of College Students, Fall 1963: State and Regional Data,* U.S. Department of Health, Education, and Welfare, 1965.

Rogoff, Natalie: "The Decision to Study Medicine," in Robert K. Merton, George G. Reader, and Patricia L. Kendall (eds.), *The Student Physician*, Harvard University Press, Cambridge, Mass., 1957.

Sedlacek, William E. (ed.): *Medical College Admission Test Handbook for Admissions Committees*, 2d ed., Association of American Medical Colleges, Evanston, Ill., 1967.

Sedlacek, William E., and Edwin B. Hutchins: "An Empirical Demonstration of Restriction of Range Artifacts in Validity Studies of the Medical College Admission Test," *Journal of Medical Education*, vol. 41, no. 3, March, 1966.

Seipp, Conrad: "Preliminary Report of a Study in the Office of Vice President for Health and Medical Affairs," *Journal of Medical Education*, vol. 42, no. 7, part 2, July, 1967.

Shell, Karl et al.: "The Educational Opportunity Bank: An Economic Analysis of a Contingent Repayment Loan Program for Higher Education," *National Tax Journal*, vol. 21, no. 1, March, 1968.

Sheps, Cecil G., Dean A. Clark, John W. Gerdes, Ethelmarie Halpern, and Nathan Hershey: *Medical Schools and Hospitals*, Association of American Medical Colleges, Evanston, Ill., 1965, published as part 2 of *Journal of Medical Education*, vol. 40, no. 9, September, 1965.

Sloan, Frank A.: "Economic Models of Physician Supply," doctoral dissertation, Harvard University, 1968.

Smythe, Cheves McC.: "Developing Medical Schools: An Interim Report," *Journal of Medical Education*, vol. 42, no. 11, November, 1967.

Somers, Herman M., and Anne R. Somers: *Medicare and the Hospitals: Issues and Prospects*, The Brookings Institution, Washington, D.C., 1967.

State of California Coordinating Council for Higher Education: *Medical Education in California*, report to the California State Legislature, Sacramento and San Francisco, Calif., January, 1963.

Statistical Abstract of the United States, 1964, Government Printing Office, Washington, D.C., 1964.

Statistical Abstract of the United States, 1967, Government Printing Office, Washington, D.C., 1967.

Statistical Abstract of the United States, 1968, Government Printing Office, Washington, D.C., 1968.

Theodore, C. N., G. E. Sutter, and J. N. Haug: *Medical School Alumni, 1967*, American Medical Association, Chicago, 1968.

Thielens, Wagner, Jr.: "Some Comparisons of Entrants to Medical School and Law School," in Robert K. Merton, George G. Reader, and Patricia

L. Kendall (eds.), *The Student Physician,* Harvard University Press, Cambridge, Mass., 1957.

"The Threat of Inflationary Erosion: The Annual Report on the Economic Status of the Profession, 1968–69," *AAUP Bulletin,* vol. 55, no. 2, June, 1969.

Toward a Long-Range Plan for Federal Financial Support for Higher Education, U.S. Department of Health, Education, and Welfare, Office of the Assistant Secretary for Planning and Evaluation, 1969.

U.S. Bureau of the Census: *Current Population Reports,* ser. P-60, no. 35, 1961; no. 39, 1963; no. 43, 1964; no. 47, 1965; no. 53, 1967; no. 59, 1969.

U.S. Bureau of the Census: *United States Census of Population, 1960: Mobility for States and State Economic Areas,* PC (2) 2B, 1963a.

U.S. Department of Health, Education, and Welfare, National Institutes of Health: "Resources Analysis," Memo 10, August, 1968.

U.S. Federal Security Agency, Public Health Service: *Conclusions and Recommendations,* report by the Surgeon General's Committee on Medical School Grants and Finances, part 1, 1951a.

U.S. Federal Security Agency, Public Health Service: *Financial Status and Needs of Medical Schools,* report by the Surgeon General's Committee on Medical School Grants and Finances, part 2, 1951b.

U.S. Office of Education: *Projections of Educational Statistics to 1975–76,* 1966.

U.S. Office of Education: *Projections of Educational Statistics to 1977–78,* 1968.

Walsh, John: "Medical Schools: Federal Funds Increase, So Do Budget Ills," *Science,* vol. 161 no. 3842, Aug. 16, 1968.

Walsh, John: "NIH: Agency and Clients React to Retrenchment," *Science,* vol. 165, no. 3900, 165, Sept. 26, 1969.

Watley, Donivan J.: "Stability of Career Choices of Talented Youth," *National Merit Scholarship Corporation Research Reports,* vol. 4, no. 2, National Merit Scholarship Corporation, Evanston, Ill., 1968.

Watley, Donivan J., and Robert C. Nichols: "Career Decisions of Talented Youth: Trends over the Past Decade," *National Merit Scholarship Corporation Research Reports,* vol. 5, no. 1, National Merit Scholarship Corporation, Evanston, Ill., 1969.

Weiskotten, Herman G. et al.: "Trends in Medical Practice: An Analysis of the Distribution and Characteristics of Medical College Graduates,

1915–1950," *Journal of Medical Education,* vol. 35, no. 12, December, 1960.

Werts, Charles E.: "Social Class and Career Choice of College Freshmen," *National Merit Scholarship Corporation Research Reports,* vol. 1, no. 8, National Merit Scholarship Corporation, Evanston, Ill., 1965.

Werts, Charles E.: "Career Changes in College," *National Merit Scholarship Corporation Research Reports,* National Merit Scholarship Corporation, Evanston, Ill., 1966a.

Werts, Charles E.: "Career Choice Patterns: Ability and Social Class," *National Merit Scholarship Corporation Research Reports,* vol. 2, no. 3, National Merit Scholarship Corporation, Evanston, Ill., 1966b.

White, Kerr L., T. Franklin Williams, and Bernard G. Greenberg: "The Ecology of Medical Care," *The New England Journal of Medicine,* vol. 265, no. 18, Nov. 2, 1961.

Whiting, J. Frank, Lee Powers, and Ward Darley: "The Financial Situation of the American Medical Student," *Journal of Medical Education,* vol. 36, no. 7, July, 1961.

Wing, Paul, and Mark S. Blumberg: *Operating Expenditures and Sponsored Research at U.S. Medical Schools: An Empirical Study,* University of California, Berkeley, Office of Health Planning, 1969. (Mimeographed.)

Index

AAMC (*see* Association of American Medical Colleges)

AAUP Bulletin, 53*n.*

Abel-Smith, Brian, 6*n.*

Adelman, Irma, 6

Agency for International Development (AID), 237

"Ailing Medical Schools Face Budget Cut Coup de Grace," 40*n.*

Allen, John S., 137*n.*

Altenderfer, Marion E., 247

American Association of University Professors (AAUP), 53*n.*

American Council on Education (ACE), 94, 95, 102*n.*

American Medical Association (AMA), 25*n.*, 62, 99, 108, 123, 157, 169*n.*, 200–201, 204, 207, 236, 237

American Medical Association Council on Medical Education and Hospitals, 123

American Medical Association Education and Research Foundation (AMA-ERF), 109

Anlyan, William G., 139, 189*n.*, 238

Association of American Medical Colleges (AAMC), 26, 27, 29, 35, 36, 53, 62, 72–74, 102, 103, 108, 110, 114, 192*n.*, 200–201, 204, 207, 236, 237, 241–242, 247

Association of Professors of Gynecology and Obstetrics, 30

Astin, Alexander W., 95, 102*n.*

Atomic Energy Commission, 204

Bane report, 197–198

Barclay, Robert W., 54*n.*

Bator, Francis M., 132

Becker, Gary, 92*n.*, 245*n.*

Benham, Lee, 154–155, 194*n.*

Berry, Ralph E., Jr., 123*n.*

Berson, Robert C., 53

Blumberg, Mark S., 34, 152, 236*n.*, 237, 242–243

Boffey, Philip M., 208

Borland, Melvin, 92*n.*

Boston University, 46

Brookings Institution, 255*n.*

Buffalo School of Medicine, 46*n.*

Bulletin of the American College of Surgeons, 210

Bunnell, Kevin P., 137*n.*, 143*n.*

Butter, Irene, 186*n.*

California, University of, 46*n.*, 143*n.*, 242

California College of Medicine, 46*n.*

California Coordinating Council for Higher Education, State of, 137*n.*, 153*n.*, 178*n.*, 260

Campbell, James A., 137*n.*, 154, 262*n.*

Campbell, Thomas J., 123, 242

Carroll, Augustus J., 124, 237, 241

Case Western Reserve University School of Medicine, 259

Caughey, John L., Jr., 60

Chiang, C. L., 6*n.*

Nichols, Robert C., 98
NIH (*see* National Institutes of Health)
Nourse, E. Shepley, 26

Olson, Stanley W., 137*n*., 154, 162*n*., 261
Opperman, K. C., 74
Ott, David J., 195–196

Page, Irvine H., 45
Panos, Robert J., 95, 102*n*., 103
Pauly, Mark V., 132*n*.
Paxton, Harry T., 210*n*.
Pechman, Joseph A., 249
Pennsylvania, University of, 100*n*.
Penrod, Kenneth E., 191*n*.
Peterson, Osler L., 126
Pettit, Lawrence K., 206
Physicians for a Growing America, 124, 198
Pittsburgh, University of, 139*n*., 259
Powers, Lee, 74
President's Commission on the Health Needs of the Nation, 56, 196–197
Professional Activity Study, 122
Project Talent, 94, 99–100
Projector, Dorothy S., 88
Public Health Service, 123, 196, 247

Rayack, Elton, 199–201
Reder, Melvin W., 154–155, 194*n*.
Reed, Louis S., 85*n*.
Report of the Committee of the Michigan Coordinating Council for Public Higher Education to Consider the Location and Sponsorship of the Expansion of Medical Education in the State of Michigan, 137*n*.
Report of the Governor's Task Force on Medical Education, The, 137*n*., 153*n*., 154, 261*n*.
Report of the National Advisory Commission on Health Manpower, 198–199
Rice, Mabel C., 163
Rogoff, Natalie, 100*n*.

Saint Louis University, 46, 47
Sedlacek, William E., 15*n*., 21, 80
Seipp, Conrad, 34
Seton Hall College of Medicine and Dentistry, 46*n*.
Shell, Karl, 226*n*.
Sheps, Cecil G., 25
Sloan, Frank A., 92–93, 133*n*.–134*n*., 155–156, 161, 186*n*., 194*n*., 246
Smith, Louis C. Remund, 102, 105
Smythe, Cheves McC., 76, 191*n*.
Social and Rehabilitation Service, 204
Social Security Act, 209*n*.
Social Security Administration, 85
Somers, Anne R., 210
Somers, Herman M., 210
Southern California, University of, 260
Southern Regional Education Board, 138*n*.
Stritch School of Medicine of Loyola University, 46, 47
Study of Medical College Costs, A, 241
Surgeon General's Committee on Medical School Grants and Finances, 39, 196
Surgeon General's Consultant Group on Medical Education, 197–198
Sutter, G. E., 56, 157

Taylor, Lester D., 123*n*.
Temple University, 139*n*., 259
Theodore, C. N., 56, 157
Thielens, Wagner, Jr., 100*n*.
"Threat of Inflationary Erosion, The: The Annual Report on the Economic Status of the Profession, 1968–69," 53*n*.
Toward a Long-range Plan for Federal Financial Support for Higher Education, 223*n*.
Tufts University, 46

U.S. Bureau of the Census, 102*n*., 103, 179, 247
U.S. Department of Agriculture, 204
U.S. Department of Defense, 204, 251
U.S. Department of Health, Education, and Welfare, 54, 205, 208*n*.
(*See also* National Institutes of Health)

This book was set in Vladimir by University Graphics,
Inc. It was printed on Vellum Offset and bound by
The Maple Press Company. The designer was Elliot Epstein;
the drawings were done by John Cordes, J. & R. Technical
Services, Inc. The editors were Herbert Waentig and
Laura Givner for McGraw-Hill Book Company and Verne A.
Stadtman and Margaret Cheney for the Carnegie Commission
on Higher Education. Frank Matonti supervised the production.